First Edition

TEACHER'S MANUAL

Common Core
Support Coach

TARGET ▶ Foundational
Mathematics ⑧

Common Core Support Coach, Target: Foundational Mathematics, First Edition, Teacher's Manual, Grade 8
T203NAM   ISBN-13: 978-1-61997-985-7

Contributing Writers: TSI Graphics   **Cover Design:** Q2A/Bill Smith

Triumph Learning® 136 Madison Avenue, 7th Floor, New York, NY 10016

Contents

Student Edition Contents

Contents

2

3

Instructional Overview

This mathematics skills and concepts program provides scaffolded instruction and support for students struggling with grade-level content required by the Common Core State Standards for Mathematics (CCSS-M). Aimed at students requiring strategic intervention—specifically, those students missing a critical foundation for grade-level understandings—*Common Core Support Coach* reflects a careful analysis of the prerequisites of key grade-level standards. This means that students will be able to rehearse and review prior skills that will ensure competency at a specific grade.

The program consists of three components:

- Student Edition Worktext
- Comprehensive Teacher's Manual with reduced, annotated Student Edition pages
- Assessment Booklet containing lesson quizzes, two performance tasks for each of the five domains, and two practice tests

Student Edition Overview

The Student Edition features 20 key lessons, focusing on a minimum of 20 standards across all five domains of the CCSS-M. These standards were chosen because they are critical components of the mathematical progressions that connect earlier standards to this grade level and from this grade level to the next. While each lesson connects to prior foundational skills and concepts, it can be viewed as an independent unit of instruction. In this way, the 20 lessons allow teachers to differentiate instructions according to the requirements of each student.

Key to the philosophy behind *Common Core Support Coach* is the recognition that math skills and concepts are part of a progression that begins early in students' lives and continues beyond their current grade level with increased complexity and depth.

For students, achieving true understanding of CCSS-M at any grade level means mastery of prior content that connects to this grade and mastery of content that connects within the grade. Often, students who cannot cope with a specific part of their grade's curriculum are missing one or more understandings that would allow mastery. *Common Core Support Coach* supplies the missing pieces.

Lesson Structure

Each lesson is divided into three parts: **Plug In**, **Power Up**, and **Ready to Go**. The first two parts provide students with a review and practice of the prerequisite content necessary for success at the targeted grade-level standard. The Plug In component reacquaints students with skills and concepts that are foundational to performing at grade level. Power Up picks up from Plug In to add another layer of prerequisite content that ensures a smooth transition to Ready to Go. This section affords an opportunity for instruction on the grade-level standard. Each part highlights key vocabulary and supplies sufficient practice to ensure mastery before moving forward. Ready to Go, the on-grade-level portion of the lesson, ends with an important emphasis on problem solving.

PLUG IN	POWER UP	GO!
Foundational Standard remediating specific content	Transitional Standard connects Foundational Standard to Target Standard	Target Standard on grade level

A Lesson Link is included to show both teachers and students how these standards connect!

LESSON LINK

PLUG IN	POWER UP	GO!
You can enlarge a figure by multiplying its side lengths by a scale factor greater than 1.	**You can reduce a figure by multiplying its side lengths by a scale factor between 0 and 1.**	I get it! I can dilate figures on the coordinate plane by multiplying each of the coordinates by the scale factor.
$2 \triangle \rightarrow 3 \triangle$ Scale factor $= 1.5$ $2 \times 1.5 = 3$	$8 \square \rightarrow 6 \square$ Scale factor $= \frac{3}{4}$ $8 \times \frac{3}{4} = 6$	

Using Support in the Classroom

The broad outline of *Common Core Support Coach*'s features suggests that the best way to use it in your classroom is to take advantage of its versatility. This means that even as *Support Coach* aims to help bring students to grade-level competency, there are many ways to implement it:

- *Common Core Support Coach* can be used with any other set of materials you are using for CCSS-M.

- The lessons do not have to be taught in a particular sequence.

- You can use *Common Core Support Coach* with one or many students at any given time.

- *Common Core Support Coach* can be used in the classroom, at home, in after-school programs, and in summer programs.

- You can use several levels of *Support Coach* at any grade to assist students who have missed earlier skills.

The most important aspect of *Common Core Support Coach* is that it digs to uncover elements that are missing from the hierarchy of math skills and concepts and assists students who have forgotten or never mastered these elements. This applies to any student who struggles when encountering new content.

Teacher's Manual: An Annotated Guide

Common Core Support Coach Teacher's Manual provides all the instructional support you need to help your students achieve mastery of key Common Core State Standards for Mathematics (CCSS-M).

Lessons in this Teacher's Manual include the following features:

- A **Lesson Overview** chart detailing objectives for each section, concepts and skills aligned to CCSS-M, and key vocabulary terms

- A list of required and suggested **Materials**

- **Spotlight on Mathematical Practice** notes that support teachers at point-of-use to develop strong mathematical behaviors in their students

- **Spotlight on Mathematical Language** provides a series of prompts using appropriate mathematical language and terms that are designed to elicit similar mathematical language from students

- **English Language Learner** notes included at point-of-use to prepare teachers for the diverse needs of the student population

- **Common Error** notes that provide insight into student misconceptions at point-of-use

- Robust **Discussion Support** that includes Prompts and Sentence Starters to facilitate mathematical discourse

- **Observation-Action tables** that outline how teachers can address specific student needs during independent practice

- A **Lesson Link** that outlines how each section of the lesson connects and works to bring the student to the on-level standard

▶ Plug In Pages

The **Lesson Overview** chart saves preparation time.

A breakdown of the lesson's components helps you plan.

The **Materials** list details the required and suggested tools for each section.

Introduce and Model outlines how to introduce a topic and model thinking and problem solving.

The Support Coach Avatars model exemplary student thinking, questioning, and problem solving!

Support is included for guiding students through the gradual release of modeling to independent practice.

Each section of the student lesson culminates in an independent practice set.

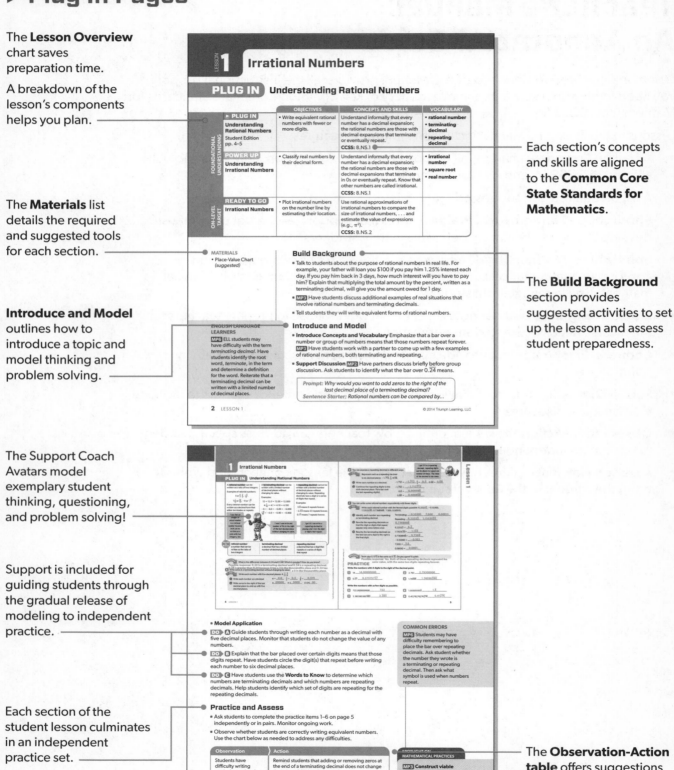

Each section's concepts and skills are aligned to the **Common Core State Standards for Mathematics**.

The **Build Background** section provides suggested activities to set up the lesson and assess student preparedness.

The **Observation-Action table** offers suggestions for addressing certain behaviors students may exhibit during independent practice.

▶ Power Up Pages

Each section of the lesson has specific objectives, concepts and skills, and key vocabulary. ———

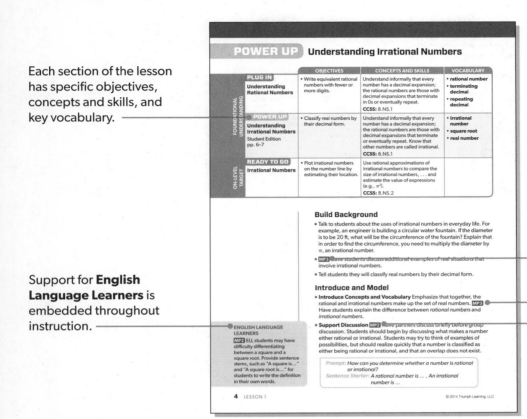

Support for **English Language Learners** is embedded throughout instruction. ———

The **Standards for Mathematical Practice** are aligned at point-of-use within instruction and other support features.

Mathematical Discourse is included in every lesson. Prompts and Sentence Starters are outlined to help facilitate discussion. ———

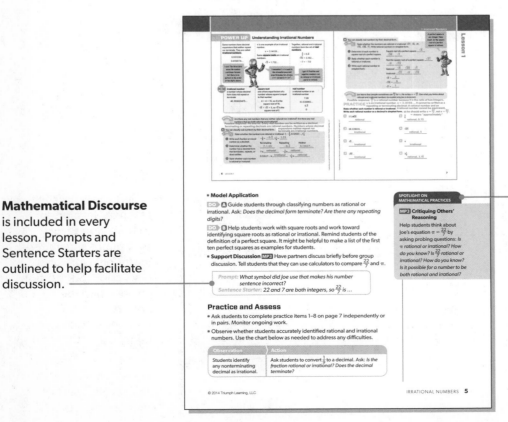

The **Spotlight on Mathematical Practices** box provides embedded professional development on the Standards for Mathematical Practice.

▶ Ready to Go Pages

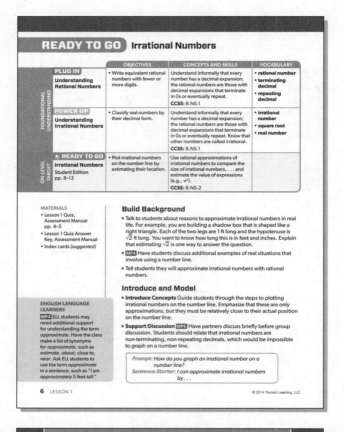

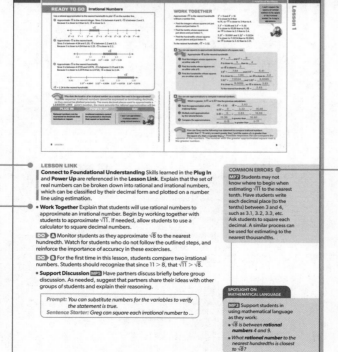

The **Lesson Link** connects the foundational skills from the Plug In and Power Up sections to the on-level standard in the Ready to Go section.

The **Ready to Go** section of the lesson often furnishes an opportunity for students to work together to build a firm base for the on-level standard.

Alongside instruction, teachers are alerted to **Common Errors** they might encounter in student work or discussion. Suggestions are included for addressing the misconceptions that might cause these errors.

▶ Ready to Go Pages

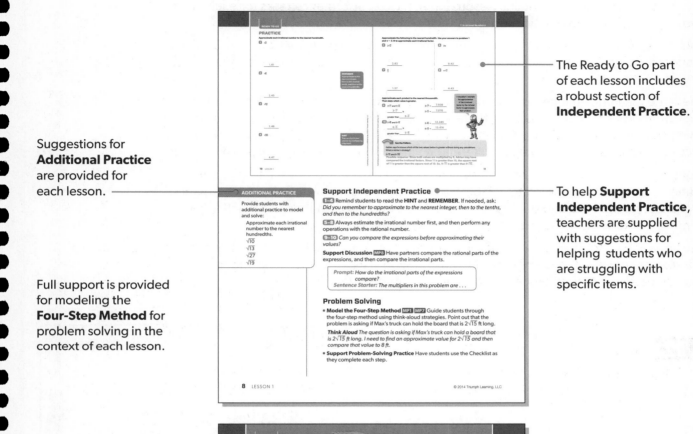

Suggestions for **Additional Practice** are provided for each lesson.

Full support is provided for modeling the **Four-Step Method** for problem solving in the context of each lesson.

The Ready to Go part of each lesson includes a robust section of **Independent Practice**.

To help **Support Independent Practice**, teachers are supplied with suggestions for helping students who are struggling with specific items.

Two full pages are dedicated to **Problem Solving**, giving students the opportunity to apply their newly acquired conceptual understandings and procedural fluencies to contextualized problem situations.

A three-part **Observation-Action table** can be used to determine whether students need more time with the lesson content or can move on to the Lesson Quiz.

Assessments

The Assessment Booklet contains lesson quizzes, two performance tasks for each of the five domains, and two practice tests.

Each Lesson Quiz helps you evaluate students' understanding of the Common Core State Standards taught in the lesson and determine whether they are prepared to move on to new material.

There are ten Performance Tasks in the Assessment Booklet—two for each Domain of the Common Core State Standards for Mathematics. The two Performance Tasks for a given Domain have a task-specific rubric. The first of the two tasks is a bit easier than the second—which allows teachers to differentiate instruction on performance task practice.

Practice Test 1 can be administered before students begin the lessons in the Student Edition. The results allow you to establish a baseline measure of students' mathematics proficiency before starting the Student Edition lessons. You can then use Practice Test 2 to measure students' progress after completing the program.

The answer keys for the Lesson Quizzes, Performance Tasks, and Practice Tests identify the correct answers, the Common Core State Standard assessed, and the alignment to the Standards for Mathematical Practice where appropriate.

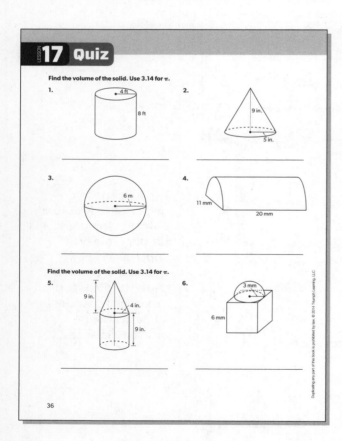

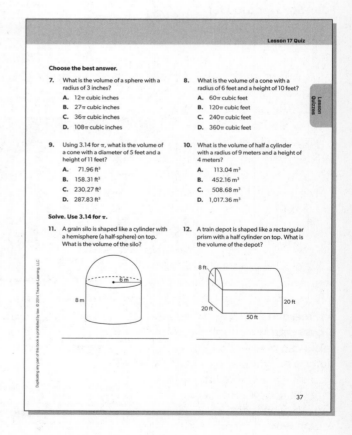

Understanding the Common Core State Standards

Adapted from the Common Core State Standards Initiative website: www.corestandards.org.

The Common Core State Standards, as created by the Council of Chief State School Officers (CCSSO) and the National Governors Association (NGA), provide a clear and consistent framework to prepare students for college and the workforce.

The Common Core State Standards for Mathematics define what students should understand and be able to do in their study of mathematics. Asking a student to understand something means asking a teacher to assess whether the student has understood it. One hallmark of mathematical understanding is the ability to justify, in a way appropriate to the student's mathematical maturity, why a particular mathematical statement is true or where a mathematical rule comes from. Mathematical understanding and procedural skill are equally important, and both are assessable using mathematical tasks of sufficient richness.

The Standards for Mathematical Practice describe varieties of expertise that mathematics educators at all levels should seek to develop in their students. These practices rest on important "processes and proficiencies" with longstanding importance in mathematics education.

The Standards for Mathematical Content are a balanced combination of procedure and understanding. Expectations that begin with the word "understand" are often especially good opportunities to connect the practices to the content. Students who lack understanding of a topic may rely on procedures too heavily. Without a flexible base from which to work, they may be less likely to consider analogous problems, represent problems coherently, justify conclusions, apply the mathematics to practical situations, use technology mindfully to work with the mathematics, explain the mathematics accurately to other students, step back for an overview, or deviate from a known procedure to find a shortcut. A lack of understanding effectively prevents a student from engaging in the mathematical practices.

The Standards set grade-specific standards but do not define the intervention methods or materials necessary to support students who are well below grade-level expectations. It is beyond the scope of the Standards to define the full range of supports appropriate for English language learners and for students with special needs. At the same time, all students must have the opportunity to learn and meet the same high standards if they are to access the knowledge and skills necessary in their post-school lives. The Standards should be read as allowing for the widest possible range of students to participate fully. No set of grade-specific standards can fully reflect the great variety in abilities, needs, learning rates, and achievement levels of students in any given classroom. However, the Standards do provide clear signposts along the way to the goal of college and career readiness for all students.

Common Core State Standards Correlation Chart

The following table matches the CCSS to the lessons in which they are addressed.

Common Core State Standards		Support Coach Lesson(s)
Domain: The Number System		
8.NS.1	Know that numbers that are not rational are called irrational. Understand informally that every number has a decimal expansion; for rational numbers show that the decimal expansion repeats eventually, and convert a decimal expansion which repeats eventually into a rational number.	1
8.NS.2	Use rational approximations of irrational numbers to compare the size of irrational numbers, locate them approximately on a number line diagram, and estimate the value of expressions (e.g., π^2). *For example, by truncating the decimal expansion of $\sqrt{2}$, show that $\sqrt{2}$ is between 1 and 2, then between 1.4 and 1.5, and explain how to continue on to get better approximations.*	1
Domain: Expressions and Equations		
6.EE.1	Write and evaluate numerical expressions involving whole-number exponents.	2
6.EE.2.c	Evaluate expressions at specific values of their variables. Include expressions that arise from formulas used in real-world problems. Perform arithmetic operations, including those involving whole-number exponents, in the conventional order when there are no parentheses to specify a particular order (Order of Operations). *For example, use the formulas $V = s^3$ and $A = 6\,s^2$ to find the volume and surface area of a cube with sides of length $s = \frac{1}{2}$.*	17
8.EE.2	Use square root and cube root symbols to represent solutions to equations of the form $x^2 = p$ and $x^3 = p$, where p is a positive rational number. Evaluate square roots of small perfect squares and cube roots of small perfect cubes. Know that $\sqrt{2}$ is irrational.	2
8.EE.3	Use numbers expressed in the form of a single digit times an integer power of 10 to estimate very large or very small quantities, and to express how many times as much one is than the other. *For example, estimate the population of the United States as 3×10^8 and the population of the world as 7×10^9, and determine that the world population is more than 20 times larger.*	3
8.EE.4	Perform operations with numbers expressed in scientific notation, including problems where both decimal and scientific notation are used. Use scientific notation and choose units of appropriate size for measurements of very large or very small quantities (e.g., use millimeters per year for seafloor spreading). Interpret scientific notation that has been generated by technology.	3
8.EE.5	Graph proportional relationships, interpreting the unit rate as the slope of the graph. Compare two different proportional relationships represented in different ways. *For example, compare a distance-time graph to a distance-time equation to determine which of two moving objects has greater speed.*	4

Common Core State Standards		Support Coach Lesson(s)
8.EE.6	Use similar triangles to explain why the slope m is the same between any two distinct points on a non-vertical line in the coordinate plane; derive the equation $y = mx$ for a line through the origin and the equation $y = mx + b$ for a line intercepting the vertical axis at b.	5
8.EE.7.a	Give examples of linear equations in one variable with one solution, infinitely many solutions, or no solutions. Show which of these possibilities is the case by successively transforming the given equation into simpler forms, until an equivalent equation of the form $x = a$, $a = a$, or $a = b$ results (where a and b are different numbers).	6
8.EE.7.b	Solve linear equations with rational number coefficients, including equations whose solutions require expanding expressions using the distributive property and collecting like terms.	6
8.EE.8.a	Understand that solutions to a system of two linear equations in two variables correspond to points of intersection of their graphs, because points of intersection satisfy both equations simultaneously.	7
8.EE.8.b	Solve systems of two linear equations in two variables algebraically, and estimate solutions by graphing the equations. Solve simple cases by inspection. *For example, $3x + 2y = 5$ and $3x + 2y = 6$ have no solution because $3x + 2y$ cannot simultaneously be 5 and 6.*	7
8.EE.8.c	Solve real-world and mathematical problems leading to two linear equations in two variables. *For example, given coordinates for two pairs of points, determine whether the line through the first pair of points intersects the line through the second pair.*	7
Domain: Functions		
8.F.1	Understand that a function is a rule that assigns to each input exactly one output. The graph of a function is the set of ordered pairs consisting of an input and the corresponding output.	8
8.F.2	Compare properties of two functions each represented in a different way (algebraically, graphically, numerically in tables, or by verbal descriptions). *For example, given a linear function represented by a table of values and a linear function represented by an algebraic expression, determine which function has the greater rate of change.*	9

Common Core State Standards		Support Coach Lesson(s)
8.F.3	Interpret the equation $y = mx + b$ as defining a linear function, whose graph is a straight line; give examples of functions that are not linear. *For example, the function $A = s^2$ giving the area of a square as a function of its side length is not linear because its graph contains the points (1,1), (2,4) and (3,9), which are not on a straight line.*	8
8.F.4	Construct a function to model a linear relationship between two quantities. Determine the rate of change and initial value of the function from a description of a relationship or from two (x, y) values, including reading these from a table or from a graph. Interpret the rate of change and initial value of a linear function in terms of the situation it models, and in terms of its graph or a table of values.	8
8.F.5	Describe qualitatively the functional relationship between two quantities by analyzing a graph (e.g., where the function is increasing or decreasing, linear or nonlinear). Sketch a graph that exhibits the qualitative features of a function that has been described verbally.	9
Domain: Geometry		
7.G.1	Solve problems involving scale drawings of geometric figures, including computing actual lengths and areas from a scale drawing and reproducing a scale drawing at a different scale.	13
7.G.5	Use facts about supplementary, complementary, vertical, and adjacent angles in a multi-step problem to write and solve simple equations for an unknown angle in a figure.	15
8.G.1	Verify experimentally the properties of rotations, reflections, and translations: a. Lines are taken to lines, and line segments to line segments of the same length. b. Angles are taken to angles of the same measure. c. Parallel lines are taken to parallel lines.	10, 11, 12
8.G.2	Understand that a two-dimensional figure is congruent to another if the second can be obtained from the first by a sequence of rotations, reflections, and translations; given two congruent figures, describe a sequence that exhibits the congruence between them.	10, 11, 12, 14
8.G.3	Describe the effect of dilations, translations, rotations, and reflections on two-dimensional figures using coordinates.	10, 11, 12, 13

Common Core State Standards		Support Coach Lesson(s)
8.G.4	Understand that a two-dimensional figure is similar to another if the second can be obtained from the first by a sequence of rotations, reflections, translations, and dilations; given two similar two-dimensional figures, describe a sequence that exhibits the similarity between them.	14
8.G.5	Use informal arguments to establish facts about the angle sum and exterior angle of triangles, about the angles created when parallel lines are cut by a transversal, and the angle-angle criterion for similarity of triangles. *For example, arrange three copies of the same triangle so that the sum of the three angles appears to form a line, and give an argument in terms of transversals why this is so.*	15
8.G.6	Explain a proof of the Pythagorean Theorem and its converse.	16
8.G.7	Apply the Pythagorean Theorem to determine unknown side lengths in right triangles in real-world and mathematical problems in two and three dimensions.	16
8.G.8	Apply the Pythagorean Theorem to find the distance between two points in a coordinate system.	16
8.G.9	Know the formulas for the volumes of cones, cylinders, and spheres and use them to solve real-world and mathematical problems.	17
Domain: Statistics and Probability		
8.SP.1	Construct and interpret scatter plots for bivariate measurement data to investigate patterns of association between two quantities. Describe patterns such as clustering, outliers, positive or negative association, linear association, and nonlinear association.	18
8.SP.2	Know that straight lines are widely used to model relationships between two quantitative variables. For scatter plots that suggest a linear association, informally fit a straight line, and informally assess the model fit by judging the closeness of the data points to the line.	19
8.SP.3	Use the equation of a linear model to solve problems in the context of bivariate measurement data, interpreting the slope and intercept. *For example, in a linear model for a biology experiment, interpret a slope of 1.5 cm/hr as meaning that an additional hour of sunlight each day is associated with an additional 1.5 cm in mature plant height.*	20

Standards for Mathematical Practice

Standards for Mathematical Practice

MP1 | **Make sense of problems and persevere in solving them.**

Mathematically proficient students start by explaining to themselves the meaning of a problem and looking for entry points to its solution. They analyze givens, constraints, relationships, and goals. They make conjectures about the form and meaning of the solution and plan a solution pathway rather than simply jumping into a solution attempt. They consider analogous problems, and try special cases and simpler forms of the original problem in order to gain insight into its solution. They monitor and evaluate their progress and change course if necessary. Older students might, depending on the context of the problem, transform algebraic expressions or change the viewing window on their graphing calculator to get the information they need. Mathematically proficient students can explain correspondences between equations, verbal descriptions, tables, and graphs or draw diagrams of important features and relationships, graph data, and search for regularity or trends. Younger students might rely on using concrete objects or pictures to help conceptualize and solve a problem. Mathematically proficient students check their answers to problems using a different method, and they continually ask themselves, "Does this make sense?" They can understand the approaches of others to solving complex problems and identify correspondences between different approaches.

MP2 | **Reason abstractly and quantitatively.**

Mathematically proficient students make sense of quantities and their relationships in problem situations. They bring two complementary abilities to bear on problems involving quantitative relationships: the ability to decontextualize—to abstract a given situation and represent it symbolically and manipulate the representing symbols as if they have a life of their own, without necessarily attending to their referents—and the ability to contextualize, to pause as needed during the manipulation process in order to probe into the referents for the symbols involved. Quantitative reasoning entails habits of creating a coherent representation of the problem at hand; considering the units involved; attending to the meaning of quantities, not just how to compute them; and knowing and flexibly using different properties of operations and objects.

Standards for Mathematical Practice

MP3 | **Construct viable arguments and critique the reasoning of others.**

Mathematically proficient students understand and use stated assumptions, definitions, and previously established results in constructing arguments. They make conjectures and build a logical progression of statements to explore the truth of their conjectures. They are able to analyze situations by breaking them into cases, and can recognize and use counterexamples. They justify their conclusions, communicate them to others, and respond to the arguments of others. They reason inductively about data, making plausible arguments that take into account the context from which the data arose. Mathematically proficient students are also able to compare the effectiveness of two plausible arguments, distinguish correct logic or reasoning from that which is flawed, and—if there is a flaw in an argument—explain what it is. Elementary students can construct arguments using concrete referents such as objects, drawings, diagrams, and actions. Such arguments can make sense and be correct, even though they are not generalized or made formal until later grades. Later, students learn to determine domains to which an argument applies. Students at all grades can listen or read the arguments of others, decide whether they make sense, and ask useful questions to clarify or improve the arguments.

MP4 | **Model with mathematics.**

Mathematically proficient students can apply the mathematics they know to solve problems arising in everyday life, society, and the workplace. In early grades, this might be as simple as writing an addition equation to describe a situation. In middle grades, a student might apply proportional reasoning to plan a school event or analyze a problem in the community. By high school, a student might use geometry to solve a design problem or use a function to describe how one quantity of interest depends on another. Mathematically proficient students who can apply what they know are comfortable making assumptions and approximations to simplify a complicated situation, realizing that these may need revision later. They are able to identify important quantities in a practical situation and map their relationships using such tools as diagrams, two-way tables, graphs, flowcharts and formulas. They can analyze those relationships mathematically to draw conclusions. They routinely interpret their mathematical results in the context of the situation and reflect on whether the results make sense, possibly improving the model if it has not served its purpose.

Standards for Mathematical Practice

MP5 | **Use appropriate tools strategically.**

Mathematically proficient students consider the available tools when solving a mathematical problem. These tools might include pencil and paper, concrete models, a ruler, a protractor, a calculator, a spreadsheet, a computer algebra system, a statistical package, or dynamic geometry software. Proficient students are sufficiently familiar with tools appropriate for their grade or course to make sound decisions about when each of these tools might be helpful, recognizing both the insight to be gained and their limitations. For example, mathematically proficient high school students analyze graphs of functions and solutions generated using a graphing calculator. They detect possible errors by strategically using estimation and other mathematical knowledge. When making mathematical models, they know that technology can enable them to visualize the results of varying assumptions, explore consequences, and compare predictions with data. Mathematically proficient students at various grade levels are able to identify relevant external mathematical resources, such as digital content located on a website, and use them to pose or solve problems. They are able to use technological tools to explore and deepen their understanding of concepts.

MP6 | **Attend to precision.**

Mathematically proficient students try to communicate precisely to others. They try to use clear definitions in discussion with others and in their own reasoning. They state the meaning of the symbols they choose, including using the equal sign consistently and appropriately. They are careful about specifying units of measure, and labeling axes to clarify the correspondence with quantities in a problem. They calculate accurately and efficiently, express numerical answers with a degree of precision appropriate for the problem context. In the elementary grades, students give carefully formulated explanations to each other. By the time they reach high school they have learned to examine claims and make explicit use of definitions.

Standards for Mathematical Practice

MP7 | **Look for and make use of structure.**

Mathematically proficient students look closely to discern a pattern or structure. Young students, for example, might notice that three and seven more is the same amount as seven and three more, or they may sort a collection of shapes according to how many sides the shapes have. Later, students will see 7×8 equals the well remembered $7 \times 5 + 7 \times 3$, in preparation for learning about the distributive property. In the expression $x^2 + 9x + 14$, older students can see the 14 as 2×7 and the 9 as $2 + 7$. They recognize the significance of an existing line in a geometric figure and can use the strategy of drawing an auxiliary line for solving problems. They also can step back for an overview and shift perspective. They can see complicated things, such as some algebraic expressions, as single objects or as being composed of several objects. For example, they can see $5 - 3(x - y)^2$ as 5 minus a positive number times a square and use that to realize that its value cannot be more than 5 for any real numbers x and y.

MP8 | **Look for and express regularity in repeated reasoning.**

Mathematically proficient students notice if calculations are repeated, and look both for general methods and for shortcuts. Upper elementary students might notice when dividing 25 by 11 that they are repeating the same calculations over and over again, and conclude they have a repeating decimal. By paying attention to the calculation of slope as they repeatedly check whether points are on the line through (1, 2) with slope 3, middle school students might abstract the equation $(y - 2)/(x - 1) = 3$. Noticing the regularity in the way terms cancel when expanding $(x - 1)(x + 1)$, $(x - 1)(x^2 + x + 1)$, and $(x - 1)(x^3 + x^2 + x + 1)$ might lead them to the general formula for the sum of a geometric series. As they work to solve a problem, mathematically proficient students maintain oversight of the process, while attending to the details. They continually evaluate the reasonableness of their intermediate results.

Irrational Numbers

PLUG IN   Understanding Rational Numbers

<table>
<tr><td colspan="2"></td><th>OBJECTIVES</th><th>CONCEPTS AND SKILLS</th><th>VOCABULARY</th></tr>
<tr>
<td rowspan="4">FOUNDATIONAL UNDERSTANDING</td>
<td>**▶ PLUG IN**

Understanding Rational Numbers
Student Edition
pp. 4–5</td>
<td>• Write equivalent rational numbers with fewer or more digits.</td>
<td>Understand informally that every number has a decimal expansion; the rational numbers are those with decimal expansions that terminate or eventually repeat.
CCSS: 8.NS.1</td>
<td>• **rational number**
• **terminating decimal**
• **repeating decimal**</td>
</tr>
<tr>
<td>**POWER UP**

Understanding Irrational Numbers</td>
<td>• Classify real numbers by their decimal form.</td>
<td>Understand informally that every number has a decimal expansion; the rational numbers are those with decimal expansions that terminate in 0s or eventually repeat. Know that other numbers are called irrational.
CCSS: 8.NS.1</td>
<td>• **irrational number**
• **square root**
• **real number**</td>
</tr>
<tr>
<td rowspan="2">ON-LEVEL TARGET</td>
<td>**READY TO GO**
Irrational Numbers</td>
<td>• Plot irrational numbers on the number line by estimating their location.</td>
<td>Use rational approximations of irrational numbers to compare the size of irrational numbers, . . . and estimate the value of expressions (e.g., π^2).
CCSS: 8.NS.2</td>
<td></td>
</tr>
</table>

MATERIALS
• Place-Value Chart *(suggested)*

Build Background

■ Talk to students about the purpose of rational numbers in real life. For example, your father will loan you $100 if you pay him 1.25% interest each day. If you pay him back in 3 days, how much interest will you have to pay him? Explain that multiplying the total amount by the percent, written as a terminating decimal, will give you the amount owed for 1 day.

■ **MP3** Have students discuss additional examples of real situations that involve rational numbers and terminating decimals.

■ Tell students they will write equivalent forms of rational numbers.

Introduce and Model

■ **Introduce Concepts and Vocabulary** Emphasize that a bar over a number or group of numbers means that those numbers repeat forever. **MP3** Have students work with a partner to come up with a few examples of rational numbers, both terminating and repeating.

■ **Support Discussion** **MP2** Have partners discuss briefly before group discussion. Ask students to identify what the bar over $0.\overline{24}$ means.

> *Prompt: Why would you want to add zeros to the right of the last decimal place of a terminating decimal?*
> *Sentence Starter: Rational numbers can be compared by...*

ENGLISH LANGUAGE LEARNERS

MP6 ELL students may have difficulty with the term *terminating decimal*. Have students identify the root word, *terminate*, in the term and determine a definition for the word. Reiterate that a terminating decimal can be written with a limited number of decimal places.

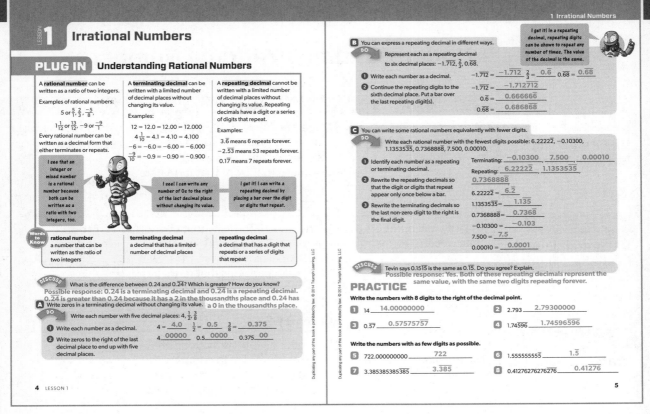

Irrational Numbers

PLUG IN Understanding Rational Numbers

A **rational number** can be written as a ratio of two integers.

Examples of rational numbers:

5 or $\frac{5}{1}$, $\frac{2}{3}$, $-\frac{5}{8}$.

$1\frac{1}{12}$ or $\frac{13}{12}$, -9 or $\frac{-9}{1}$

Every rational number can be written as a decimal form that either terminates or repeats.

I see that an integer or mixed number is a rational number because both can be written as a ratio with two integers, too.

I see I can write any number of 0s to the right of the last decimal place without changing its value.

I get it! I can write a repeating decimal by placing a bar over the digit or digits that repeat.

A **terminating decimal** can be written with a limited number of decimal places without changing its value.

Examples:

$12 = 12.0 = 12.00 = 12.000$
$4\frac{1}{10} = 4.1 = 4.10 = 4.100$
$-6 = -6.0 = -6.00 = -6.000$
$\frac{-9}{10} = -0.9 = -0.90 = -0.900$

A **repeating decimal** cannot be written with a limited number of decimal places without changing its value. Repeating decimals have a digit or a series of digits that repeat.

Examples:

$3.\overline{6}$ means 6 repeats forever.
$-2.\overline{53}$ means 53 repeats forever.
$0.1\overline{7}$ means 7 repeats forever.

Words to Know

rational number a number that can be written as the ratio of two integers

terminating decimal a decimal that has a limited number of decimal places

repeating decimal a decimal that has a digit that repeats or a series of digits that repeat

DISCUSS What is the difference between 0.24 and $0.\overline{24}$? Which is greater? How do you know?
Possible response: 0.24 is a terminating decimal and $0.\overline{24}$ is a repeating decimal. $0.\overline{24}$ is greater than 0.24 because it has a 2 in the thousandths place and 0.24 has a 0 in the thousandths place.

A Write zeros in a terminating decimal without changing its value.

DO Write each number with five decimal places: 4, $\frac{1}{2}$, $\frac{3}{8}$.

❶ Write each number as a decimal. $4 = \underline{4.0}$ $\frac{1}{2} = \underline{0.5}$ $\frac{3}{8} = \underline{0.375}$

❷ Write zeros to the right of the last decimal place to end up with five decimal places. $4.\underline{00000}$ $0.5\underline{0000}$ $0.375\underline{00}$

4 LESSON 1

---

1 Irrational Numbers

B You can express a repeating decimal in different ways.

DO Represent each as a repeating decimal to six decimal places: $-1.7\overline{12}$, $\frac{2}{3}$, $0.\overline{68}$.

❶ Write each number as a decimal. $-1.7\overline{12} = \underline{-1.7\overline{12}}$ $\frac{2}{3} = \underline{0.\overline{6}}$ $0.\overline{68} = \underline{0.\overline{68}}$

❷ Continue the repeating digits to the sixth decimal place. Put a bar over the last repeating digit(s).
$-1.7\overline{12} = \underline{-1.712712}$
$0.\overline{6} = \underline{0.666666}$
$0.\overline{68} = \underline{0.686868}$

I get it! In a repeating decimal, repeating digits can be shown to repeat any number of times. The value of the decimal is the same.

C You can write some rational numbers equivalently with fewer digits.

DO Write each rational number with the fewest digits possible: $6.2222\overline{2}$, -0.10300, $1.1353\overline{535}$, $0.7368\overline{888}$, 7.500, 0.00010.

❶ Identify each number as a repeating or terminating decimal.
Terminating: $\underline{-0.10300}$ $\underline{7.500}$ $\underline{0.00010}$
Repeating: $\underline{6.2222\overline{2}}$ $\underline{1.1353\overline{535}}$

❷ Rewrite the repeating decimals so that the digit or digits that repeat appear only once below a bar.
$0.7368\overline{888}$
$6.2222\overline{2} = \underline{6.\overline{2}}$

❸ Rewrite the terminating decimals so the last non-zero digit to the right is the final digit.
$1.1353\overline{535} = \underline{1.1\overline{35}}$
$0.7368\overline{888} = \underline{0.736\overline{8}}$
$-0.10300 = \underline{-0.103}$
$7.500 = \underline{7.5}$
$0.00010 = \underline{0.0001}$

DISCUSS Tevin says $0.15\overline{15}$ is the same as $0.\overline{15}$. Do you agree? Explain.
Possible response: Yes. Both of these repeating decimals represent the same value, with the same two digits repeating forever.

PRACTICE

Write the numbers with 8 digits to the right of the decimal point.

1 14 $\underline{14.00000000}$

2 2.793 $\underline{2.79300000}$

3 $0.\overline{57}$ $\underline{0.57575757}$

4 $1.74\overline{596}$ $\underline{1.74596596}$

Write the numbers with as few digits as possible.

5 722.000000000 $\underline{722}$

6 1.555555555 $\underline{1.\overline{5}}$

7 3.385385385385 $\underline{3.\overline{385}}$

8 0.41276276276276 $\underline{0.41\overline{276}}$

5

• **Model Application**

DO ▶ A Guide students through writing each number as a decimal with five decimal places. Monitor that students do not change the value of any numbers.

DO ▶ B Explain that the bar placed over certain digits means that those digits repeat. Have students circle the digit(s) that repeat before writing each number to six decimal places.

DO ▶ C Have students use the **Words to Know** to determine which numbers are terminating decimals and which numbers are repeating decimals. Help students identify which set of digits are repeating for the repeating decimals.

Practice and Assess

• Ask students to complete the practice items 1–6 on page 5 independently or in pairs. Monitor ongoing work.

• Observe whether students are correctly writing equivalent numbers. Use the chart below as needed to address any difficulties.

Observation	Action
Students have difficulty writing equivalent rational numbers.	Remind students that adding or removing zeros at the end of a terminating decimal does not change the value of the number. Have students circle the digit(s) that repeat. Remind them that placing a bar over the first set of repeating decimals is the mathematical convention for representing repeating digits.

COMMON ERRORS

MP6 Students may have difficulty remembering to place the bar over repeating decimals. Ask student whether the number they wrote is a terminating or repeating decimal. Then ask what symbol is used when numbers repeat.

SPOTLIGHT ON MATHEMATICAL PRACTICES

MP3 Construct viable arguments

Help students explain their reasoning by asking probing questions: *How can you use a place-value chart to compare these numbers?*

Understanding Irrational Numbers

		OBJECTIVES	CONCEPTS AND SKILLS	VOCABULARY
FOUNDATIONAL UNDERSTANDING	**PLUG IN** **Understanding Rational Numbers**	• Write equivalent rational numbers with fewer or more digits.	Understand informally that every number has a decimal expansion; the rational numbers are those with decimal expansions that terminate in 0s or eventually repeat. **CCSS:** 8.NS.1	• **rational number** • **terminating decimal** • **repeating decimal**
	▶ POWER UP **Understanding Irrational Numbers** Student Edition pp. 6–7	• Classify real numbers by their decimal form.	Understand informally that every number has a decimal expansion; the rational numbers are those with decimal expansions that terminate or eventually repeat. Know that other numbers are called irrational. **CCSS:** 8.NS.1	• **irrational number** • **square root** • **real number**
ON-LEVEL TARGET	**READY TO GO** **Irrational Numbers**	• Plot irrational numbers on the number line by estimating their location.	Use rational approximations of irrational numbers to compare the size of irrational numbers, . . . and estimate the value of expressions (e.g., π^2). **CCSS:** 8.NS.2	

Build Background

- Talk to students about the uses of irrational numbers in everyday life. For example, an engineer is building a circular water fountain. If the diameter is to be 20 ft, what will be the circumference of the fountain? Explain that in order to find the circumference, you need to multiply the diameter by π, an irrational number.

- **MP3** Have students discuss additional examples of real situations that involve irrational numbers.

- Tell students they will classify real numbers by their decimal form.

Introduce and Model

- **Introduce Concepts and Vocabulary** Emphasize that together, the rational and irrational numbers make up the set of real numbers. **MP3** Have students explain the difference between *rational numbers* and *irrational numbers*.

- **Support Discussion** **MP2** Have partners discuss briefly before group discussion. Students should begin by discussing what makes a number either rational or irrational. Students may try to think of examples of possibilities, but should realize quickly that a number is classified as either being rational or irrational, and that an overlap does not exist.

> *Prompt: How can you determine whether a number is rational or irrational?*
> *Sentence Starter: A rational number is … . An irrational number is …*

ENGLISH LANGUAGE LEARNERS

MP2 ELL students may have difficulty differentiating between a square and a square root. Provide sentence stems, such as "A square is…" and "A square root is…" for students to write the definition in their own words.

POWER UP — Understanding Irrational Numbers

Some numbers have decimal expansions that neither repeat nor terminate. They are called **irrational numbers**.

6.931558...
0.4198174...

I see! The three dots mean the number continues forever, but there is no pattern in the order of the digits shown.

π is one example of an irrational number.

π = 3.14159...

Some **square roots** are irrational numbers.

$\sqrt{3}$ = 1.732...

I remember! π is used in the circumference and area formulas for circles: $C = \pi d$ and $A = \pi r^2$.

Together, rational and irrational numbers form the set of **real numbers**.

$\frac{4}{9} = 0.\overline{4}$
$\sqrt{10} = 3.162...$
$-7 = -7.0$

I got it! Positive and negative numbers can be rational or irrational, and 0 is rational.

Words to Know

irrational number a number whose decimal form does not repeat or terminate

48.395620475...

square root one of two equal factors of a number whose square is equal to that number

$4 \times 4 = 16$, so 4 is the square root of 16.
$\sqrt{5} \times \sqrt{5} = 5$, so $\sqrt{5}$ is the square root of 5.

real number a rational number or an irrational number

7.28
53.535982...
$0.\overline{3}$
0

DISCUSS Are there any real numbers that are neither rational nor irrational? Are there any real numbers that are both rational and irrational?
Possible response: No and no. Every real number can be written as a decimal. Terminating or repeating decimals are rational numbers. Numbers whose decimal expansions neither repeat nor terminate are irrational numbers.

A DO You can classify real numbers by their decimal form.
State whether the numbers are rational or irrational: 7, $-\frac{2}{9}$, 0.12627..., $1\frac{1}{4}$

1. Write each fraction or mixed number as a decimal. $-\frac{2}{9} = -0.\overline{2}$, $1\frac{1}{4} = 1.25$

2. Determine whether the number has a decimal form that terminates, repeats, or does neither.

Terminating	Repeating	Neither
7; 1.25	$-0.\overline{2}$	0.12627...

7 is __rational__ $-\frac{2}{9}$ is __rational__
0.12627... is __irrational__ $1\frac{1}{4}$ is __rational__

3. State whether each number is rational or irrational.

B DO You can classify real numbers by their decimal form.
State whether the numbers are rational or irrational: $\sqrt{21}$, $\sqrt{4}$, $\sqrt{\pi}$, $\sqrt{15}$, $\sqrt{36}$, $\sqrt{1}$. Write rational numbers in simplest form.

A perfect square is any integer times itself. So the square root of a perfect square is rational.

1. Determine if each number is square root of a perfect square.

Square root of a perfect square: $\sqrt{4}$
$\sqrt{36}$ $\sqrt{1}$

2. State whether each number is rational or irrational.

Not the square root of a perfect square: $\sqrt{21}$
$\sqrt{\pi}$ $\sqrt{15}$

3. Write each rational number in simplest form.

Rational: $\sqrt{4}$ $\sqrt{36}$ $\sqrt{1}$
Irrational: $\sqrt{21}$ $\sqrt{\pi}$ $\sqrt{15}$

$\sqrt{4} = $ __2__
$\sqrt{36} = $ __6__
$\sqrt{1} = $ __1__

DISCUSS Joe learns that people sometimes use $\frac{22}{7}$ for π. He writes π = $\frac{22}{7}$. Use what you know about rational and irrational numbers to explain why Joe is incorrect.
Possible response: $\frac{22}{7}$ is a rational number because it is the ratio of two integers. π is an irrational number. π ≈ 3.14159.... It cannot be written as a repeating or terminating decimal. A rational number and an irrational number cannot be equivalent, so he should write π ≈ $\frac{22}{7}$, not π = $\frac{22}{7}$. ≈ means "approximately"

PRACTICE
State whether each number is rational or irrational.
Write each rational number as a decimal in simplest form.

1. 17.34$\overline{05}$ __rational__
2. $\frac{3}{4}$ __rational, 0.75__
3. 58.539035... __irrational__
4. $\sqrt{25}$ __rational, 5__
5. $\sqrt{5}$... __irrational__
6. π __irrational__
7. $\sqrt{51}$... __irrational__
8. $3\frac{1}{6}$ __rational, 3.1$\overline{6}$__

• Model Application

DO A Guide students through classifying numbers as rational or irrational. Ask: *Does the decimal form terminate? Are there any repeating digits?*

DO B Help students work with square roots and work toward identifying square roots as rational or irrational. Remind students of the definition of a perfect square. It might be helpful to make a list of the first ten perfect squares as examples for students.

• **Support Discussion** **MP3** Have partners discuss briefly before group discussion. Tell students that they can use calculators to compare $\frac{22}{7}$ and π.

Prompt: What symbol did Joe use that makes his number sentence incorrect?
Sentence Starter: 22 and 7 are both integers, so $\frac{22}{7}$ is ...

Practice and Assess

• Ask students to complete practice items 1–8 on page 7 independently or in pairs. Monitor ongoing work.

• Observe whether students accurately identified rational and irrational numbers. Use the chart below as needed to address any difficulties.

Observation	Action
Students identify any nonterminating decimal as irrational.	Ask students to convert $\frac{1}{9}$ to a decimal. Ask: *Is the fraction rational or irrational? Does the decimal terminate?*

SPOTLIGHT ON MATHEMATICAL PRACTICES

MP3 Critiquing Others' Reasoning

Help students think about Joe's equation π = $\frac{22}{7}$ by asking probing questions: *Is π rational or irrational? How do you know? Is $\frac{22}{7}$ rational or irrational? How do you know? Is it possible for a number to be both rational and irrational?*

		OBJECTIVES	CONCEPTS AND SKILLS	VOCABULARY
FOUNDATIONAL UNDERSTANDING	**PLUG IN** **Understanding Rational Numbers**	• Write equivalent rational numbers with fewer or more digits.	Understand informally that every number has a decimal expansion; the rational numbers are those with decimal expansions that terminate in 0s or eventually repeat. **CCSS:** 8.NS.1	• **rational number** • **terminating decimal** • **repeating decimal**
	POWER UP **Understanding Irrational Numbers**	• Classify real numbers by their decimal form.	Understand informally that every number has a decimal expansion; the rational numbers are those with decimal expansions that terminate in 0s or eventually repeat. Know that other numbers are called irrational. **CCSS:** 8.NS.1	• **irrational number** • **square root** • **real number**
ON-LEVEL TARGET	▶ **READY TO GO** **Irrational Numbers** Student Edition pp. 8–13	• Plot irrational numbers on the number line by estimating their location.	Use rational approximations of irrational numbers to compare the size of irrational numbers, . . . and estimate the value of expressions (e.g., π^2). **CCSS:** 8.NS.2	

MATERIALS

• Lesson 1 Quiz, Assessment Manual pp. 4–5
• Lesson 1 Quiz Answer Key, Assessment Manual
• Index cards (*suggested*)

ENGLISH LANGUAGE LEARNERS

MP4 ELL students may need additional support for understanding the term *approximate*. Have the class make a list of synonyms for *approximate*, such as *estimate, about, close to, near*. Ask ELL students to use the term *approximate* in a sentence, such as "I am *approximately* 5 feet tall."

Build Background

■ Talk to students about reasons to approximate irrational numbers in real life. For example, you are building a shadow box that is shaped like a right triangle. Each of the two legs are 1 ft long and the hypotenuse is $\sqrt{2}$ ft long. You want to know how long this is in feet and inches. Explain that estimating $\sqrt{2}$ is one way to answer the question.

■ **MP4** Have students discuss additional examples of real situations that involve using a number line.

■ Tell students they will approximate irrational numbers with rational numbers.

Introduce and Model

■ **Introduce Concepts** Guide students through the steps to plotting irrational numbers on the number line. Emphasize that these are only approximations, but they must be relatively close to their actual position on the number line.

■ **Support Discussion** **MP6** Have partners discuss briefly before group discussion. Students should relate that irrational numbers are non-terminating, non-repeating decimals, which would be impossible to graph on a number line.

> *Prompt: How do you graph an irrational number on a number line?*
> *Sentence Starter: I can approximate irrational numbers by . . .*

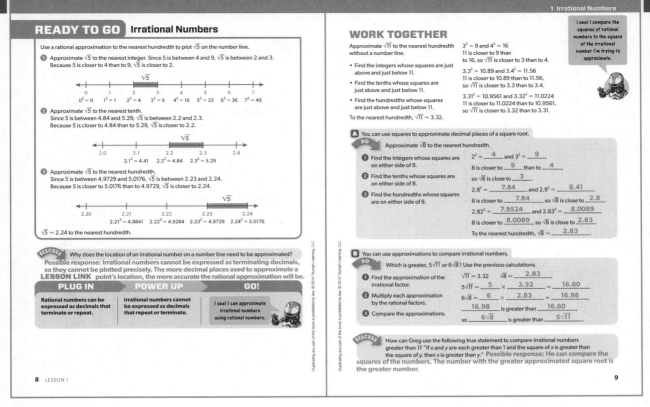

READY TO GO Irrational Numbers

Use a rational approximation to the nearest hundredth to plot $\sqrt{5}$ on the number line.

1. Approximate $\sqrt{5}$ to the nearest integer. Since 5 is between 4 and 9, $\sqrt{5}$ is between 2 and 3. Because 5 is closer to 4 than to 9, $\sqrt{5}$ is closer to 2.

$\sqrt{5}$

$0^2 = 0$ $1^2 = 1$ $2^2 = 4$ $3^2 = 9$ $4^2 = 16$ $5^2 = 25$ $6^2 = 36$ $7^2 = 49$

2. Approximate $\sqrt{5}$ to the nearest tenth. Since 5 is between 4.84 and 5.29, $\sqrt{5}$ is between 2.2 and 2.3. Because 5 is closer to 4.84 than to 5.29, $\sqrt{5}$ is closer to 2.2.

$\sqrt{5}$

$2.1^2 = 4.41$ $2.2^2 = 4.84$ $2.3^2 = 5.29$

3. Approximate $\sqrt{5}$ to the nearest hundredth. Since 5 is between 4.9729 and 5.0176, $\sqrt{5}$ is between 2.23 and 2.24. Because 5 is closer to 5.0176 than to 4.9729, $\sqrt{5}$ is closer to 2.24.

$\sqrt{5}$

$2.21^2 = 4.8841$ $2.22^2 = 4.9284$ $2.23^2 = 4.9729$ $2.24^2 = 5.0176$

$\sqrt{5} \approx 2.24$ to the nearest hundredth.

DISCUSS Why does the location of an irrational number on a number line need to be approximated? Possible response: Irrational numbers cannot be expressed as terminating decimals, so they cannot be plotted precisely. The more decimal places used to approximate a point's location, the more accurate the rational approximation will be.

LESSON LINK

PLUG IN	POWER UP	GO!
Rational numbers can be expressed as decimals that terminate or repeat.	Irrational numbers cannot be expressed as decimals that repeat or terminate.	I see! I can approximate irrational numbers using rational numbers.

8 LESSON 1

WORK TOGETHER

Approximate $\sqrt{11}$ to the nearest hundredth without a number line.

- Find the integers whose squares are just above and just below 11.
- Find the tenths whose squares are just above and just below 11.
- Find the hundredths whose squares are just above and just below 11.

To the nearest hundredth, $\sqrt{11} \approx 3.32$.

$3^2 = 9$ and $4^2 = 16$
11 is closer to 9 than to 16, so $\sqrt{11}$ is closer to 3 than to 4.

$3.3^2 = 10.89$ and $3.4^2 = 11.56$
11 is closer to 10.89 than to 11.56, so $\sqrt{11}$ is closer to 3.3 than to 3.4.

$3.31^2 = 10.9561$ and $3.32^2 = 11.0224$
11 is closer to 11.0224 than to 10.9561, so $\sqrt{11}$ is closer to 3.32 than to 3.31.

I see! I compare the squares of rational numbers to the square of the irrational number I'm trying to approximate.

A You can use squares to approximate decimal places of a square root.

DO Approximate $\sqrt{8}$ to the nearest hundredth.

1. Find the integers whose squares are on either side of 8.

$2^2 = \underline{4}$ and $3^2 = \underline{9}$
8 is closer to $\underline{9}$ than to $\underline{4}$, so $\sqrt{8}$ is close to $\underline{3}$.

2. Find the tenths whose squares are on either side of 8.

$2.8^2 = \underline{7.84}$ and $2.9^2 = \underline{8.41}$
8 is closer to $\underline{7.84}$, so $\sqrt{8}$ is close to $\underline{2.8}$.

3. Find the hundredths whose squares are on either side of 8.

$2.82^2 = \underline{7.9524}$ and $2.83^2 = \underline{8.0089}$
8 is closer to $\underline{8.0089}$, so $\sqrt{8}$ is close to $\underline{2.83}$.

To the nearest hundredth, $\sqrt{8} \approx \underline{2.83}$.

B You can use approximations to compare irrational numbers.

DO Which is greater, $5\sqrt{11}$ or $6\sqrt{8}$? Use the previous calculations.

1. Find the approximation of the irrational factor.

$\sqrt{11} \approx 3.32$ $\sqrt{8} \approx \underline{2.83}$

2. Multiply each approximation by the rational factors.

$5\sqrt{11} \approx \underline{5} \times \underline{3.32} = \underline{16.60}$
$6\sqrt{8} \approx \underline{6} \times \underline{2.83} = \underline{16.98}$

3. Compare the approximations.

$\underline{16.98}$ is greater than $\underline{16.60}$
so $\underline{6\sqrt{8}}$ is greater than $\underline{5\sqrt{11}}$

DISCUSS How can Greg use the following true statement to compare irrational numbers greater than 1? "If x and y are each greater than 1 and the square of x is greater than the square of y, then x is greater than y." Possible response: He can compare the squares of the numbers. The number with the greater approximated square root is the greater number.

9

LESSON LINK

Connect to Foundational Understanding Skills learned in the **Plug In** and **Power Up** are referenced in the **Lesson Link**. Explain that the set of real numbers can be broken down into rational and irrational numbers, which can be classified by their decimal form and plotted on a number line using estimation.

- **Work Together** Explain that students will use rational numbers to approximate an irrational number. Begin by working together with students to approximate $\sqrt{11}$. If needed, allow students to use a calculator to square decimal numbers.

DO **A** Monitor students as they approximate $\sqrt{8}$ to the nearest hundredth. Watch for students who do not follow the outlined steps, and reinforce the importance of accuracy in these excercises.

DO **B** For the first time in this lesson, students compare two irrational numbers. Students should recognize that since $11 > 8$, that $\sqrt{11} > \sqrt{8}$.

- **Support Discussion** **MP5** Have partners discuss briefly before group discussion. As needed, suggest that partners share their ideas with other groups of students and explain their reasoning.

> **Prompt:** You can substitute numbers for the variables to verify the statement is true.
> **Sentence Starter:** Greg can square each irrational number to …

COMMON ERRORS

MP7 Students may not know where to begin when estimating $\sqrt{11}$ to the nearest tenth. Have students write each decimal place (to the tenths) between 3 and 4, such as 3.1, 3.2, 3.3, etc. Ask students to square each decimal. A similar process can be used for estimating to the nearest thousandths.

SPOTLIGHT ON MATHEMATICAL LANGUAGE

MP3 Support students in using mathematical language as they work:

- $\sqrt{8}$ is between **rational numbers** 4 and 9.
- What **rational number** to the nearest hundredths is closest to $\sqrt{8}$?

PRACTICE

Approximate each irrational number to the nearest hundredth.

1 $\sqrt{2}$

_____1.41_____

2 $\sqrt{6}$

_____2.45_____

3 $\sqrt{12}$

_____3.46_____

4 $\sqrt{20}$

_____4.47_____

REMEMBER
Approximate to the nearest integer, then to the nearest tenth, and then to the nearest hundredth.

HINT
You can check your answer by multiplying it by itself.

Approximate the following to the nearest hundredth. Use your answers to problem 1 and $\pi \approx 3.14$ to approximate each irrational factor.

5 $2\sqrt{2}$

_____2.82_____

6 3π

_____9.42_____

7 $\frac{\pi}{2}$

_____1.57_____

8 $\pi\sqrt{2}$

_____4.43_____

Approximate each product to the nearest thousandth. Then state which value is greater.

9 $3\sqrt{7}$ and $5\sqrt{2}$

$3\sqrt{7} \approx$ _____7.938_____

$3\sqrt{7}$ is

$5\sqrt{2} \approx$ _____7.070_____

greater than _____$5\sqrt{2}$_____.

10 $5\sqrt{6}$ and $6\sqrt{5}$

$5\sqrt{6} \approx$ _____12.245_____

$6\sqrt{5}$ is

$6\sqrt{5} \approx$ _____13.416_____

greater than _____$5\sqrt{6}$_____.

I remember! I multiply the approximation of the irrational factor by the rational factor to approximate their product.

DISCUSS

See the Pattern.

Adrian says he knows which of the two values below is greater without doing any calculations. What is Adrian's strategy?

$9\sqrt{11}$ and $9\sqrt{10}$

Possible response: Since both values are multiplied by 9, Adrian may have compared the irrational factors. Since 11 is greater than 10, the square root of 11 is greater than the square root of 10. So, $9\sqrt{11}$ is greater than $9\sqrt{10}$.

ADDITIONAL PRACTICE

Provide students with additional practice to model and solve:

Approximate each irrational number to the nearest hundredths.

$\sqrt{10}$
$\sqrt{13}$
$\sqrt{27}$
$\sqrt{19}$

Support Independent Practice

1–4 Remind students to read the **HINT** and **REMEMBER**. If needed, ask: *Did you remember to approximate to the nearest integer, then to the tenths, and then to the hundredths?*

5–8 Always estimate the irrational number first, and then perform any operations with the rational number.

9–10 *Can you compare the expressions before approximating their values?*

Support Discussion **MP8** Have partners compare the rational parts of the expressions, and then compare the irrational parts.

> *Prompt: How do the irrational parts of the expressions compare?*
>
> *Sentence Starter: The multipliers in this problem are . . .*

Problem Solving

- **Model the Four-Step Method** **MP1** **MP7** Guide students through the four-step method using think-aloud strategies. Point out that the problem is asking if Max's truck can hold the board that is $2\sqrt{15}$ ft long.

  Think Aloud The question is asking if Max's truck can hold a board that is $2\sqrt{15}$ ft long. I need to find an approximate value for $2\sqrt{15}$ and then compare that value to 8 ft.

- **Support Problem-Solving Practice** Have students use the Checklist as they complete each step.

READY TO GO

PROBLEM SOLVING

PAINTING A CIRCLE

READ Max needs to bring wooden boards to a construction site. His truck can hold a board that is up to 8 ft long. Will his truck hold a board that is $2\sqrt{15}$ ft long? Find the length of the board to the nearest thousandth.

PLAN
- What are you asked to find? __whether the truck can hold the board__
- What do you need to know? __the approximate length of the board to the nearest thousandth__
- How do you solve the problem? __Approximate the length of the board.__

SOLVE
1. Find the integers whose squares are just above and just below 15. __3__^{2} = 9 and __4__^{2} = 16 $\sqrt{15}$ is closer to __4__
2. Find the tenths whose squares are just above and just below 15. $3.8^2 =$ __14.44__, $3.9^2 =$ __15.21__ $\sqrt{15}$ is closer to __3.9__
3. Find the hundredths whose squares are just above and just below 15. $3.87^2 =$ __14.9769__, $3.88^2 =$ __15.0544__ $\sqrt{15}$ is closer to __3.87__
4. Find the thousandths whose squares are just above and just below 15. $3.872^2 =$ __14.992384__ $3.873^2 =$ __15.000129__ $\sqrt{15}$ is closer to __3.873__
5. Find the product of the rational approximation and 2. $2 \times$ __3.873__ = __7.746__ ft

> I can work backward to check my answer. That can show me if I've made a mistake in my calculations.

CHECK Divide the product by 2. Then square the quotient. The solution should be very close to 15.
__7.746__ ÷ 2 = __3.873__
__3.873__^{2} = __15.000129__
So, $2\sqrt{15} =$ __7.746__

The length of the board to the nearest thousandth is __7.746__ ft.
The board __will fit__ inside the bed of the Max's truck.

PRACTICE
Use the problem-solving steps to help you.

1. Two legs of a right triangle measure 4 cm and 7 cm. The length of its hypotenuse is $\sqrt{65}$. Approximate the length of the hypotenuse to the nearest thousandth.

CHECKLIST
☐ READ ☐ PLAN ☐ SOLVE ☐ CHECK

8.062 cm

2. The area of the square floor measures 107 ft². Find the approximate length of each side of the floor by approximating $\sqrt{107}$ to the nearest thousandth.

CHECKLIST
☐ READ ☐ PLAN ☐ SOLVE ☐ CHECK

10.344 ft

3. Gary wants to rent space at the community garden. He can choose one space with an area of $16\sqrt{17}$ ft² and another space with an area of $17\sqrt{15}$ ft². If Gary wants to rent the larger plot, which should he choose? Explain.

CHECKLIST
☐ READ ☐ PLAN ☐ SOLVE ☐ CHECK

$16\sqrt{17}$ ft²; Possible response: $16\sqrt{17}$ ft² (approximately 65.968 ft²) is greater than $17\sqrt{15}$ ft² (approximately 65.841 ft²).

Prompt: Between which two integers is $\sqrt{65}$?
Prompt: Is $\sqrt{107}$ greater than or less than 10? How do you know?
Prompt: Without doing any calculations, how can you tell which is greater, $\sqrt{17}$ or $\sqrt{15}$?

- **Explore Student Thinking** **MP3** Invite students to explain their answers to their partners and encourage discussion about why each student believes they are correct.

Assess

- Use the table below to observe whether students accurately approximate irrational numbers.
- When all students are ready, assign the Lesson 1 Quiz.

	Observation	Action
1	Errors in approximating values of irrational numbers are frequent; general confusion about irrational numbers	Remind students to start their estimation with integers. Then to tenths, hundredths, thousands, etc.
2	Performs calculations correctly, but does not approximate to the nearest decimal place indicated.	Have students review the decimal place values.
3	Calculates, compares, and reasons completely and correctly.	Assign the Lesson 1 Quiz.

Square Roots and Cube Roots

PLUG IN Evaluating Square Numbers

		OBJECTIVES	CONCEPTS AND SKILLS	VOCABULARY
FOUNDATIONAL UNDERSTANDING	▶ **PLUG IN** **Evaluating Square Numbers** Student Edition pp. 14–15	• Evaluate square numbers. • Evaluate expressions that include square numbers.	Evaluate numerical expressions involving whole-number exponents. **CCSS:** 6.EE.1	• **power** • **base** • **exponent** • **square number**
	POWER UP **Evaluating Cube Numbers**	• Evaluate cube numbers. • Evaluate expressions that include cube numbers.	Evaluate numerical expressions involving whole-number exponents. **CCSS:** 6.EE.1	• **cube number**
ON-LEVEL TARGET	**READY TO GO** **Square Roots and Cube Roots**	• Evaluate square roots of small perfect squares. • Evaluate cube roots of small perfect cubes. • Solve problems that include square and cube roots.	Evaluate square roots of small perfect squares and cube roots of small perfect cubes. **CCSS:** 8.EE.2	• **square root** • **principal square root** • **cube root**

MATERIALS
- Math Tool: Grid Paper, p. A11 (Student Edition p. 229)

Build Background

- Talk to students about real-life situations that involve using square numbers. For example, a contractor needs to tile a square floor with 1-ft^2 tiles. The length of each side of the square is 1 ft. How many tiles will she need?

- **MP8** Have students discuss additional examples of real situations that involve square numbers.

- Tell students they will use multiplication to find the value of squared numbers.

Introduce and Model

- **Introduce Concepts and Vocabulary** Guide students through the information about squaring numbers. Use **Words to Know** to clarify their understanding of vocabulary. **MP7** Have students explain how to find the first five *square numbers*.

- **Support Discussion** **MP2** Have partners discuss briefly before group discussion. As needed, direct students to **Words to Know** and have them identify the *base* and *exponent*.

> *Prompt:* How is squaring a number different than multiplying by 2? How is it the same?
> *Sentence Starter:* Squaring a number means multiplying by...

SPOTLIGHT ON MATHEMATICAL PRACTICES

MP3 Critiquing Others' Reasoning

Help students correct Paulo's reasoning by asking them to use the Words to Know in their responses: *What error did Paulo make with the base? with the exponent? How is a power different than a multiple?*

LESSON 2 — Square Roots and Cube Roots

PLUG IN — Evaluating Square Numbers

You can write repeated multiplication as a **power**. The **base** is the repeated factor. The **exponent** is the number of times the factor repeats.

base 3^2 exponent

power

I see! The exponent is written above and to the right of the base.

To evaluate a base raised to an exponent, write a multiplication expression with the base for each factor. The exponent indicates the number of times the base is used as a factor.

$7^2 = 7 \times 7 = 49$

I get it! The base is the number you multiply, and the exponent tells you how many factors there are.

When you evaluate an integer base with an exponent of 2, the resulting integer is called a **square number**.

You read 4^2 as "4 squared."

Since $4^2 = 16$,

16 is a square number.

So any integer that can be written as a power with an exponent of 2 is a square number.

Words to Know

power
an expression of repeated multiplication

5^2 is the second power of 5.

5^3 is the third power of 5.

base
the repeated factor in a power

base 5^2

exponent
the raised number in a power that indicates the number of times the base is used as a factor

5^2 exponent

square number
the product of an integer multiplied by itself

Since $5^2 = 25$,

25 is a square number.

DISCUSS Paulo says that 8^2 equals 16 because $8 \times 2 = 16$. How would you help Paulo correct his mistake? Possible response: Paulo misunderstands the meaning of an exponent. The exponent, 2, tells you how many times the base is used as a factor. 8^2 means $8 \times 8 = 64$.

A You can multiply to evaluate square numbers.

DO Evaluate 6^2, 8^2, and 1^2.

① Write the power as repeated multiplication.

$6^2 = 6 \times \underline{6}$, $8^2 = \underline{8} \times \underline{8}$, $1^2 = \underline{1} \times \underline{1}$

② Multiply.

$6 \times 6 = \underline{36}$, $8 \times 8 = \underline{64}$, $1 \times 1 = \underline{1}$

B You can write repeated multiplication of two identical factors as a power.

DO Write 5×5 and 2×2 as powers.

	5×5	2×2
① Identify the base.	The base is $\underline{5}$	The base is $\underline{2}$
② Identify the exponent.	The exponent is $\underline{2}$	The exponent is $\underline{2}$
③ Write the power.	$5 \times 5 = \boxed{5}^{\boxed{2}}$	$2 \times 2 = \boxed{2}^{\boxed{2}}$

C You can evaluate expressions that include powers.

DO Evaluate $7^2 - 2^2$.

① Evaluate each power in the expression.

$7^2 - 2^2$
$= 7 \times \underline{7} - \underline{2} \times \underline{2}$

② Carry out the remaining operations.

$= 49 - \underline{4}$
$49 - \underline{4} = \underline{45}$

I remember! The order of operations says that I have to multiply before I add or subtract.

DISCUSS Simon and Ada evaluate $4^2 + 5^2$ differently. Simon says to add first, and then evaluate 9^2. Ada says to evaluate 4^2 and 5^2 first, and then add. Who is right, and why? Possible response: Ada is correct. The order of operations says to evaluate exponents as multiplication before adding. The correct answer is 41.

PRACTICE

Evaluate each power.

1 10^2

$\underline{10} \times \underline{10} = \underline{100}$

2 15^2

$\underline{15} \times \underline{15} = \underline{225}$

Write each repeated multiplication as a power.

3 7×7

$\underline{7^2}$

4 12×12

$\underline{12^2}$

Evaluate each expression.

5 $5^2 + 10^2$

$= \underline{5} \times \underline{5} + \underline{10} \times \underline{10}$
$= \underline{25} + \underline{100}$
$= \underline{125}$

6 $9^2 - 3^2$

$= \underline{9} \times \underline{9} - \underline{3} \times \underline{3}$
$= \underline{81} - \underline{9}$
$= \underline{72}$

• Model Application

DO A Make sure students understand that writing a squared number in expanded form means writing the base multiplied by the base.

DO B Explain that any number multiplied by itself can be written as a power of 2.

DO C Remind students of the order of operations. Exponents must be simplified before subtracting.

• **Support Discussion** **MP1** Have partners briefly discuss similarities and differences before group discussion. Ask students to recall the order of operations.

> *Prompt: Why is it important to apply the order of operations when solving this expression?*
> *Sentence Starter: The order of operations determines…*

Practice and Assess

• Ask students to complete practice items 1–6 on page 15 independently or in pairs. Monitor ongoing work.

• Use the chart below as needed to address any difficulties.

Observation	Action
Students have difficulty evaluating expressions containing exponents.	Provide grid paper for students to model square numbers. The base is the length and the width of the square. The total area of the square is the value of the squared number.

COMMON ERRORS

Students may mistakenly multiply the base by 2 instead of by itself. Remind students that the *exponent* tells how many times to multiply the *base* by itself. Have students draw squares on grid paper, and then identify the base and exponent represented by the model.

ENGLISH LANGUAGE LEARNERS

MP1 ELL students may need additional support understanding the different uses of the term *base*. Make flash cards showing the different uses, such as a baseball base, the base of a triangle, and the base of an exponential number.

		OBJECTIVES	CONCEPTS AND SKILLS	VOCABULARY
FOUNDATIONAL UNDERSTANDING	**PLUG IN** Evaluating Square Numbers	• Evaluate square numbers. • Evaluate expressions that include square numbers.	Evaluate numerical expressions involving whole-number exponents. **CCSS:** 6.EE.1	• **power** • **base** • **exponent** • **square number**
	▶ POWER UP Evaluating Cube Numbers Student Edition pp. 16–17	• Evaluate cube numbers. • Evaluate expressions that include cube numbers.	Evaluate numerical expressions involving whole-number exponents. **CCSS:** 6.EE.1	• **cube number**
ON-LEVEL TARGET	**READY TO GO** Square Roots and Cube Roots	• Evaluate square roots of small perfect squares. • Evaluate cube roots of small perfect cubes. • Solve problems that include square and cube roots.	Evaluate square roots of small perfect squares and cube roots of small perfect cubes. **CCSS:** 8.EE.2	• **square root** • **principal square root** • **cube root**

MATERIALS

• Base-10 unit cubes and thousands cubes *(suggested)*

Build Background

■ Talk to students about real-life situations that involve cube numbers. For example, a shipping box is 2 ft long, 2 ft wide, and 2 ft high. What is the volume of the box? Explain that since the box is a cube the volume can be found by calculating 2^3.

■ **MP8** Have students discuss other uses of cube numbers in real life.

■ Tell students they will use multiplication to find the value of cubed numbers.

Introduce and Model

■ **Introduce Concepts and Vocabulary** Guide students through the information about cube numbers. Emphasize that similar to squared numbers, where the base is multiplied by itself twice, the value of a cubed number is the base multiplied by itself three times. Use **Words to Know** to clarify their understanding of vocabulary. **MP7** Have students explain the similarities and differences between a *square number* and a *cube number*.

■ **Support Discussion** **MP4** Have partners discuss briefly before group discussion. Students can use unit cubes and thousands cubes to model their reasoning.

> *Prompt: Can any number be modeled as a cube? Explain.*
> *Sentence Starter: Only numbers that have three…*

SPOTLIGHT ON MATHEMATICAL LANGUAGE

MP6 Support students in using mathematical language as they work.

■ *What is the **base**?*

■ *What is the **exponent**?*

■ *How are base and exponent used to write a number as a **power**?*

POWER UP Evaluating Cube Numbers

When you raise an integer to the 3rd power, the result is called a **cube number**.

2^3 is read as "2 cubed."

To evaluate a power with an exponent of 3, write as a multiplication expression using the base for each of the three factors.

$4^3 = 4 \times 4 \times 4 = 16 \times 4 = 64$

I get it! Any power with an exponent of 3 is equal to a cube number.

I see! 64 is a cube number because it is equal to 4^3.

Words to Know

cube number
a number that is the product of the same three integer factors
125 is a cube number because $5 \times 5 \times 5 = 125$.

DISCUSS Why is a cube a good model for a cube number, such as 125?
All edges of a cube are the same length. So its length, width, and height have the same value. The volume of the cube is equal to this value cubed. So $5^3 = 125$ just as a cube with an edge length of 5 has a volume of 125 cubic units.

A You can multiply to evaluate cube numbers.

DO Evaluate 10^3 and 3^3.

❶ Write the power as repeated multiplication.

$10^3 = \underline{10} \times \underline{10} \times \underline{10}$, $3^3 = \underline{3} \times \underline{3} \times \underline{3}$

❷ Multiply.

$10 \times 10 \times 10 = \underline{1,000}$, $3 \times 3 \times 3 = \underline{27}$

B You can write repeated multiplication of three identical factors as a power.

DO Write $8 \times 8 \times 8$ and $2 \times 2 \times 2$ as powers.

❶ Identify the base. $8 \times 8 \times 8$ $2 \times 2 \times 2$

❷ Identify the exponent. The base is $\underline{8}$ The base is $\underline{2}$
The exponent is $\underline{3}$ The exponent is $\underline{3}$

❸ Write the power. $8 \times 8 \times 8 = \boxed{8}^{\boxed{3}}$ $2 \times 2 \times 2 = \boxed{2}^{\boxed{3}}$

I remember! The number being multiplied is the base. The number of times the base is used as a factor is the exponent.

C You can evaluate expressions with cube numbers.

DO Evaluate $2^3 + 4^3$.

To find a cube number, I can multiply the first two factors, then multiply that product by the third factor. So $2 \times 2 \times 2$ is 4×2, or 8.

❶ Evaluate each power in the expression.

$2^3 + 4^3$
$= 2 \times \underline{2} \times \underline{2} + \underline{4} \times \underline{4} \times \underline{4}$

❷ Carry out the remaining operations.

$= 8 + \underline{64}$
$= \underline{72}$

DISCUSS Hector says that 1 is a square number. Maggie says that 1 is a cube number. Who is correct? Explain. Possible response: Both are correct. 1 is an integer. $1^2 = 1 \times 1 = 1$, so 1 is a square number. $1^3 = 1 \times 1 \times 1 = 1 \times 1 = 1$, so 1 is also a cube number.

PRACTICE

Evaluate each power.

1 9^3
$= \underline{9} \times \underline{9} \times \underline{9}$
$= \underline{81} \times \underline{9}$
$= \underline{729}$

2 12^3
$= \underline{12} \times \underline{12} \times \underline{12}$
$= \underline{144} \times \underline{12}$
$= \underline{1,728}$

Write each expression as a power.

3 $4 \times 4 \times 4$
$\underline{4^3}$

4 $7 \times 7 \times 7$
$\underline{7^3}$

Evaluate each expression.

5 $8^3 - 3^3$
$= \underline{8} \times \underline{8} \times \underline{8} - \underline{3} \times \underline{3} \times \underline{3}$
$= \underline{512} - \underline{27}$
$= \underline{485}$

6 $2^3 + 1^3$
$= \underline{2} \times \underline{2} \times \underline{2} + \underline{1} \times \underline{1} \times \underline{1}$
$= \underline{8} + \underline{1}$
$= \underline{9}$

• Model Application

DO A Explain that evaluating a cubed number is similar to evaluating a squared number, except that the base is used as a factor one additional time.

DO B Explain that any number used as a factor 3 times can be written as a power of 3.

DO C Remind students of the order of operations. Exponents must be simplified before adding.

• **Support Discussion** MP2 MP3 Have partners briefly discuss before group discussion. Suggest students write equations to justify their reasoning.

Prompt: What is the difference between using 1 as a repeated factor and using some greater number as a repeated factor?
Sentence Starter: The values of 1^2 and 1^3 are…

Practice and Assess

• Ask students to complete practice items 1–6 on page 17 independently or in pairs. Monitor ongoing work.

• Use the chart below as needed to address any difficulties.

Observation	Action
Students do not simplify the cubed numbers before adding or subtracting.	Explain that the order of operations ensures that the same problem always gives the same result. Expressions must be solved in the following order: parentheses, exponents, multiplication and division, and addition and subtraction.

SPOTLIGHT ON MATHEMATICAL PRACTICES

MP2 Reason Abstractly

Help students reason about multiplication patterns. *Is there another number that behaves similar to 1 when it is squared or cubed? What is it?*

ENGLISH LANGUAGE LEARNERS

MP6 ELL students may need additional support understanding abstract language such as "4 cubed." Remind students that saying "4 cubed" is the same as saying "4 to the power of 3" or "4 to the third power."

Square Roots and Cube Roots

		OBJECTIVES	CONCEPTS AND SKILLS	VOCABULARY
FOUNDATIONAL UNDERSTANDING	**PLUG IN** **Evaluating Square Numbers**	• Evaluate square numbers. • Evaluate expressions that include square numbers.	Evaluate numerical expressions involving whole-number exponents. **CCSS:** 6.EE.1	• **power** • **base** • **exponent** • **square number**
	POWER UP **Evaluating Cube Numbers**	• Evaluate cube numbers. • Evaluate expressions that include cube numbers.	Evaluate numerical expressions involving whole-number exponents. **CCSS:** 6.EE.1	• **cube number**
ON-LEVEL TARGET	▶ **READY TO GO** **Square Roots and Cube Roots** Student Edition pp. 18–23	• Evaluate square roots of small perfect squares. • Evaluate cube roots of small perfect cubes. • Solve problems that include square and cube roots.	Evaluate square roots of small perfect squares and cube roots of small perfect cubes. **CCSS:** 8.EE.2	• **square root** • **principal square root** • **cube root**

MATERIALS

• Lesson 2 Quiz, Assessment Manual pp. 6–7
• Lesson 2 Quiz Answer Key, Assessment Manual
• Math Tool: Dot Paper, p. A2 (Student Edition p. 211)
• Base 10 thousands cube (*suggested*)

COMMON ERRORS

Students may misread the root symbol as division. Point out that the root symbol has a leading tail to distinguish it from a division bracket. The exponent of the power is written above the tail. When there is no exponent written with the root symbol, the exponent of 2 is understood.

Build Background

- Talk to students about real-life situation in which a square root or a cube root of a number may need to be known. For example, a mosaic is made by arranging small square tiles to create a design. The artist needs to build a square frame to contain the 121 mosaic tiles. What should be the length and width of the frame? Remind students that a characteristic of a square is congruent sides.

- **MP1** Have students discuss methods to find two equal factors given the product.

- Tell students they will use multiplication patterns to identify the square and cube roots of numbers.

Introduce and Model

- **Introduce Concepts and Vocabulary** Guide students through the information about finding square roots and cube roots. Use **Words to Know** to clarify their understanding of vocabulary. **MP4** Have students explain the relationship between square numbers and square roots (cube numbers and cube roots).

- **Support Discussion** **MP7** Have partners discuss briefly before group discussion. Refer students back to **Words to Know** *square number* and *square root* as they construct their explanations.

> *Prompt: What is the difference between a square number and a square root? Are there other similar examples?*
> *Sentence Starter: The difference between a square number and a square root is…*

14 LESSON 2

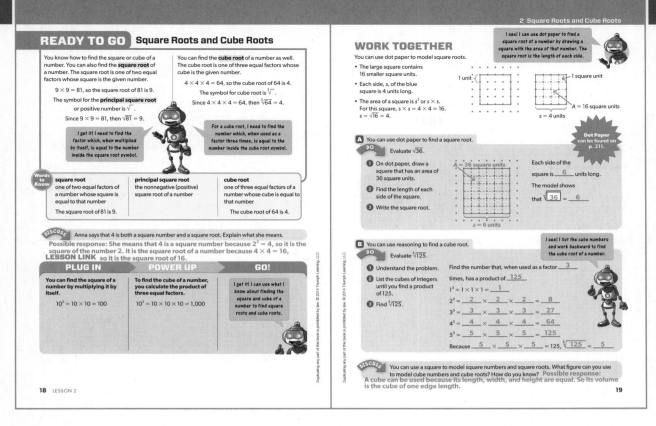

READY TO GO Square Roots and Cube Roots

You know how to find the square or cube of a number. You can also find the **square root** of a number. The square root is one of two equal factors whose square is the given number.

$9 \times 9 = 81$, so the square root of 81 is 9.

The symbol for the **principal square root** or positive number is $\sqrt{}$.

Since $9 \times 9 = 81$, then $\sqrt{81} = 9$.

I get it! I need to find the factor which, when multiplied by itself, is equal to the number inside the square root symbol.

You can find the **cube root** of a number as well. The cube root is one of three equal factors whose cube is the given number.

$4 \times 4 \times 4 = 64$, so the cube root of 64 is 4.

The symbol for cube root is $\sqrt[3]{}$.

Since $4 \times 4 \times 4 = 64$, then $\sqrt[3]{64} = 4$.

For a cube root, I need to find the number which, when used as a factor three times, is equal to the number inside the cube root symbol.

Words to Know

square root	principal square root	cube root
one of two equal factors of a number whose square is equal to that number. The square root of 81 is 9.	the nonnegative (positive) square root of a number	one of three equal factors of a number whose cube is equal to that number. The cube root of 64 is 4.

DISCUSS Anna says that 4 is both a square number and a square root. Explain what she means.
Possible response: She means that 4 is a square number because $2^2 = 4$, so it is the square of the number 2. It is the square root of a number because $4 \times 4 = 16$, so it is the square root of 16.

LESSON LINK

PLUG IN	POWER UP	GO!
You can find the square of a number by multiplying it by itself. $10^2 = 10 \times 10 = 100$	To find the cube of a number, you calculate the product of three equal factors. $10^3 = 10 \times 10 \times 10 = 1{,}000$	*I get it! I can use what I know about finding the square and cube of a number to find square roots and cube roots.*

18 LESSON 2

WORK TOGETHER
You can use dot paper to model square roots.
- The large square contains 16 smaller square units.
- Each side, s, of the blue square is 4 units long.
- The area of a square is s^2 or $s \times s$. For this square, $s \times s = 4 \times 4 = 16$. $s = \sqrt{16} = 4$.

I see! I can use dot paper to find a square root of a number by drawing a square with the area of that number. The square root is the length of each side.

1 unit   1 square unit   A = 16 square units   s = 4 units

A You can use dot paper to find a square root.
DO Evaluate $\sqrt{36}$.
1. On dot paper, draw a square that has an area of 36 square units.
2. Find the length of each side of the square.
3. Write the square root.

A = 36 square units   s = 6 units

Each side of the square is **6** units long.
The model shows that $\sqrt{36} = 6$.

Dot Paper can be found on p. 211.

B You can use reasoning to find a cube root.
DO Evaluate $\sqrt[3]{125}$.
1. Understand the problem. Find the number that, when used as a factor **3** times, has a product of **125**.
2. List the cubes of integers until you find a product of 125.
3. Find $\sqrt[3]{125}$.

$1^3 = 1 \times 1 \times 1 = 1$
$2^3 = 2 \times 2 \times 2 = 8$
$3^3 = 3 \times 3 \times 3 = 27$
$4^3 = 4 \times 4 \times 4 = 64$
$5^3 = 5 \times 5 \times 5 = 125$
Because $5 \times 5 \times 5 = 125$, $\sqrt[3]{125} = 5$.

I see! I list the cube numbers and work backward to find the cube root of a number.

DISCUSS You can use a square to model square numbers and square roots. What figure can you use to model cube numbers and cube roots? How do you know? Possible response: A cube can be used because its length, width, and height are equal. So its volume is the cube of one edge length.

19

LESSON LINK

Connect to Foundational Understanding Skills learned in the **Plug In** and **Power Up** are referenced in the **Lesson Link**. Explain that a square number is the product of two equal factors. A cube number is the product of three equal factors. The root of square or cube number is the base.

- **Work Together** Explain that students will use dot paper to model finding the square root of a number. Remind students that the area of a square is found by multiplying the length and the width. Have students count the units in both the length and the width. The square root of a square number is the length of one side of the area model.

DO A Monitor students as they draw a 6-by-6 square on dot paper. As needed, assist students in identifying the multiplication pattern of square numbers. Ask: *what is the area of a 2-by-2 square? A 3-by-3 square?*

DO B Monitor students as they expand the multiplication patterns to identify the cube root. Say, *the area of a 2-by-2 square is 4. If there are 2 layers of 4 cubes, how many cubes are there in all?* $2 \times 2 \times 2 = 4 \times 2 = 8$. *So, 2 is the cube root of 8.*

- **Support Discussion** MP Have partners briefly discuss before group discussion. Encourage students to discuss how the area of a square is related to a cube having the same length and width.

Prompt: If you have a model of a cube, how can you find the cube root? How can you find the cube number?
Sentence Starter: Since the length, width, and height of a cube are all equal, the cube root is equal to...

ENGLISH LANGUAGE LEARNERS

MP6 ELL students may need additional clarification of the difference between a square and a cube. Draw a square and point out that there are two equal measurements in a square: length and width. Hold up a base-10 thousands cube. Point out that there are three equal measurements in a cube: length, width, and height.

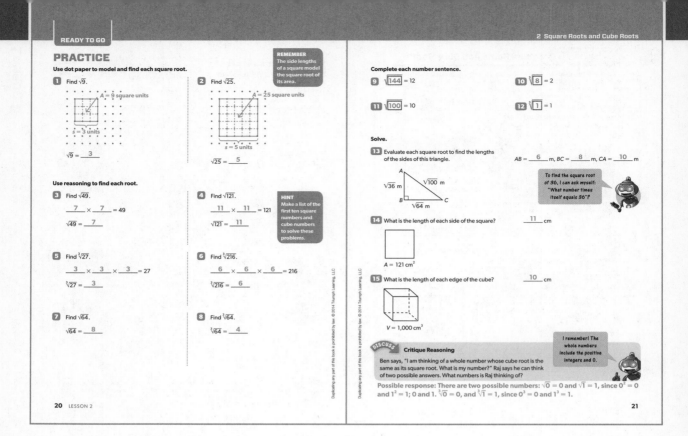

READY TO GO

PRACTICE

Use dot paper to model and find each square root.

1 Find $\sqrt{9}$.

$A = 9$ square units

$s = 3$ units

$\sqrt{9} = \underline{3}$

2 Find $\sqrt{25}$.

$A = 25$ square units

$s = 5$ units

$\sqrt{25} = \underline{5}$

> **REMEMBER**
> The side lengths of a square model the square root of its area.

Use reasoning to find each root.

3 Find $\sqrt{49}$.

$\underline{7} \times \underline{7} = 49$

$\sqrt{49} = \underline{7}$

4 Find $\sqrt{121}$.

$\underline{11} \times \underline{11} = 121$

$\sqrt{121} = \underline{11}$

> **HINT**
> Make a list of the first ten square numbers and cube numbers to solve these problems.

5 Find $\sqrt[3]{27}$.

$\underline{3} \times \underline{3} \times \underline{3} = 27$

$\sqrt[3]{27} = \underline{3}$

6 Find $\sqrt[3]{216}$.

$\underline{6} \times \underline{6} \times \underline{6} = 216$

$\sqrt[3]{216} = \underline{6}$

7 Find $\sqrt{64}$.

$\sqrt{64} = \underline{8}$

8 Find $\sqrt[3]{64}$.

$\sqrt[3]{64} = \underline{4}$

Complete each number sentence.

9 $\sqrt{\boxed{144}} = 12$

10 $\sqrt[3]{\boxed{8}} = 2$

11 $\sqrt{\boxed{100}} = 10$

12 $\sqrt[3]{\boxed{1}} = 1$

Solve.

13 Evaluate each square root to find the lengths of the sides of this triangle.

$\sqrt{36}$ m $\sqrt{100}$ m $\sqrt{64}$ m

$AB = \underline{6}$ m, $BC = \underline{8}$ m, $CA = \underline{10}$ m

> To find the square root of 36, I can ask myself: "What number times itself equals 36"?

14 What is the length of each side of the square? $\underline{11}$ cm

$A = 121$ cm^2

15 What is the length of each edge of the cube? $\underline{10}$ cm

$V = 1,000$ cm^3

> I remember! The whole numbers include the positive integers and 0.

DISCUSS **Critique Reasoning**

Ben says, "I am thinking of a whole number whose cube root is the same as its square root. What is my number?" Raj says he can think of two possible answers. What numbers is Raj thinking of?

Possible response: There are two possible numbers: $\sqrt{0} = 0$ and $\sqrt{1} = 1$, since $0^2 = 0$ and $1^2 = 1$; 0 and 1. $\sqrt[3]{0} = 0$, and $\sqrt[3]{1} = 1$, since $0^3 = 0$ and $1^3 = 1$.

20 LESSON 2

21

ADDITIONAL PRACTICE

Provide students with additional practice to model and solve:

$\sqrt{100} = ?$ $\sqrt[3]{8} = ?$

$10 = \sqrt{x}$ $7 = \sqrt[3]{z}$

SPOTLIGHT ON MATHEMATICAL PRACTICES

MP2 **Reason Abstractly**

I am a number that has both a square root and a cube root. My square root is less than 10. My cube root is half my square root. What number am I?

Encourage students to discuss strategies for solving the riddle such as making an organized list or looking for number patterns. Students should find the $8^2 = 64$ and $4^3 = 64$.

Support Independent Practice

1–8 Remind students to read the **HINT** and **REMEMBER**. If needed, have them read the problems aloud as they translate the root symbol into words. Remind students that when there is no number designated with the root symbol, square root is implied.

9–12 *If you are given the root, what do you need to do to find the square or cube number?*

13–15 *What do you know about the lengths of the sides of squares and the lengths of the edges of cubes?*

- **Support Discussion** **MP7** Have partners discuss briefly before group discussion. As needed, suggest that students make a list of square roots and cube roots.

> **Prompt:** *What are some examples of whole numbers? Is zero a whole number? Is one a whole number?*
> **Sentence Starter:** *Two whole numbers whose cube root and square root are equal…*

Problem Solving

- **Model the Four-Step Method** **MP2** Guide students through the four-step method using think-aloud strategies. Point out that the volume is given. Students are asked to find the *cube root*.

Think Aloud The box is a cube, therefore each of the edges must be the same length. To find the volume of a rectangular prism, you multiply the length, width, and height. Since the box has the same length, width, and height, you can find the cube root of 729 to find the dimensions of the box.

PROBLEM SOLVING

READY TO GO

GIFT BOXES

READ

The owner of a gift shop wants to order boxes that have a volume of 729 cubic inches. If she selects a cube-shaped box, what will the dimensions of the box be?

PLAN

- What is the problem asking you to find?

  You need to find the dimensions of the box shaped like a __cube__.

- What do you need to know to solve the problem?

  You need to know that the length, width, and height of a cube are equal.

  You can use the __volume__ of the cube-shaped box to find its __edge length__.

- How can you solve the problem?

  Use the formula $V = s^3$ and what you know about __cube__ roots to solve the problem.

SOLVE

Write the formula. $\qquad V = s^3$

Substitute the volume for V. $\qquad \dfrac{729}{} = s^3$

Find the cube root to solve for s. $\qquad \sqrt[3]{729} = s$

Think: what number cubed equals 729? $\qquad \underline{9} = s$

$\underline{9} \times \underline{9} \times \underline{9} = \underline{729}$

CHECK

Find the volume of a right rectangular prism where each edge length is __9__ inches.

The volume should be equal to __729__ cubic inches.

The volume of a right rectangular prism is the product of the area of the base, B, and the height, h.

The base of a cube is a square.

$B = (\underline{9})^2 = \underline{9} \times \underline{9} = \underline{81}$

The volume of the prism is the product of the base and the height.

$V = B \times h = \underline{81} \times \underline{9} = \underline{729}$

The dimensions of the box are __9__ inches by __9__ inches by __9__ inches.

> I remember! A cube is one type of right rectangular prism.

22 LESSON 2

PRACTICE

Use the problem-solving steps to help you.

Find the square root or cube root to solve each problem.

> Don't forget to include units for side lengths.

1 The area of the square rug in Milo's classroom is 16 square feet. What is length of each side of the rug?

4 feet

CHECKLIST
- [ ] READ
- [ ] PLAN
- [ ] SOLVE
- [ ] CHECK

2 A fish tank in a restaurant is shaped like a cube. It can hold 27 cubic feet of water. What is its height?

3 feet

CHECKLIST
- [ ] READ
- [ ] PLAN
- [ ] SOLVE
- [ ] CHECK

3 Marsha stores her school supplies in a cube-shaped box with a volume of 512 in.³. She sees that each face of the box is a square. What is the length of each edge of the top of the box?

8 in.

CHECKLIST
- [ ] READ
- [ ] PLAN
- [ ] SOLVE
- [ ] CHECK

23

- **Support Problem-Solving Practice** Have students use the Checklist as they complete each step.

  Prompt: How do you know if you are finding the square root or the cube root?

  Prompt: How can you use square roots to estimate a cube root?

  Prompt: What multiplication sentence could you write to find the product 512?

- **Explore Student Thinking** **MP8** Invite students to share how they used the information in the problems to write an expression used to find the solution.

SPOTLIGHT ON MATHEMATICAL LANGUAGE

MP6 Support students in using mathematical language as they work:

- The word **cubic** is a form of the word cube.
- What are the characteristics of a cube?
- When a measurement is given in cubic units, what does that tell you about the number?

Assess

- Use the table below to address any difficulties.

	Observation	Action
1	Errors when finding the square or cube of a number are frequent. Confusion about the meaning of square and cube roots.	Provide students with grid paper and base-10 blocks as they continue to work with square and cube numbers. Encourage students to model each number and explain their thinking.
2	Makes occasional errors when finding the square or cube of a number. Understands the meaning of square and cube root, but makes occasional computation errors.	Provide additional practice problems based on real-life situations. Have students write their own word problems that involve finding the square or cube of a number or finding the square or cube root of a number.
3	Simplifies squared and cubed numbers and identifies square and cube roots accurately.	Assign the Lesson 2 Quiz.

Scientific Notation

PLUG IN — Expressing Magnitude

		OBJECTIVES	CONCEPTS AND SKILLS	VOCABULARY
FOUNDATIONAL UNDERSTANDING	**▶ PLUG IN** **Expressing Magnitude** Student Edition pp. 24–25	• Use division to compare numbers. • Express numbers as a number of times greater than another number. • Solve problems using number comparisons.	Express how many times greater one number is than another. **CCSS:** 8.EE.3	
	POWER UP **Converting Between Scientific Notation and Standard Form**	• Write numbers in scientific notation. • Write the standard form of numbers given in scientific notation.	Understand scientific notation and convert numbers in standard form to scientific notation and vice versa. **CCSS:** 8.EE.3	• **scientific notation**
ON-LEVEL TARGET	**READY TO GO** **Scientific Notation**	• Multiply numbers that are written in scientific notation. • Divide numbers that are written in scientific notation.	Perform operations with numbers expressed in scientific notation. **CCSS:** 8.EE.4	

MATERIALS
• Different colored counters *(suggested)*

COMMON ERRORS
Students may automatically assume that the greater number is the dividend. This assumption is only true if the solution is greater than 1. Remind students to use keywords to help identify the relationship between the values.

Build Background

■ Talk to students about situations that might involve comparing one number to another. For example, the highest mountain in the world is Mt. Everest. It is more than 2 times the height of Pikes Peak in Colorado.

■ **MP4** Have students discuss other examples of comparing numbers using the number of times one value is greater than another.

■ Tell students they will use multiplication and division to compare numbers.

Introduce and Model

■ **Introduce Concepts** Guide students through the information about comparing numbers. Remind students that multiplication and division are inverse operations. Multiplication joins equal groups together, and division takes equal groups apart.

■ **Support Discussion** **MP1** Have partners discuss briefly before group discussion.

> *Prompt: If you say a number is 4 times as great as another. What does this mean?*
> *Sentence Starter: The word "times" means …*

LESSON 3 — Scientific Notation

PLUG IN — Expressing Magnitude

If you wanted to describe how many times as great a number a is than the number b, you can use multiplication. To show that a is 6 times as great as b, write $a = 6b$.

How do you show that 24 is 8 times as great as 3? Write: $24 = 8 \times 3$

So this is a new way to compare numbers.

You can also use division to describe how many times as great a number c is than d. To show that c is 5 times as great as d, write $c \div d = 5$.

How do you show that 10 is 5 times as great as 2? Write: $10 \div 2 = 5$

I get it! I can divide to find how many times as great one number is as another.

You can express how numbers are related in problem situations. Sarah ran 42 miles this week and 21 miles last week. How many times as great as 21 is 42?

$$21)\overline{42}$$
$$-42$$
$$0$$

I see! Sarah ran two times as far this week as last week.

DISCUSS Minnie says the word "times" is used to describe multiplication. She asks how this is related to questions where she is asked "how many times as great" one number is as another. What would you tell her?
Possible response: Just as 'times' is used to describe multiplication of two factors, you can use 'how many times as great' to relate a factor to a product.

A You can use division to find how many times as great one number is as another.

DO How many times as great as 25 is 250? How many times as great as 10 is 250? How many times as great as 5 is 250?

1 Divide.
$250 \div 25 =$ __10__ $250 \div 10 =$ __25__ $250 \div 5 =$ __50__

2 Express how many times as great one number is as another.
250 is __10__ times as great as 25.
250 is __25__ times as great as 10.
250 is __50__ times as great as 5.

B You can express how many times as great one number is as another.

I see! The number of times one number is as great as another can be less than 1.

DO How many times as great as 100 is 25? How many times as great as 100 is 50?

1 Divide. $25 \div 100 = \frac{1}{4}$ $50 \div 100 = \frac{1}{2}$

2 Express how many times as great one number is as another.
25 is $\frac{1}{4}$ times as great as 100.
50 is $\frac{1}{2}$ times as great as 100.

C You can solve problems using number comparisons.

DO Aiden sold 30 coupon books for a fund-raiser. Jaxon sold 4 times as many coupon books as Aiden. How many coupon books did Jaxon sell?

1 Identify the given values.   Aiden sold __30__ coupon books.
2 Write a multiplication or division equation for the comparison.   Jaxon sold __4__ times as many as Aiden.
$4 \times 30 = 120$
Jaxon sold __120__ coupon books.

DISCUSS Alexandra visited the same number of web pages today as her sister. She said, "I've visited one times as many web pages as you today." Does this statement make sense?
Possible response: Yes. If each one visited n web pages, the multiplication equation that compares the numbers is $n \times 1 = n$. So n is one times as great as itself.

PRACTICE

Solve.

1 How many times as great as 9 is 36?   __4__

2 How many times as great as 7 is 105?   __15__

3 How many times as great as 30 is 180?   __6__

4 How many times as great as 50 is 5?   __$\frac{1}{10}$__

5 An art teacher has 63 erasers. A math teacher has 21 erasers. How many times as great is the art teacher's number of erasers as the math teacher's?   __3__

6 One car dealer has 72 cars on her lot. Another car dealer has 36 cars on her lot. How many times as great is the first dealer's number of cars as the second dealer's?   __2__

7 A builder uses 36 tiles for the kitchen floor and 9 tiles for the bathroom floor. How many times as great is the number of tiles for the kitchen floor as for the bathroom floor?   __4__

8 A university has 3 vans to transport fans from the parking lot to the basketball arena. There are 75 times as many fans as there are vans. How many fans need to be transported?   __225__

24 LESSON 3   25

• Model Application

DO **A** Remind students that the question can also be phrased as multiplication: *250 is how many times greater than 25? 250 = x · 25*

DO **B** Guide students to recognize that when the final number is less that the comparative number, the solution will be less than 1. For example, 25 is less than 100, so 25 is less then 1 times as great as 100.

DO **C** *If Jaxon sold 4 times as many coupon books as Aiden did, did Jaxon sell more or less than the number Aiden sold? How do you know?*

• **Support Discussion** **MP2** Have partners discuss briefly before group discussion. If needed, suggest students choose a number to represent the number of Web pages Alexandra visited.

> *Prompt: What is true about the product of 1 and any number?*
> *Sentence Starter: The product of 1 and any number is equal to…*

Practice and Assess

• Ask students to complete practice items 1–8 on page 25 independently or in pairs. Monitor ongoing work.

• Observe whether students can write each problem as an algebraic equation. Use the chart below as needed to address any difficulties.

Observation	Action
Students have difficulty identifying the relationship between values.	Suggest that students circle the greater number being referred to in each description.

SPOTLIGHT ON MATHEMATICAL PRACTICES

MP1 Make Sense of Problems

Mathematically proficient students start by explaining to themselves the meaning of a problem and looking for entry points to its solution. Since multiplication and division are inverse operations, either operation can be used to solve these problems. Students may find they prefer one method over another.

ENGLISH LANGUAGE LEARNERS

MP1 ELL students may need additional support understanding the abstract language "times as great." Use different colored counters to demonstrate and use phrasing that names the objects such as "There are 4 times as many red counters as blue counters."

Converting Between Scientific Notation and Standard Form

		OBJECTIVES	CONCEPTS AND SKILLS	VOCABULARY
FOUNDATIONAL UNDERSTANDING	**PLUG IN** **Expressing Magnitude**	• Use division to compare numbers. • Express numbers as a number of times greater than another number. • Solve problems using number comparisons.	Express how many times greater one number is than another. **CCSS:** 8.EE.3	
	▶ POWER UP **Converting Between Scientific Notation and Standard Form** Student Edition pp. 26–27	• Write numbers in scientific notation. • Write the standard form of numbers given in scientific notation.	Understand scientific notation and convert numbers in standard form to scientific notation and vice versa. **CCSS:** 8.EE.3	• **scientific notation**
ON-LEVEL TARGET	**READY TO GO** **Scientific Notation**	• Multiply numbers that are written in scientific notation. • Divide numbers that are written in scientific notation.	Perform operations with numbers expressed in scientific notation. **CCSS:** 8.EE.4	

MATERIALS
• Colored pencils *(suggested)*

COMMON ERRORS
Students may write numbers in scientific notation with a coefficient greater than 10. Remind students that the coefficient must be greater than or equal to 1 and less than 10.

Build Background
▪ Talk to students about examples of very large numbers. For example, scientists often use very large numbers. The mass of the sun is 1,988,920,000,000,000,000,000,000,000,000 kilograms.
▪ **MP4** Have students discuss other examples of very large numbers.
▪ Tell students they will learn an abbreviated method for writing very large numbers.

Introduce and Model
▪ **Introduce and Model** Guide the students through the information about writing numbers in scientific notation. Explain that scientific notation uses decimal values times 10 to a power. Use **Words to Know** to clarify their understanding of vocabulary. **MP7** Have students describe the relationship between the number of zeros in 500 million to the exponent of the same number written in scientific notation.

▪ **Support Discussion** **MP2** Have partners discuss briefly before group discussion. Students can use abstract reasoning by referring back to the examples.

> *Prompt: Is the first factor of a number written in scientific notation always a single digit? Explain.*
> *Sentence Starter: The number of digits in numbers from 1 to less than 10 depends on…*

POWER UP
Converting Between Scientific Notation and Standard Form

A number in **scientific notation** is the product of a factor greater than or equal to 1 and less than 10, and a power of ten.

$$3 \times 10^9$$

To convert a number in scientific notation to standard form, expand the power of 10 and multiply it by the other factor.

$$5 \times 10^8 = 5 \times 100,000,000$$
$$= 500,000,000$$

To convert a number in standard form to scientific notation, first move the decimal point to form the factor equal to or greater than 1 and less than 10. Then use the number of places the decimal point moves as the power of 10.

$$0.000026 = 000002.6 \times 10^{-5}$$

$$340,000 = 3.40000 \times 10^5$$

I see! Scientific notation is a way to write a number using a multiplication expression.

So scientific notation lets me write a number with many zeros between the decimal point and a nonzero digit in an equivalent form.

I see! Numbers greater than or equal to 10 have positive exponents. Numbers less than 1 have negative exponents.

Words to Know

scientific notation
a way to express numbers using a multiplication expression in which the first factor, the coefficient, is a number that is greater than or equal to 1 and less than 10, and the second factor is a power of 10

$$3 \times 10^4 = 3 \times 10,000 = 30,000$$
$$0.025 = 2.5 \times 10^{-2}$$

DISCUSS Marcus wants to write 50,000 using scientific notation. He writes 50×10^3. Is he correct? Explain. **Possible response:** No, the first factor in scientific notation should be greater than or equal to 1 and less than 10. Possible response: 50 is greater than 10. The correct coefficient is 5. The power of 10 is then 10^4. He should write 5×10^4.

A You can write numbers in scientific notation.

DO Write 53,000 in scientific notation.

1. Move the decimal point to form the factor greater than or equal to 1 and less than 10. 5 . 3 000

2. Count the number of places the decimal point moved. The decimal point moved $\underline{4}$ places.

3. Write this number as the exponent for the power of 10. $10^{\boxed{4}}$

4. Write the first factor and the power of 10 as a multiplication expression. $5 . 3 \times 10^{\boxed{4}}$

B You can write numbers in scientific notation in standard form.

DO Write 1.81×10^{-6} in standard form.

I know the number will be between 0 and 1 because the exponent is negative.

1. Determine the location of the decimal point based on the exponent of the power of 10. The exponent of the power of 10 is $\underline{-6}$. The decimal point will be $\underline{6}$ places to the $\underline{\text{left}}$.

2. Write the number in standard form. 0.00000181

DISCUSS Ashton says if he wrote 3.1×10^{-3} in standard form, it would be a negative number. How would you explain his mistake? **Possible response:** The number will be positive and between 0 and 1. The exponent indicates where the decimal point will be, not whether the number will be positive or negative.

PRACTICE

Rewrite each number in standard form.

1. 5×10^6
5,000,000

2. 3×10^{-10}
0.0000000003

3. 6.5×10^{-3}
0.0065

4. 7.7×10^{-4}
0.00077

5. 9.7×10^9
9,700,000,000

6. 8×10^7
80,000,000

Rewrite each number in scientific notation.

7. 0.000000001
1×10^{-9}

8. 40,000,000,000
4×10^{10}

9. 0.00000098
9.8×10^{-7}

10. 900,000,000
9×10^8

11. 0.00000000041
4.1×10^{-10}

12. 0.00000089
8.9×10^{-7}

26 LESSON 3

27

Model Application

DO A Guide students to count the number of places the decimal needs to be moved to in order to represent a number n: $1 \leq n < 10$.

DO B Guide students to recognize that when the exponent is positive, the standard form is a whole number. Therefore, when the exponent is negative, the standard form is a decimal number.

Support Discussion MP4 Have partners discuss briefly before group discussion. Encourage students to use examples and number patterns to help support their answers.

Prompt: What does the negative exponent of a number written in scientific notation tell you?
Sentence Starter: The negative exponent indicates …

Practice and Assess

- Ask students to complete practice items 1–12 on page 27 independently or in pairs. Monitor ongoing work.
- Observe whether students accurately write the correct form of the number. Use the chart below as needed to address any difficulties.

Observation	Action
Students have difficulty writing the standard form of a number given in scientific notation.	Have students write the first factor. Then, starting at the decimal and moving to the left for negative exponents or to the right for positive exponents, have students make loops equal to the exponent in order to locate the decimal point.

ENGLISH LANGUAGE LEARNERS

MP4 Use colored pencils to show the decimal "moving" as students convert from standard form to scientific notation. Use one color if decimal is moving from right to left (negative exponent) and a different color if decimal is moving from left to right (positive exponent).

SPOTLIGHT ON MATHEMATICAL LANGUAGE

MP6 Support students in using mathematical language as they work:
- The number 53,000 is written in **standard form**.
- The number 1.81×10^{-6} is written in **scientific notation**.

		OBJECTIVES	CONCEPTS AND SKILLS	VOCABULARY
FOUNDATIONAL UNDERSTANDING	**PLUG IN** **Expressing Magnitude**	• Use division to compare numbers. • Express numbers as a number of times greater than another number. • Solve problems using number comparisons.	Express how many times greater one number is than another. **CCSS:** 8.EE.3	
	POWER UP **Converting Between Scientific Notation and Standard Form**	• Write numbers in scientific notation. • Write the standard form of numbers given in scientific notation.	Understand scientific notation and convert numbers in standard form to scientific notation and vice versa. **CCSS:** 8.EE.3	• **scientific notation**
ON-LEVEL TARGET	▶ **READY TO GO** **Scientific Notation** Student Edition pp. 28–33	• Multiply numbers that are written in scientific notation. • Divide numbers that are written in scientific notation.	Perform operations with numbers expressed in scientific notation. **CCSS:** 8.EE.4	

MATERIALS

- Lesson 3 Quiz, Assessment Manual pp. 8–9
- Lesson 3 Quiz Answer Key, Assessment Manual

SPOTLIGHT ON MATHEMATICAL LANGUAGE

MP6 Support students in using mathematical language as they work:

- *What is the* **coefficient** *in a number written in scientific notation?*
- *What is the* **base** *in a number written in scientific notation?*

Build Background

- Talk to students about situations that might require multiplying or dividing numbers written in scientific notation. For example, the mass of the sun is 333,000 times as great as the mass of Earth. So, the mass of Earth is equal to $(1.98892 \times 10^{30}) \div (3.33 \times 10^5)$.

- **MP4** Have students discuss additional examples of real situations that involve multiplying and dividing numbers written in scientific notation.

Introduce and Model

- **Introduce Concepts** Emphasize that division is one way to compare how many times as great one number is as another.

- **Support Discussion** **MP3** Have partners discuss briefly before group discussion. Encourage students to express the steps in order.

> *Prompt: How can you multiply two numbers written in scientific notation?*
>
> *Sentence Starter: To multiply two numbers written in scientific notation, first multiply the …*

LESSON LINK

Connect to Foundational Understanding Skills learned in the **Plug In** and **Power Up** are referenced in the **Lesson Link**. Explain that division is one way to compare how many times as great one number is as another. When comparing very large or very small numbers, it is useful to write the numbers in scientific notation before dividing.

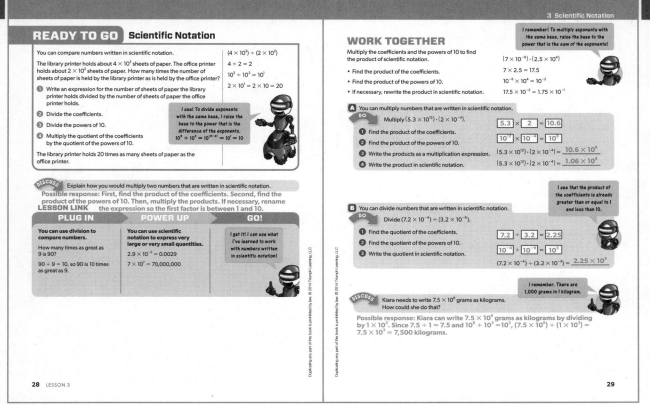

- **Work Together** Explain that students will find the product or quotient of numbers written in scientific notation. Remind students that only exponential numbers with like bases can be multiplied or divided. Since the base of an exponential number is always written as a power of 10, the product or quotient of the bases is always 10 to the sum or difference of the powers.

DO **A** Monitor students as they find the product of two numbers written in scientific notation. Remind students that multiplication is commutative, so the order of the factors can be changed without affecting the product. $(5.3 \times 10^{12}) \cdot (2 \times 10^{-4})$ can be rewritten as $(5.3 \times 2) \cdot (10^{12} \times 10^{-4})$.

DO **B** Monitor students as they find the quotient of two numbers written in scientific notation. Remind students that fractions are another way to show division. $\frac{(7.2 \times 10^{-4})}{(3.2 \times 10^{-9})}$ can be rewritten as $\frac{7.2}{3.2} \cdot \frac{10^{-4}}{10^{-9}}$. Simplify each fraction and write the solution as a product of a decimal number and a power of 10.

- **Support Discussion** MP6 Have partners discuss briefly before group discussion. Suggest students write 1 kilogram in terms of grams in scientific notation. Then write an equation to divide the numbers written in scientific notation.

> *Prompt:* How many grams are equal to 1 kilogram? Will the number of kilograms be greater than or less than the number of grams?
> *Sentence Starter:* To convert grams to kilograms…

ENGLISH LANGUAGE LEARNERS

MP6 Traditionally, the *coefficient* is the constant multiplied by a variable, and a *base* is the number being raised to a power. Remind students that the terms *coefficient* and *base* have slightly different meanings when working with numbers written in scientific notation.

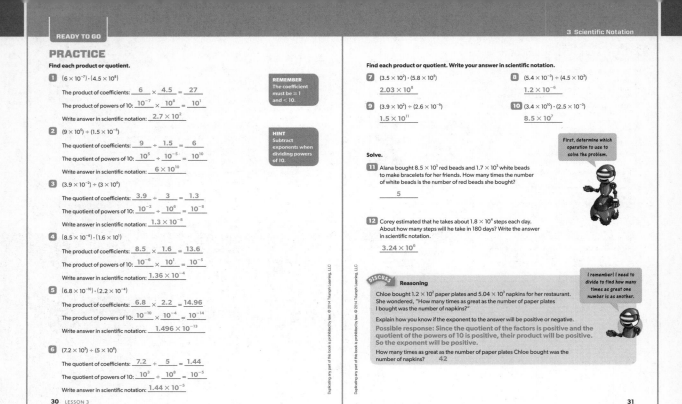

READY TO GO

PRACTICE

Find each product or quotient.

1 $(6 \times 10^{-7}) \cdot (4.5 \times 10^{8})$

The product of coefficients: $\underline{6} \times \underline{4.5} = \underline{27}$

The product of powers of 10: $\underline{10^{-7}} \times \underline{10^{8}} = \underline{10^{1}}$

Write answer in scientific notation: $\underline{2.7 \times 10^{2}}$

2 $(9 \times 10^{5}) \div (1.5 \times 10^{-5})$

The quotient of coefficients: $\underline{9} \div \underline{1.5} = \underline{6}$

The quotient of powers of 10: $\underline{10^{5}} \div \underline{10^{-5}} = \underline{10^{10}}$

Write answer in scientific notation: $\underline{6 \times 10^{10}}$

3 $(3.9 \times 10^{-2}) \div (3 \times 10^{6})$

The quotient of coefficients: $\underline{3.9} \div \underline{3} = \underline{1.3}$

The quotient of powers of 10: $\underline{10^{-2}} \div \underline{10^{6}} = \underline{10^{-8}}$

Write answer in scientific notation: $\underline{1.3 \times 10^{-8}}$

4 $(8.5 \times 10^{-6}) \cdot (1.6 \times 10^{1})$

The product of coefficients: $\underline{8.5} \times \underline{1.6} = \underline{13.6}$

The product of powers of 10: $\underline{10^{-6}} \times \underline{10^{1}} = \underline{10^{-5}}$

Write answer in scientific notation: $\underline{1.36 \times 10^{-4}}$

5 $(6.8 \times 10^{-10}) \cdot (2.2 \times 10^{-4})$

The product of coefficients: $\underline{6.8} \times \underline{2.2} = \underline{14.96}$

The product of powers of 10: $\underline{10^{-10}} \times \underline{10^{-4}} = \underline{10^{-14}}$

Write answer in scientific notation: $\underline{1.496 \times 10^{-13}}$

6 $(7.2 \times 10^{3}) \div (5 \times 10^{8})$

The quotient of coefficients: $\underline{7.2} \div \underline{5} = \underline{1.44}$

The quotient of powers of 10: $\underline{10^{3}} \div \underline{10^{8}} = \underline{10^{-5}}$

Write answer in scientific notation: $\underline{1.44 \times 10^{-5}}$

REMEMBER
The coefficient must be ≥ 1 and < 10.

HINT
Subtract exponents when dividing powers of 10.

Find each product or quotient. Write your answer in scientific notation.

7 $(3.5 \times 10^{2}) \cdot (5.8 \times 10^{5})$

$\underline{2.03 \times 10^{8}}$

8 $(5.4 \times 10^{-3}) \div (4.5 \times 10^{3})$

$\underline{1.2 \times 10^{-6}}$

9 $(3.9 \times 10^{2}) \div (2.6 \times 10^{-9})$

$\underline{1.5 \times 10^{11}}$

10 $(3.4 \times 10^{10}) \cdot (2.5 \times 10^{-3})$

$\underline{8.5 \times 10^{7}}$

First, determine which operation to use to solve the problem.

Solve.

11 Alana bought 8.5×10^{3} red beads and 1.7×10^{3} white beads to make bracelets for her friends. How many times the number of white beads is the number of red beads she bought?

$\underline{\quad 5 \quad}$

12 Corey estimated that he takes about 1.8×10^{4} steps each day. About how many steps will he take in 180 days? Write the answer in scientific notation.

$\underline{3.24 \times 10^{6}}$

DISCUSS

Reasoning

Chloe bought 1.2×10^{5} paper plates and 5.04×10^{3} napkins for her restaurant. She wondered, "How many times as great as the number of paper plates I bought was the number of napkins?"

Explain how you know if the exponent to the answer will be positive or negative.

Possible response: Since the quotient of the factors is positive and the quotient of the powers of 10 is positive, their product will be positive. So the exponent will be positive.

How many times as great as the number of paper plates Chloe bought was the number of napkins? $\underline{42}$

I remember! I need to divide to find how many times as great one number is as another.

Provide students with additional practice to model and solve:

$(3.06 \times 10^{4}) \cdot (3.22 \times 10^{-6})$

$(8.748 \times 10^{-8}) \div (1.62 \times 10^{2})$

$(4.03 \times 10^{12}) \cdot (2.35 \times 10^{-7})$

$(6.825 \times 10^{-5}) \div (2.1 \times 10^{-9})$

ENGLISH LANGUAGE LEARNERS

MP1 If students have difficulty remembering the terms *product*, *quotient*, *coefficient*, or *base*, suggest they write each word on an index card with a definition and example. Students should keep these reference cards handy as they work through the problems.

Support Independent Practice

1–6 Remind students to read the **HINT** and **REMEMBER**. If needed, remind students to use the commutative property of multiplication to rewrite the expressions before finding the product or quotient.

7–10 Remind students to pay close attention to the sign of the exponent before simplifying the base of the scientific notation.

11–12 Encourage students to write an algebraic expression for the word problem before solving. Interpreting the meaning of the questions can help students accurately set up the expression.

- **Support Discussion** **MP1** Have students write an algebraic expression. Remind students to put parentheses around each number in scientific notation to avoid issues with the order of operations.

> *Prompt:* What determines whether the exponent of a number written in scientific notation will be positive or negative?
>
> *Sentence Starter:* The value of a number that has a positive exponent when written in exponential form will be…

Problem Solving

- **Model the Four-Step Method** **MP2** **MP4** Guide students through the four-step method using think-aloud strategies. Point out that the problem is asking for the relationship between the amount of chlorine and the amount of water.

Think Aloud There are 1.92×10^{6} milligrams of chlorine divided equally among 6.4×10^{5} liters of water, or $\frac{chlorine}{water}$.

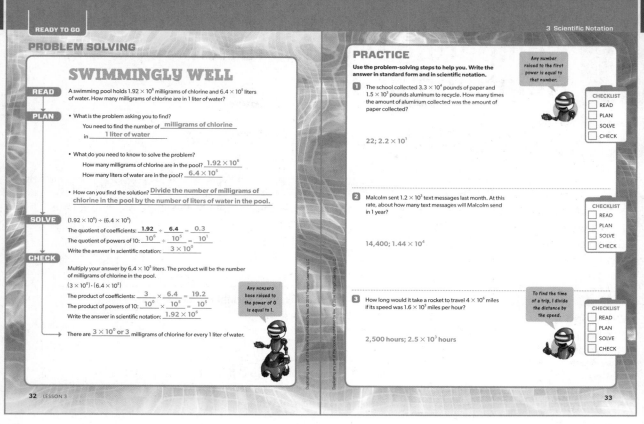

- **Support Problem-Solving Practice** Have students use the Checklist as they complete each step.

> **Prompt:** *Which is the greater number?*
> **Prompt:** *How is 14.4 × 10³ written in scientific notation?*
> **Prompt:** *Which is the dividend and which is the divisor?*

- **Explore Student Thinking** MP2 Invite students to share their reasoning and problem-solving strategies.

MP2 Reason Abstractly and Quantitatively

Help students think about the meaning of the values in word problems. Since every value written in scientific notation is from 1 to less than 10, comparing the exponent of the base is a quick way to determine which number is the greater value.

Assess

- Use the table below to address any difficulties as needed before the quiz.

	Observation	Action
1	Frequent errors in setting up expressions and finding solutions. General confusion about multiplying and dividing numbers written in scientific notation.	Model picking out keywords in the problems. For example, *how much* implies an unknown amount. Model writing the expressions using both multiplication and division to help students understand the relationship between the operations.
2	Occasional errors in setting up expressions or finding solutions. Some misunderstanding about multiplying and dividing numbers in scientific notation.	Encourage students to list the information given in the problem. For example, in Problem 1, the list would include the following: paper: 3.3×10^4 pounds; aluminum: 1.5×10^3 pounds; paper > aluminum. Ask: *How many times greater?*
3	Accurately multiplies and divides numbers in scientific notation.	Assign the Lesson 3 Quiz.

Comparing Proportional Relationships

PLUG IN Unit Rate and Slope of a Line

		OBJECTIVES	CONCEPTS AND SKILLS	VOCABULARY
FOUNDATIONAL UNDERSTANDING	**▶ PLUG IN** **Unit Rate and Slope of a Line** Student Edition pp. 34–35	• Find the slope of a graph to determine the unit rate.	Interpret the unit rate as the slope of the graph. **CCSS:** 8.EE.5	• **unit rate** • **slope**
	POWER UP **Graphing a Proportional Relationship**	• Graph proportional relationships from tables and verbal descriptions.	Graph proportional relationships. **CCSS:** 8.EE.5	
ON-LEVEL TARGET	**READY TO GO** **Comparing Proportional Relationships**	• Compare proportional relationships represented in different ways.	Compare two different proportional relationships represented in different ways. **CCSS:** 8.EE.5	

MATERIALS

• Highlighters (*suggested*)
• graphing calculator (*suggested*)
• graph of $y = 2x$ (*suggested*)

ENGLISH LANGUAGE LEARNERS

MP8 ELL students may find it difficult to find the slope of a line. Provide students with a graph of the line $y = 2x$. Using one color highlighter, have students draw and label the rise. Using another color highlighter, have students draw and label the run. Then have students find the slope of the line using the format shown below.

$$\text{slope} = \frac{\text{rise}}{\text{run}} = \frac{\text{change in } y}{\text{change in } x} = \frac{2}{1}$$

Students should highlight the words *rise* and *run* to match their graphs. Have students use this as a reference.

Build Background

■ Talk to students about reasons to find unit rates from graphs in real life. For example, the cost of 2, 3, and 4 concert tickets is $24, $36, and $48. What is the cost of 1 concert ticket? Explain that by graphing this relationship you can find the unit rate, which will answer this question.

■ **MP4** Have students discuss additional examples of real situations that involve finding the unit rate from a graph.

■ Tell students they will work on finding the slope of a graph to determine the unit rate.

Introduce and Model

■ **Introduce Concepts and Vocabulary** Guide students through the information about unit rates and slope. Emphasize that the *slope* is also called the rate of change. The *slope* of a line can be positive or negative. Use **Words to Know** to clarify their understanding of vocabulary. **MP4** Have students write the everyday usage of the terms *unit rate* and *slope*. Then have students compare those definitions to the mathematical definitions.

■ **Support Discussion** **MP7** Have partners discuss briefly before group discussion. As needed, remind students of how a constant rate of change is represented graphically.

> *Prompt: What is true about the rate of change for this graph?*
> *Sentence Starter: To calculate the slope …*

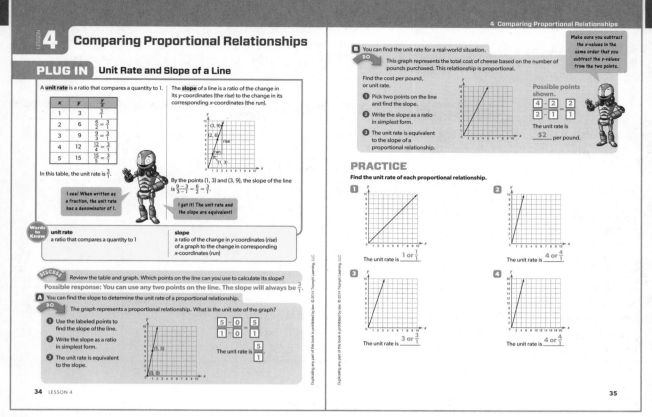

Model Application

DO **A** Guide students as they find the slope of the line to determine the unit rate. Remind students that it does not matter which two points you use to find the slope.

DO **B** Monitor students as they find and interpret the unit rate. Remind students that the slope of the line is the unit rate.

COMMON ERRORS
When finding the slope of a line, students may write the change in y in the denominator and the change of x in the numerator. Remind students of the definition of slope.

Practice and Assess

- Ask students to complete practice items 1–4 on page 35 independently or in pairs. Monitor ongoing work.

- Observe whether students are correctly finding the unit rate. Use the chart below as needed to address any difficulties.

Observation	Action
Students have difficulty finding the slope.	Have students practice finding the slope of a line using a graphing calculator. Students should work in pairs. Provide students with a list of equations to graph in the form $y = mx$, where m represents the slope of the graph. One student should graph the equation on the calculator. The other student should find the slope from the graph. Students should alternate roles.

Graphing a Proportional Relationship

		OBJECTIVES	CONCEPTS AND SKILLS	VOCABULARY
FOUNDATIONAL UNDERSTANDING	**PLUG IN** Unit Rate and Slope of a Line	• Find the slope of a graph to determine the unit rate.	Interpret the unit rate as the slope of the graph. **CCSS:** 8.EE.5	• **unit rate** • **slope**
	▶ POWER UP Graphing a Proportional Relationship Student Edition pp. 36–37	• Graph proportional relationships from tables and verbal descriptions.	Graph proportional relationships. **CCSS:** 8.EE.5	
ON-LEVEL TARGET	**READY TO GO** Comparing Proportional Relationships	• Compare proportional relationships represented in different ways.	Compare two different proportional relationships represented in different ways. **CCSS:** 8.EE.5	

MATERIALS

- Math Tool: Coordinate Grid, p. A12 (Student Edition p. 231)
- Index cards (suggested)
- Highlighters (suggested)

ENGLISH LANGUAGE LEARNERS

MP3 Students may need additional support in identifying proportional relationships from graphs. Make sets of index cards. On the front of the card, provide a graph of a proportional or nonproportional relationship. Then on the back provide the answer. Working in pairs, students should discuss whether the graph shows a proportional relationship.

Build Background

- Talk to students about reasons to graph proportional relationships. For example, Annie paid $7, $10.50, and $14 for 2, 3, and 4 ice cream sundaes. What is the cost of 1 sundae? Explain that this question can be answered by graphing this proportional relationship.

- **MP4** Have students discuss additional examples of real situations in which they would graph proportional relationships.

- Tell students they will graph proportional relationships from tables and descriptions.

Introduce and Model

- **Introduce and Model** Guide students through the information about proportional relationships. Emphasize that the graph of a proportional relationship must contain the point (0, 0) and be a straight line.

- **Support Discussion** **MP3** Have partners discuss briefly before group discussion. As needed, remind students that the slope of a proportional relationship must be constant.

> Prompt: What are the characteristics of a graph of a
> proportional relationship?
> Sentence Starter: The graph of a proportional relationship...

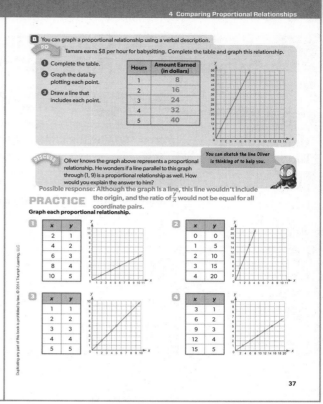

POWER UP   Graphing a Proportional Relationship

In a proportional relationship, the ratios of the quantities compared are the same.

You can use the values in the table as coordinate pairs to create a graph of the proportional relationship.

Weight (in pounds)	Cost (in dollars)	Ratio
1	2	$\frac{2}{1}$
2	4	$\frac{4}{2} = \frac{2}{1}$
3	6	$\frac{6}{3} = \frac{2}{1}$
4	8	$\frac{8}{4} = \frac{2}{1}$

I see! Since each of the ratios can be written as $\frac{2}{1}$, the table shows a proportional relationship.

I remember! The graph of a proportional relationship is a line that passes through the origin.

Ming bought 10 pounds of meat for $30. If this relationship between cost and weight were graphed, how would she know if the relationship was proportional?
Possible response: The ratio of cost and weight should be constant, so the graph should be linear and pass through the origin.

A You can identify a proportional relationship by graphing a table of data.

Graph the relationship shown in the table.
1. Plot each point.
2. Connect the points with a line.
3. Determine if the line passes through the origin.

x	y
1	4
2	8
3	12
4	16
5	20

The line includes the origin. The table represents a proportional relationship.

B You can graph a proportional relationship using a verbal description.

Tamara earns $8 per hour for babysitting. Complete the table and graph this relationship.
1. Complete the table.
2. Graph the data by plotting each point.
3. Draw a line that includes each point.

Hours	Amount Earned (in dollars)
1	8
2	16
3	24
4	32
5	40

Oliver knows the graph above represents a proportional relationship. He wonders if a line parallel to this graph through (1, 9) is a proportional relationship as well. How would you explain the answer to him?

You can sketch the line Oliver is thinking of to help you.

Possible response: Although the graph is a line, this line wouldn't include the origin, and the ratio of $\frac{y}{x}$ would not be equal for all coordinate pairs.

PRACTICE
Graph each proportional relationship.

1

x	y
2	1
4	2
6	3
8	4
10	5

2

x	y
0	0
1	5
2	10
3	15
4	20

3

x	y
1	1
2	2
3	3
4	4
5	5

4

x	y
3	1
6	2
9	3
12	4
15	5

36 LESSON 4

37

Model Application

DO **A** Guide students through the steps of graphing a table of data to determine if a relationship is proportional. If needed, remind students of how to graph ordered pairs on the coordinate plane.

DO **B** Guide students in completing the table of data. Monitor that students graph the line correctly.

Support Discussion **MP3** Have partners discuss briefly before group discussion. As needed, remind students of the definition of a parallel line.

> *Prompt:* How could you determine if the parallel line is proportional?
>
> *Sentence Starter:* I would explain to Oliver...

Practice and Assess

- Ask students to complete practice items 1–4 on page 37 independently or in pairs. Monitor ongoing work.
- Observe whether students correctly graph proportional relationships. Use the chart below as needed to address any difficulties.

Observation	Action
Students do not graph proportional relationships correctly.	Have students review how to graph points on the coordinate grid. Using blank coordinate grids, students should highlight the x-coordinates of the table with the same color as the x-axis and highlight the y-coordinates of the table with the same color as the y-axis.

READY TO GO — Comparing Proportional Relationships

		OBJECTIVES	CONCEPTS AND SKILLS	VOCABULARY
FOUNDATIONAL UNDERSTANDING	**PLUG IN** Unit Rate and Slope of a Line	• Find the slope of a graph to determine the unit rate.	Interpret the unit rate as the slope of the graph. **CCSS:** 8.EE.5	• **unit rate** • **slope**
	POWER UP Graphing a Proportional Relationship	• Graph proportional relationships from tables and verbal descriptions.	Graph proportional relationships. **CCSS:** 8.EE.5	
ON-LEVEL TARGET	**► READY TO GO** Comparing Proportional Relationships Student Edition pp. 38–43	• Compare proportional relationships represented in different ways.	Compare two different proportional relationships represented in different ways. **CCSS:** 8.EE.5	

MATERIALS

- Lesson 4 Quiz, Assessment Manual pp. 10–11
- Lesson 4 Quiz Answer Key, Assessment Manual
- Highlighters (*suggested*)

ENGLISH LANGUAGE LEARNERS

MP8 Students may need additional support for understanding how to identify the unit rate from an equation. Have students practice identifying the unit rate in given equations. Give students a list of equations that contain negative, decimal, and fraction coefficients of *x*. Students should highlight the entire coefficient of *x*.

Build Background

- Talk to students about reasons to compare proportional relationships that are represented in different ways. For example, Alexis wants to buy a photo printer. The number of photos, *y*, that the ZOOM printer can print in *x* minutes is represented by $y = 4x$. Printer LX can print 3, 6, and 9 photos in 1 minute, 2 minutes, and 3 minutes. If Alexis wanted to buy the photo printer with the faster unit rate, which printer should she buy? Explain that by comparing the unit rates of these proportional relationships you can answer this question.

- **MP4** Have students discuss additional examples of real situations that require comparing proportional relationships.

- Tell students they will compare proportional relationships that are represented in different ways.

Introduce and Model

- **Introduce Concepts and Vocabulary** Guide students through the information about how proportional relationships can be represented in tables, graphs, and equations. Emphasize that *k* represents the slope of the line, the unit rate, and the constant rate of change.

- **Support Discussion** **MP3** Have partners discuss briefly before group discussion. If needed, recall how to identify the unit rate from an equation.

> *Prompt: What is different about these two equations?*
> *Sentence Starter: The equation has...*

READY TO GO — Comparing Proportional Relationships

Proportional relationships can be represented using a table or graph.

x	2	4	6	8	10
y	3	6	9	12	15

The unit rate is $\frac{1.5}{1}$.

The slope is $\frac{3}{2}$ or 1.5.

Another way to represent a proportional relationship is with an equation.

All proportional relationships have the form $y = kx$, where k is any nonzero number and represents the unit rate (or slope).

The equation is $y = 1.5x$.

I know this is a proportional relationship because the ratio $\frac{y}{x}$ is constant in the table, and because the graph is a line that passes through the origin.

I see! To find the unit rate of a proportional relationship expressed as an equation, I can just look at the coefficient of x.

DISCUSS Compare the proportional relationship $y = 3x$ to $y = 1.5x$. Which has a greater unit rate? How do you know?

$y = 3x$. Possible response: $y = 3x$ has a greater unit rate because $3 > 1.5$.

LESSON LINK

PLUG IN

You can determine the unit rate of a proportional relationship by finding the constant ratio $\frac{y}{x}$ in a table of values or the slope of its graph.

x	1	2	3	4	5
y	4	8	12	16	20

POWER UP

You can graph a proportional relationship, which is represented by a line that passes through the origin.

GO!

I see! I can compare proportional relationships represented as graphs, tables, or equations by finding the unit rate.

WORK TOGETHER

You can compare two proportional relationships by finding their unit rates.

- Find Sherine's unit rate.
- Find Devon's unit rate.
- Compare the unit rates.

I see! The words "constant rate" let me know that these relationships are proportional.

Sherine and Devon each handed out flyers at a constant rate. Sherine made a table of the number of flyers she handed out, and Devon made a graph. Who handed out flyers at a greater rate?

Sherine's Table

Flyers Passed Out over Time

Hours	Flyers
0	0
1	7
2	14
3	21
4	28

Devon's Graph

Flyers Passed Out over Time

The unit rate is the change in quantity per unit of measure.

Sherine's rate $= \frac{\text{change in flyers}}{\text{change in hours}} = \frac{14 - 7 \text{ flyers}}{2 - 1 \text{ hours}} = \frac{7 \text{ flyers}}{1 \text{ hour}} = 7$ flyers per hour

The slope of a graph is equal to the unit rate.

$$\text{Slope} = \frac{\text{change in y-coordinates}}{\text{change in x-coordinates}}$$

Slope of Devon's graph $= \frac{15 - 10 \text{ flyers}}{3 - 2 \text{ hours}} = \frac{5 \text{ flyers}}{1 \text{ hour}} = 5$ flyers per hour

Sherine's rate is greater.

A You can compare proportional relationships that are represented in different ways.

DO Dwayne used the equation $y = 3.25x$ to represent the total cost when buying x gallons of gasoline in City A. Dena created a table to represent the total cost when buying x gallons of gasoline in City B. Which city sells gasoline at a lower unit rate?

x	2	4	6	8	10
y	6.40	12.80	19.20	25.60	32.00
$\frac{y}{x}$	$\frac{6.40}{2} = 3.20$	$\frac{12.80}{4} = 3.20$	$\frac{19.20}{6} = 3.20$	$\frac{25.60}{8} = 3.20$	$\frac{32.00}{10} = 3.20$

① Identify the unit rate for City A. The equation $y = 3.25x$ represents City A.

② Calculate the unit rate for City B. The unit rate is __3.20__.

③ Compare unit rates. __3.25__ > __3.20__. City __B__ sells gasoline at a lower unit rate.

DISCUSS If you know the table of values for a proportional relationship, how could you express the relationship as an equation? Possible response: Calculate the unit rate by finding $\frac{y}{x}$. Then write the unit rate as k, the coefficient, in the equation $y = kx$.

LESSON LINK

Connect to Foundational Understanding Skills learned in the **Plug In** and **Power Up** are referenced in the **Lesson Link**. Explain that proportional relationships can be represented in tables, graphs, equations, and descriptions. Proportional relationships represented in different ways can be compared. To compare these relationships, find and interpret the unit rates.

- **Work Together** Explain that students will compare proportional relationships that are presented in different ways (tables, graphs, equations, and descriptions) by comparing their unit rates.

DO **A** Monitor students as they identify the unit rate for each relationship. Remind students that after finding the unit rates they need to answer the question by comparing the unit rates.

- **Support Discussion** **MP1** Have partners discuss briefly before group discussion. As needed, have students explain how to find a unit rate from a table, a graph, and an equation.

> *Prompt: How do you find the unit rate from a table?*
> *Sentence Starter: To express the relationship as an equation …*

SPOTLIGHT ON MATHEMATICAL PRACTICES

MP1 Make Sense of Problems

- Help students think about unit rates by asking these probing questions: *When finding the unit rate from the table, does it matter which pair of values you use? Why or why not? How is the unit rate represented in an equation? How could you check that your equation is correct using the table of values?*

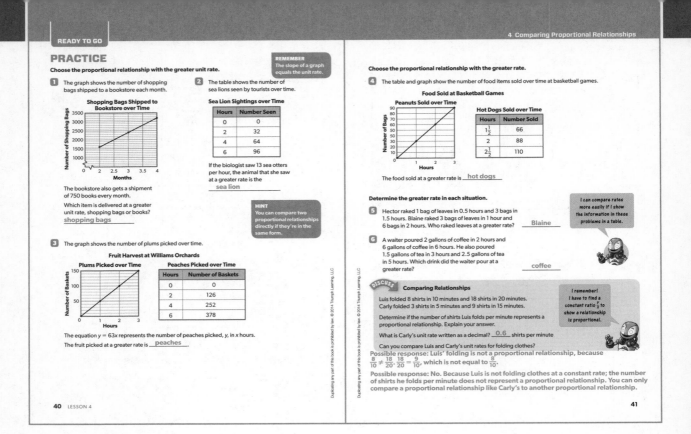

READY TO GO

PRACTICE

Choose the proportional relationship with the greater unit rate.

REMEMBER
The slope of a graph equals the unit rate.

1 The graph shows the number of shopping bags shipped to a bookstore each month.

Shopping Bags Shipped to Bookstore over Time

The bookstore also gets a shipment of 750 books every month.

Which item is delivered at a greater unit rate, shopping bags or books?
shopping bags

2 The table shows the number of sea lions seen by tourists over time.

Sea Lion Sightings over Time

Hours	Number Seen
0	0
2	32
4	64
6	96

If the biologist saw 13 sea otters per hour, the animal that she saw at a greater rate is the
sea lion

HINT
You can compare two proportional relationships directly if they're in the same form.

3 The graph shows the number of plums picked over time.

Fruit Harvest at Williams Orchards

Plums Picked over Time

Peaches Picked over Time

Hours	Number of Baskets
0	0
2	126
4	252
6	378

The equation $y = 63x$ represents the number of peaches picked, y, in x hours.
The fruit picked at a greater rate is _peaches_

Choose the proportional relationship with the greater rate.

4 The table and graph show the number of food items sold over time at basketball games.

Food Sold at Basketball Games

Peanuts Sold over Time

Hot Dogs Sold over Time

Hours	Number Sold
$1\frac{1}{2}$	66
2	88
$2\frac{1}{2}$	110

The food sold at a greater rate is _hot dogs_

Determine the greater rate in each situation.

5 Hector raked 1 bag of leaves in 0.5 hours and 3 bags in 1.5 hours. Blaine raked 3 bags of leaves in 1 hour and 6 bags in 2 hours. Who raked leaves at a greater rate? _Blaine_

I can compare rates more easily if I show the information in these problems in a table.

6 A waiter poured 2 gallons of coffee in 2 hours and 6 gallons of coffee in 6 hours. He also poured 1.5 gallons of tea in 3 hours and 2.5 gallons of tea in 5 hours. Which drink did the waiter pour at a greater rate? _coffee_

DISCUSS Comparing Relationships

Luis folded 8 shirts in 10 minutes and 18 shirts in 20 minutes. Carly folded 3 shirts in 5 minutes and 9 shirts in 15 minutes.

Determine if the number of shirts Luis folds per minute represents a proportional relationship. Explain your answer.

What is Carly's unit rate written as a decimal? _0.6_ shirts per minute

I remember! I have to find a constant ratio $\frac{y}{x}$ to show a relationship is proportional.

Can you compare Luis and Carly's unit rates for folding clothes?
Possible response: Luis' folding is not a proportional relationship, because $\frac{8}{10} \ne \frac{18}{20}$; $\frac{18}{20} = \frac{9}{10}$, which is not equal to $\frac{8}{10}$.

Possible response: No. Because Luis is not folding clothes at a constant rate; the number of shirts he folds per minute does not represent a proportional relationship. You can only compare a proportional relationship like Carly's to another proportional relationship.

ADDITIONAL PRACTICE

Provide students with additional practice to model and solve:

Lee earns $15 per lawn he mows. JD earns $32 for mowing 2 lawns and $64 for mowing 4 lawns. Who charges a greater lawn mowing rate?

Train A travels 160 miles per hour. Train B can travel 300 miles in 2 hours and 600 miles 4 hours. Which train travels at the faster rate?

SPOTLIGHT ON MATHEMATICAL PRACTICES

MP2 Model with Mathematics

- Help students think about the relationships by asking the probing questions: *Are both relationships proportional? Can you compare the unit rates of proportional and nonproportional relationships? Why or why not?*

Support Independent Practice

1–4 Remind students to read the **HINT** and **REMEMBER**. If needed, ask: *How did you identify the unit rate from a table? a graph? an equation? a description? How did you determine which relationship had a greater rate?*

5–6 *What was the unit rate for each relationship?*

- **Support Discussion MP4** Have partners discuss briefly before group discussion. As needed, have students discuss how to compare proportional relationships.

> *Prompt: What are the characteristics of a proportional relationship?*
> *Sentence Starter: You can/cannot compare the relationships…*

Problem Solving

- **Model the Four-Step Method MP1 MP4** Guide students through the four-step method using think-aloud strategies. Point out the clue words *as quickly as possible*.

Think Aloud To determine which faucet flows faster, I need to compare the unit rates for both faucets.

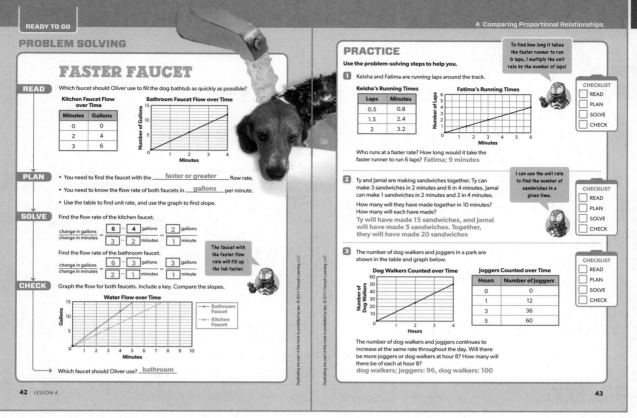

READY TO GO

PROBLEM SOLVING

FASTER FAUCET

READ Which faucet should Oliver use to fill the dog bathtub as quickly as possible?

Kitchen Faucet Flow over Time

Minutes	Gallons
0	0
2	4
3	6

Bathroom Faucet Flow over Time

PLAN
- You need to find the faucet with the ___faster or greater___ flow rate.
- You need to know the flow rate of both faucets in ___gallons___ per minute.
- Use the table to find unit rate, and use the graph to find slope.

SOLVE Find the flow rate of the kitchen faucet.

$$\frac{\text{change in gallons}}{\text{change in minutes}} = \frac{6 - 4 \text{ gallons}}{3 - 2 \text{ minutes}} = \frac{2 \text{ gallons}}{1 \text{ minute}}$$

Find the flow rate of the bathroom faucet.

$$\frac{\text{change in gallons}}{\text{change in minutes}} = \frac{6 - 3 \text{ gallons}}{2 - 1 \text{ minutes}} = \frac{3 \text{ gallons}}{1 \text{ minute}}$$

The faucet with the faster flow rate will fill up the tub faster.

CHECK Graph the flow for both faucets. Include a key. Compare the slopes.

Water Flow over Time

— Bathroom Faucet
— Kitchen Faucet

Which faucet should Oliver use? ___bathroom___

42 LESSON 4

PRACTICE
Use the problem-solving steps to help you.

1 Keisha and Fatima are running laps around the track.

Keisha's Running Times

Laps	Minutes
0.5	0.8
1.5	2.4
2	3.2

Fatima's Running Times

To find how long it takes the faster runner to run 6 laps, I multiply the unit rate by the number of laps!

CHECKLIST
☐ READ
☐ PLAN
☐ SOLVE
☐ CHECK

Who runs at a faster rate? How long would it take the faster runner to run 6 laps? **Fatima; 9 minutes**

2 Ty and Jamal are making sandwiches together. Ty can make 3 sandwiches in 2 minutes and 6 in 4 minutes. Jamal can make 1 sandwiches in 2 minutes and 2 in 4 minutes. How many will they have made together in 10 minutes? How many will each have made? **Ty will have made 15 sandwiches, and Jamal will have made 5 sandwiches. Together, they will have made 20 sandwiches**

I can use the unit rate to find the number of sandwiches in a given time.

CHECKLIST
☐ READ
☐ PLAN
☐ SOLVE
☐ CHECK

3 The number of dog walkers and joggers in a park are shown in the table and graph below.

Dog Walkers Counted over Time

Joggers Counted over Time

Hours	Number of Joggers
0	0
1	12
3	36
5	60

CHECKLIST
☐ READ
☐ PLAN
☐ SOLVE
☐ CHECK

The number of dog walkers and joggers continues to increase at the same rate throughout the day. Will there be more joggers or dog walkers at hour 8? How many will there be of each at hour 8? **dog walkers; joggers: 96, dog walkers: 100**

43

- **Support Problem-Solving Practice** Have students use the Checklist as they complete each step.

> **Prompt:** *Which is the faster rate, the greater number or smaller number?*
> **Prompt:** *How did you find the unit rate for each person?*
> **Prompt:** *What is the unit rate for the walkers? joggers?*

- **Explore Student Thinking** **MP6** Invite students to explain how they compared the unit rates. Have partners compare their work on a problem and describe their results.

COMMON ERRORS
When solving problems that involve comparing proportional relationships, students may interpret numbers incorrectly. For example, which is a better buy—$5 per pack or $4 per pack? Students may select the greater number instead of the smaller number.

Assess

- Use the table below to address any difficulties as needed.

1
Observation	Action
Errors in finding unit rates are frequent; general confusion about comparing proportional relationships.	Have students make a chart on how to find the unit rate from tables, graphs, equations, and descriptions. Students should provide an example for each representation and steps to follow.

2
Observation	Action
Makes occasional errors when finding unit rates; some understanding of comparing proportional relationships.	Provide additional practice problems for comparing proportional relationships. Have students review how to find the unit rate from tables, graphs, equations, and descriptions.

3
Observation	Action
Compares proportional relationships accurately.	Assign the Lesson 4 Quiz.

COMPARING PROPORTIONAL RELATIONSHIPS **33**

PLUG IN Finding the Slope of a Line

	OBJECTIVES	CONCEPTS AND SKILLS	VOCABULARY
FOUNDATIONAL UNDERSTANDING ▶ **PLUG IN** **Finding the Slope of a Line** Student Edition pp. 44–45	• Find the slope of a line from two points. • Identify the slope and y-intercept from a graph or equation.	Find the slope of a line given two distinct points. Identify the slope and y-intercept from a graph or from an equation. **CCSS:** 8.EE.6	• **slope** • **y-intercept**
POWER UP **Writing the Equation of a Line**	• Write the equation of a line.	Write an equation in the form $y = mx$ for a line through the origin and write an equation in the form $y = mx + b$ for a line intercepting the vertical axis at b. **CCSS:** 8.EE.6	
ON-LEVEL TARGET **READY TO GO** **Slope**	• Determine if the slopes of two segments on a line are the same.	Confirm that the slopes of two segments on a line are the same. **CCSS:** 8.EE.6	

MATERIALS

- Math Tool: Coordinate Grid, p. A13 (Student Edition p. 233)
- Index cards (*suggested*)

ENGLISH LANGUAGE LEARNERS

MP6 Students may need extra support in remembering what the variables m and b represent in the equation $y = mx + b$. On an index card, have students write the equation and label the variables. Below the diagram, have students write the definitions of *slope* and *y-intercept* in their own words. Students should use this card as a reference as they work through the exercises.

Build Background

- Talk to students about reasons to find the slope in real life. For example, the cost of 2 pounds of trail mix is $5 and the cost of 4 pounds is $10. What is the cost of one pound of trail mix? Explain that by finding the slope you can answer this question.
- **MP4** Have students discuss additional examples of real situations that involve finding the slope of a line.
- Tell students they will work on finding the slope of a line.

Introduce and Model

- **Introduce Concepts and Vocabulary** Guide students through the information about slopes and y-intercepts. Emphasize that when finding the slope from two points it does not matter which point you designate as the first point (x, y). What matters is that you subtract the x-values in the same order as you subtracted the y-values. Use **Words to Know** to clarify their understanding of vocabulary. **MP6** Have students discuss the terms *slope* and *y-intercept* with a partner.
- **Support Discussion** **MP1** Have partners discuss briefly before group discussion. As needed, remind students of ways to determine the slope of a line.

> *Prompt: How can you find the slope of a line?*
> *Sentence Starter: The slope is positive/negative because…*

LESSON 5 Slope

PLUG IN Finding the Slope of a Line

The **slope** of a line is the ratio of the change in the y-values to the change in the corresponding x-values.

Slope = $\dfrac{\text{change in y-values}}{\text{change in x-values}}$ = $\dfrac{5-2}{8-2} = \dfrac{3}{6} = \dfrac{1}{2}$

The **y-intercept** is where a line crosses the y-axis.

(0, 1) ← y-intercept is 1.

The equation of a line can be written in the form $y = mx + b$, where the slope of the line is m, and the y-intercept is b.

I see! I choose two coordinate pairs and then divide the difference of the y-values by the difference of the corresponding x-values.

The y-intercept is the y-coordinate of the point where the line intersects the y-axis.

I get it! The slope is $m = \frac{1}{2}$, and the y-intercept is $b = 1$, so the equation of the line is $y = \frac{1}{2}x + 1$.

Words to Know

slope
a ratio of the change in y-coordinates (*rise*) of a graph to the change in corresponding x-coordinates (*run*)

y-intercept
the y-coordinate of the point at which a line crosses the y-axis

DISCUSS Will the slope of the line through the points (1, 6) and (7, −2) be positive or negative? How do you know? **Negative. Possible response: The slope of the line is negative. Using the slope formula, $m = \dfrac{\text{change in y-values}}{\text{change in x-values}} = \dfrac{6-(-2)}{1-7} = \dfrac{8}{(-6)} = -\dfrac{4}{3}$.**

A You can use the slope formula $m = \dfrac{y_2 - y_1}{x_2 - x_1}$ to find the slope of a line.

DO Find the slope of the line through points (5, 1) and (−4, 3).

1. Choose (x_1, y_1) and (x_2, y_2).

2. Write the slope formula. Substitute for x_1, x_2, y_1, and y_2.

3. Subtract. Simplify, if possible.

$(x_1, y_1) = (5, 1)$ $(x_2, y_2) = (\boxed{-4}, \boxed{3})$

slope = $\dfrac{y_2 - y_1}{x_2 - x_1} = \dfrac{3 - \boxed{1}}{\boxed{-4} - 5} = \dfrac{\boxed{2}}{\boxed{-9}}$

44 LESSON 5

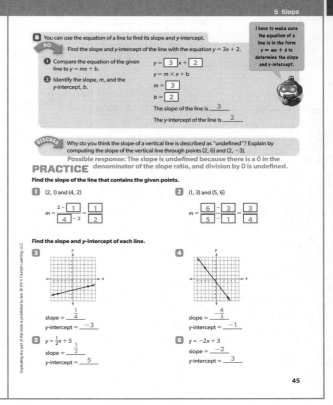

B You can use the equation of a line to find its slope and y-intercept.

DO Find the slope and y-intercept of the line with the equation $y = 3x + 2$.

1. Compare the equation of the given line to $y = mx + b$.

2. Identify the slope, m, and the y-intercept, b.

$y = \boxed{3}x + \boxed{2}$
$y = m \times x + b$
$m = \boxed{3}$
$b = \boxed{2}$

The slope of the line is ___3___

The y-intercept of the line is ___2___

I have to make sure the equation of a line is in the form $y = mx + b$ to determine the slope and y-intercept.

DISCUSS Why do you think the slope of a vertical line is described as "undefined"? Explain by computing the slope of the vertical line through points (2, 6) and (2, −3). **Possible response: The slope is undefined because there is a 0 in the denominator of the slope ratio, and division by 0 is undefined.**

PRACTICE

Find the slope of the line that contains the given points.

1 (2, 2) and (4, 2)

$m = \dfrac{2 - \boxed{1}}{\boxed{4} - 2} = \dfrac{\boxed{1}}{\boxed{2}}$

2 (1, 3) and (5, 6)

$m = \dfrac{\boxed{6} - \boxed{3}}{\boxed{5} - \boxed{1}} = \dfrac{\boxed{3}}{\boxed{4}}$

Find the slope and y-intercept of each line.

3

slope = $\dfrac{\boxed{1}}{\boxed{4}}$
y-intercept = ___−3___

4

slope = $-\dfrac{\boxed{4}}{\boxed{3}}$
y-intercept = ___−1___

5 $y = \frac{1}{2}x + 5$

slope = $\dfrac{\boxed{1}}{\boxed{2}}$
y-intercept = ___5___

6 $y = -2x + 3$

slope = ___−2___
y-intercept = ___3___

45

• Model Application

DO ▶ A Remind students that it does not matter which point they designate as x_1 and y_1.

DO ▶ B Monitor students as they find the slope and y-intercept from an equation. Explain that in order to identify the slope and y-intercept from an equation, the equation must be written in the form $y = mx + b$.

• **Support Discussion MP3** Have partners discuss briefly before group discussion. As needed, have students review if the denominator of a fraction can be zero.

> **Prompt:** What are the characteristics of a vertical line?
> **Sentence Starter:** The slope of a vertical line is described as undefined because…

Practice and Assess

• Ask students to complete practice items 1–6 on page 45 independently or in pairs. Monitor ongoing work.

• Use the chart below as needed to address any difficulties.

Observation	Action
Students have difficulty finding the slope.	Students may find it difficult to find the slope of a line if given two points. Provide students with blank coordinate grids. Have students graph the given points and connect the points with a straight line. Students can calculate the slope by finding the rise and run.

Writing the Equation of a Line

		OBJECTIVES	CONCEPTS AND SKILLS	VOCABULARY
FOUNDATIONAL UNDERSTANDING	**PLUG IN** **Finding the Slope of a Line**	• Find the slope of a line from two points. • Identify the slope and *y*-intercept from a graph or equation.	Find the slope of a line given two distinct points. Identify the slope and *y*-intercept from a graph or from an equation. **CCSS:** 8.EE.6	• **slope** • ***y*-intercept**
	▶ **POWER UP** **Writing the Equation of a Line** Student Edition pp. 46–47	• Write the equation of a line.	Write an equation in the form $y = mx$ for a line through the origin and write an equation in the form $y = mx + b$ for a line intercepting the vertical axis at *b*. **CCSS:** 8.EE.6	
ON-LEVEL TARGET	**READY TO GO** **Slope**	• Determine if the slopes of two segments on a line are the same.	Confirm that the slopes of two segments on a line are the same. **CCSS:** 8.EE.6	

MATERIALS

• Math Tool: Coordinate Grid, p. A13 (Student Edition p. 233)
• Index cards *(suggested)*
• Highlighters *(suggested)*

ENGLISH LANGUAGE LEARNERS

MP7 Students may need additional support in identifying the *y*-intercept when given two points. On an index card, have students write these steps. First, identify the ordered pair that has zero as an *x*-value. Second, highlight the *y*-value that is paired with the *x*-value of zero. This is the *y*-intercept. Third, write the *y*-value for *b* in the equation $y = mx + b$.

Build Background

■ Talk to students about reasons to write equations for given lines. For example, a taxicab company charges a flat fee of $2 plus $0.90 per mile. How much would a taxicab ride for 15 miles cost? Explain that this question can be answered by writing an equation in the form $y = mx + b$.

■ **MP4** Have students discuss additional examples of real situations in which they would write an equation of a line.

■ Tell students they will write equations of lines in the form $y = mx + b$.

Introduce and Model

■ **Introduce and Model** Guide students through the information about writing equations of lines in the form $y = mx + b$. Emphasize that if the graph crosses the origin, the value of *b* is zero.

■ **Support Discussion** **MP3** Have partners discuss briefly before group discussion. As needed, remind students that the slope of a line is constant.

> *Prompt: How can you test your answer to this question?*
> *Sentence Starter: The slope does/does not change…*

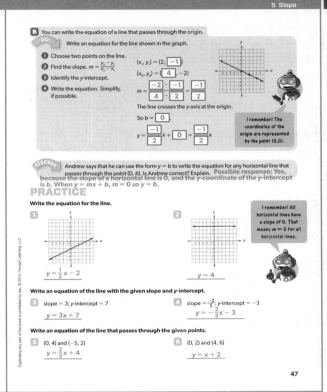

POWER UP Writing an Equation of a Line

You can write the equation of a line from its graph using the form $y = mx + b$.

❶ **Find the slope.** Choose two points on the line, and use the slope formula to calculate the slope. Using the points $(-3, -1)$ and $(2, 4)$:

$$m = \frac{\text{change in } y\text{-values}}{\text{change in } x\text{-values}}$$

$$= \frac{y_2 - y_1}{x_2 - x_1}$$

$$= \frac{4 - (-1)}{2 - (-3)}$$

$$= \frac{5}{5}$$

$$= 1$$

I see! If I know the slope and y-intercept of a line, then I can write an equation for the line.

❷ **Find the y-intercept.** Identify where the line crosses the y-axis.

The line crosses the y-axis at (0, 2).

The y-intercept is 2.

❸ **Substitute the slope, m, and the y-intercept, b, in the equation $y = mx + b$.**

$y = mx + b$

$y = x + 2$ is an equation for the line.

The x and y in the equation represent all the possible coordinate pairs of points on the line.

DISCUSS Does the slope change, depending on which point you assign as (x_1, y_1) or (x_2, y_2)? Explain. Possible response: No, you can assign either point as (x_1, y_1) or (x_2, y_2). You may start substituting with x_2 and y_2 or x_1 and y_1.

A You can write the equation of a line if given the slope and y-intercept.

DO What is the equation of a line that has a slope of 8 and a y-intercept of -2?

❶ Identify m and b. $m = \boxed{8}$

❷ Substitute the slope, m, and the y-intercept, b, in the equation $y = mx + b$. $b = \boxed{-2}$

$y = mx + b$

$y = \boxed{8}x + \boxed{-2}$

❸ Write the equation. $y = \underline{8x - 2}$

I remember! m stands for slope and b represents the y-intercept.

46   LESSON 5

B You can write the equation of a line that passes through the origin.

DO Write an equation for the line shown in the graph.

❶ Choose two points on the line.

❷ Find the slope. $m = \frac{y_2 - y_1}{x_2 - x_1}$ $(x_1, y_1) = (2, \boxed{-1})$

❸ Identify the y-intercept. $(x_2, y_2) = (\boxed{4}, -2)$

❹ Write the equation. Simplify, if possible. $m = \frac{\boxed{-2} - \boxed{-1}}{\boxed{4} - \boxed{2}} = \frac{\boxed{-1}}{\boxed{2}}$

The line crosses the y-axis at the origin.

So $b = \boxed{0}$.

$y = \frac{\boxed{-1}}{\boxed{2}}x + \boxed{0} = \frac{\boxed{-1}}{\boxed{2}}x$

I remember! The coordinates of the origin are represented by the point (0,0).

DISCUSS Andrew says that he can use the form $y = b$ to write the equation for any horizontal line that passes through the point (0, b). Is Andrew correct? Explain. Possible response: Yes, because the slope of a horizontal line is 0, and the y-coordinate of the y-intercept is b. When $y = mx + b$, $m = 0$ so $y = b$.

PRACTICE

Write the equation for the line.

1.

$y = \frac{1}{2}x - 2$

2.

I remember! All horizontal lines have a slope of 0. That means $m = 0$ for all horizontal lines.

$y = 4$

Write an equation of the line with the given slope and y-intercept.

3. slope = 3; y-intercept = 7

$y = 3x + 7$

4. slope = $\frac{-2}{5}$; y-intercept = -3

$y = -\frac{2}{5}x - 3$

Write an equation of the line that passes through the given points.

5. (0, 4) and (-5, 2)

$y = \frac{2}{5}x + 4$

6. (0, 2) and (4, 6)

$y = x + 2$

47

• Model Application

DO A Monitor students as they write the equation of the line. If needed, tell students that when given the slope and y-intercept, all they need to do is substitute the correct values into the equation.

DO B Guide students in identifying the slope and y-intercept from a graph. Explain to students that when identifying the y-intercept they need to find the point that has an x-value of zero.

• **Support Discussion** **MP3** Have partners discuss briefly before group discussion. Remind students of the definition of a horiztonal line.

> *Prompt:* What are the characteristics of a horizontal line?
> *Sentence Starter:* Andrew is correct/not correct because…

MP3 Construct Viable Arguments

Help students think about Andrew's statement by having them graph a horizontal line. Students should find the slope and y-intercept and then substitute the values into the equation.

Practice and Assess

• Ask students to complete practice items 1 and 2 on page 47 independently or in pairs. Monitor ongoing work.

• Use the chart below as needed to address any difficulties.

Observation	Action
Students do not correctly write the equation of a line when given two points.	Provide students with blank coordinate grids and ask them to graph the line. Students should plot the given points and connect the points with a straight line. From the graph, students should be able to see where the graph crosses the y-axis and calculate the slope. Then the students can substitute the values into the equation $y = mx + b$.

		OBJECTIVES	CONCEPTS AND SKILLS	VOCABULARY
FOUNDATIONAL UNDERSTANDING	**PLUG IN** Finding the Slope of a Line	• Find the slope of a line from two points. • Identify the slope and *y*-intercept from a graph or equation.	Find the slope of a line given two distinct points. Identify the slope and *y*-intercept from a graph or from an equation. **CCSS:** 8.EE.6	• **slope** • **y-intercept**
	POWER UP Writing the Equation of a Line	• Write the equation of a line.	Write an equation in the form $y = mx$ for a line through the origin and write an equation in the form $y = mx + b$ for a line intercepting the vertical axis at *b*. **CCSS:** 8.EE.6	
ON-LEVEL TARGET	▶ **READY TO GO** Slope Student Edition pp. 48–53	• Determine if the slopes of two segments on a line are the same.	Confirm that the slopes of two segments on a line are the same. **CCSS:** 8.EE.6	

MATERIALS

• Lesson 5 Quiz, Assessment Manual pp. 12–13
• Lesson 5 Quiz Answer Key, Assessment Manual
• Math Tool: Coordinate Grid, p. A13 (Student Edition p. 233)
• Highlighters *(suggested)*

ENGLISH LANGUAGE LEARNERS

MP6 Students may need additional support in understanding the geometry terms used in this lesson. Have students write what they know about the terms *segment* and *endpoint*. Have students share their definitions. Clarify any errors. If needed, provide students with drawings of various lines. Working with a partner, students should identify the segments and endpoints.

Build Background

■ Talk to students about reasons to determine if the slopes of two segments on a line are the same. For example, the Smith family drove 180 miles in 3 hours. The Jackson family drove 120 miles in 2 hours. If the families continue driving at these rates, will they drive 300 miles in the same amount of time? Explain that by determining if the slopes are on the same line you can answer this question.

■ **MP4** Have students discuss additional examples of real situations that require determining if the slopes of two segments on a line are the same.

■ Tell students they will determine if the slopes of two segments on a line are the same.

Introduce and Model

■ **Introduce Concepts and Vocabulary** Guide students through the information about how to determine if the slopes of two segments on a line are the same. Emphasize that the slopes have to be equal in order for the segments to be on the same line.

■ **Support Discussion** **MP3** Have partners discuss briefly before group discussion. If needed, recall that the slope of a line is constant.

> *Prompt: What is true about the slope of a line?*
> *Sentence Starter: Margarita can conclude that...*

READY TO GO | Slope

You can use any two points on a line to find the slope of the line.
You can compare the slopes of two segments of the line to show this.

❶ Use the points $(0, -3)$ and $(3, -1)$ to find the slope of the line.

$$m = \frac{-1 - (-3)}{3 - 0}$$
$$= \frac{2}{3}$$

❷ Use the points $(3, -1)$ and $(9, 3)$ to find the slope of the line.

$$m = \frac{3 - (-1)}{9 - 3}$$
$$= \frac{4}{6}$$
$$= \frac{2}{3}$$

❸ Compare the slopes.

$$\frac{2}{3} = \frac{2}{3}$$

The slopes are equal.

I get it! Every segment of a line will have the same slope!

DISCUSS Margarita looks at a table of x-y values and calculates the slope using one pair of points. She uses another pair of points and calculates a different slope. What can Margarita conclude about a graph of those points?
Possible response: The values in the table do not represent points on the same line.

LESSON LINK

PLUG IN	POWER UP	GO!
You can find the slope and y-intercept of a line given any two points on the line, its graph, or its equation.	You can use the slope and y-intercept of a line to write an equation for the line.	*I get it! I can investigate slope and y-intercept further to better understand the characteristics of lines!*

Slope: $m = \frac{5}{8}$

y-intercept: $b = -2$
$$y = mx + b$$
$$y = \frac{5}{8}x + (-2)$$
$$= \frac{5}{8}x - 2$$

slope: $m = \frac{1}{2}$

y-intercept: $b = 1$

WORK TOGETHER

Use two pairs of points to confirm the slope of a line.

- This line includes the points $(-1, 6)$, $(1, 2)$, $(2, 0)$, and $(5, -6)$.
- The slope between $(-1, 6)$ and $(1, 2)$ is $-\frac{4}{2}$, or -2.
- The slope between $(2, 0)$ and $(5, -6)$ is $\frac{-6}{3} = -\frac{2}{1}$, or -2.
- The slope of the line is the same with either pair of points.

I could also use any other two pairs of points on this line to confirm the slope.

A You can use slope to check whether three points lie on the same line.

DO Determine if the points $(0, 6)$, $(3, 3)$, and $(6, -1)$ are on the same line.

❶ Find the slope between any two of the three points.

Use $(0, 6)$ and $(3, 3)$.

$$m = \frac{\boxed{3} - \boxed{6}}{\boxed{3} - \boxed{0}} = \frac{\boxed{-3}}{\boxed{3}} = \boxed{-1}$$

❷ Now find the slope between two other points.

Use $(3, 3)$ and $(6, -1)$.

$$m = \frac{\boxed{-1} - \boxed{3}}{\boxed{6} - \boxed{3}} = \frac{\boxed{-4}}{\boxed{3}}$$

❸ Compare the slopes to determine if the points are on the same line.

The three points **are not** on the same line
because the slopes are **not equal**.

B You can determine if two segments that share an endpoint are on the same line.

DO Determine if two segments, one with endpoints $(0, 2)$ and $(4, 3)$ and one with endpoints $(0, 2)$ and $(8, 4)$, lie along the same line.

❶ Find the slope of the first segment.

Use $(0, 2)$ and $(4, 3)$.

$$m = \frac{\boxed{3} - \boxed{2}}{\boxed{4} - \boxed{0}} = \frac{\boxed{1}}{\boxed{4}}$$

❷ Find the slope of the second segment.

Now use $(0, 2)$ and $(8, 4)$.

$$m = \frac{\boxed{4} - \boxed{2}}{\boxed{8} - \boxed{0}} = \frac{\boxed{2}}{\boxed{8}} = \frac{\boxed{1}}{\boxed{4}}$$

The slopes are **equal**. The 3 points **are** on the same line.

DISCUSS Will a line segment that is part of a larger line segment always have the same slope as the larger line segment? Explain. Possible response: Yes, you can calculate the slope using any two points on the shorter segment, which can then be used to calculate the slope of the larger segment. The slopes will be equal.

LESSON LINK

Connect to Foundational Understanding Skills learned in the **Plug In** and **Power Up** are referenced in the **Lesson Link**. Explain that you can use slope to determine whether points lie on the same line and to determine if two segments are on the same line.

- **Work Together** Explain that students will use slope to determine whether points lie on the same line and whether two line segments are on the same line.

DO A Explain to students they need to compare the slopes in order to determine whether the points lie on the same line. In order to do this, they must find the slope between one set of ordered pairs and then find the slope between another set of ordered pairs.

DO B Explain to students they need to compare the slopes in order to determine whether the segments are on the same line. The slopes must be equal for the segments to be on the same line.

- **Support Discussion** **MP3** Have partners discuss briefly before group discussion. As needed, have students explain what is true about the slope of a line.

> **Prompt:** How can you determine the slope of a line segment?
> **Sentence Starter:** Yes/No, the smaller line …

SPOTLIGHT ON MATHEMATICAL PRACTICES

MP3 Construct Viable Arguments

Use Math Tool: Coordinate Grid to help students think about this question. Ask students to draw a line on their graph. Students should identify a small segment on the line and then find the slope. Then, find the slope of the larger line. Students should then compare the slopes.

PRACTICE

READY TO GO

Solve.

1 A line segment has endpoints at $(-2, 5)$ and $(1, 4)$. Another line segment has endpoints at $(1, 4)$ and $(2, 7)$. Are the line segments parts of the same line?

Coordinate Grid can be found on p.213

Find the slope of the first line segment.

$$m = \frac{4 - \boxed{5}}{\boxed{1} - (-2)} = \frac{\boxed{-1}}{\boxed{3}}$$

Find the slope of the second line segment.

$$m = \frac{\boxed{7} - 4}{2 - \boxed{1}} = \frac{\boxed{3}}{\boxed{1}} = \boxed{3}$$

HINT
You can check your answer by graphing the segments on a coordinate grid.

Are the line segments on the same line? Explain.
Possible response: No. The slopes are not equal, so the segments cannot be on the same line.

2 Choose two pairs of points on the line to show the slope of the line is the same.
Possible points are shown.

REMEMBER
Any two pairs of points on the line will show the same slope.

Use points ($\boxed{3}$, $\boxed{4}$) and ($\boxed{2}$, $\boxed{3}$).

$$m = \frac{\boxed{3} - \boxed{4}}{\boxed{2} - \boxed{3}} = \frac{\boxed{-1}}{\boxed{-1}} = \boxed{1}$$

Now use points ($\boxed{2}$, $\boxed{3}$) and ($\boxed{4}$, $\boxed{5}$).

$$m = \frac{\boxed{5} - \boxed{3}}{\boxed{4} - \boxed{2}} = \frac{\boxed{2}}{\boxed{2}} = \boxed{1}$$

Are the slopes the same? ___ **yes**

3 Use the endpoints of two segments along this line to show that the slopes of the segments are the same.
Possible points are shown.
For points $(-2, -3)$ and $(1, 1)$, $m = \frac{4}{3}$.
For points $(1, 1)$ and $(4, 5)$, $m = \frac{4}{3}$.

Are the slopes of the segments the same? ___ **yes**

50 LESSON 5

Solve.

4 Two line segments are part of the line $y = -\frac{1}{5}x + 10$. What is the slope of each segment?
$-\frac{1}{5}$

5 Barb drew a line through the origin and point $(2, 3)$. Jamal drew a line through the origin and point $(4, 6)$. How can you tell that Barb and Jamal drew the same line?
Possible response: Because the segments formed by each point and the origin have the same slope and share an endpoint, the segments lie along the same line.

Use the slope formula to determine if the three points lie on a line.

6 $(-3, -2), (-1, 3), (3, 13)$
For points $(-3, -2)$ and $(-1, 3)$, $m = \frac{5}{2}$.
For points $(-1, 3)$ and $(3, 13)$, $m = \frac{5}{2}$.
Do the points lie on the same line? Explain.

Yes, because the slopes are equal

I see! I can think of any two points as the endpoints of a segment.

7 $(-3, 11), (2, 7), (6, 3)$
For points $(-3, 11)$ and $(2, 7)$, $m = -\frac{4}{5}$.
For points $(2, 7)$ and $(6, 3)$, $m = -1$.
Do the points lie on the same line? Explain.

No, because the slopes are not equal

DISCUSS   **Reasoning with Graphs**

Do any segments within each of these graphs share an endpoint? Explain.
Possible response: Yes, all three lines share the point (0,1), so there are segments within each line that have (0,1) as an endpoint.

I get it! I can relate the steepness of a line with the value of its slope.

$m = \frac{1}{4}$ $m = 1$ $m = 4$

What do you notice about the slopes as the lines gets steeper?
As the line gets steeper, the slope increases.

51

ADDITIONAL PRACTICE

Provide students with additional practice to model and solve:

Use the slope formula to determine if the three points lie on a line.

a. $(2, 5), (4, 10), \left(-1, -2\frac{1}{2}\right)$

b. $(3, 9), (-2, -6), (-1, 3)$

A line segment has endpoints at $(-1, 3)$ and $(1, 1)$. Another line segment has endpoints at $(1, 1)$ and $(-1, -1)$. Are the line segments parts of the same line? Explain.

SPOTLIGHT ON MATHEMATICAL PRACTICES

MP7 Look for Structure

Have students graph all three lines on the same coordinate grid, label each line, and highlight the value of the slope. Ask: *What do you notice about the slope and the steepness of the line?*

Support Independent Practice

1–3 Remind students to read the **HINT** and **REMEMBER**. If needed, ask: *How did you know if two line segments are on the same line?*

4–5 *How did you determine the slope from the equation? What point do both lines have in common?*

6–7 *What has to be true for the points to lie on the same line?*

- **Support Discussion MP7** Have partners discuss briefly before group discussion. As needed, have students discuss how to find the slope if given a graph.

> **Prompt:** Why do you think the slope of a line is referred to as the steepness of the line?
> **Sentence Starter:** I notice that...

Problem Solving

- **Model the Four-Step Method MP1 MP4** Guide students through the four-step method using think-aloud strategies. Point out that the problem tells you to write an equation to find the pressure at 100 meters.

  Think Aloud To find the pressure at 100 meters, I need to write an equation in the form $y = mx + b$.

- **Support Problem-Solving Practice** Have students use the Checklist as they complete each step.

READY TO GO

PROBLEM SOLVING

UNDERWATER PRESSURE

READ The units of measure for pressure are called atmospheres. The pressure at sea level is 1 atmosphere. At a depth of 20 meters, the pressure is 3 atmospheres. Write an equation, and find the pressure at a depth of 100 meters.

PLAN
- You need to find the number of atmospheres at a depth of __100 meters__
- Use (0, 1) for the pressure at __sea level__.
- Use __(20, 3)__ for the pressure at a depth of 20 meters.
- Use the points to find the __slope__.
- Use the measure of pressure at __sea level__ as the y-intercept.
- Use $y = mx + b$ and substitute __100__ for x.

SOLVE Write an equation.

The slope, $m = \dfrac{3-1}{20-0} = \dfrac{2}{20} = \dfrac{1}{10}$

The y-intercept is __1__. The equation is $y = \dfrac{1}{10}x + 1$.

Find the number of atmospheres at a depth of 100 meters: $y = \dfrac{1}{10}(100) + 1 = 11$

CHECK Write an ordered pair for the atmosphere at a depth of 100 meters. (100, 11)
Check that this point and the given two points lie on the same line.

The slope between (0, 1) and (20, 3) is $\dfrac{1}{10}$

The slope between (20, 3) and (100, 11) is: $m = \dfrac{11-3}{100-20} = \dfrac{8}{80} = \dfrac{1}{10}$

The slopes are __the same__, so the points __lie along the same line__.

At a depth of 100 meters, the pressure is __11__ atmospheres.

52 | LESSON 5

PRACTICE

Use the problem-solving steps to help you.

> I see! For the company to perform any repair work, a customer is charged for making an appointment. That amount is the y-intercept!

1 A computer repair company charges $50 for an appointment. For 2 hours of repair work, it charges a total of $120. What is the total charge for 5 hours of repair work?

The total charge is $225 for 5 hours of repair work.

CHECKLIST
- READ
- PLAN
- SOLVE
- CHECK

2 At dawn, the temperature is 70°F. The temperature falls at the same rate for the rest of the day. In 4 hours, the temperature is 60°F. What is the temperature 6 hours after dawn?

The temperature is 55°F 6 hours after dawn.

CHECKLIST
- READ
- PLAN
- SOLVE
- CHECK

3 Jennie works for a cell phone company. She earns $250 per week plus commissions she makes on sales. One week, she had sales of $1000, and her pay was $275. How much would her pay be if she had sales of $2,000?

She will earn $300.

CHECKLIST
- READ
- PLAN
- SOLVE
- CHECK

53

> **Prompt:** How will you find the amount the company charges per hour?
> **Prompt:** How will you find the amount the temperature is dropping each hour?
> **Prompt:** How much does Jennie earn per $1,000 she sells?

- **Explore Student Thinking** MP6 Invite students to explain how they solved their equation. Have partners compare their work on a problem and describe their results.

COMMON ERRORS
When using the slope formula, students may make mistakes with integer operations. Remind students to pay attention to the signs.

Assess

- Use the table below to address any difficulties as needed.

	Observation	Action
1	Errors in finding slope are frequent; general confusion about how to determine if the slopes of two segments on a line are the same.	Have students work in pairs. Students should make a presentation of how to determine whether the slopes of two segments on a line are the same.
2	Makes occasional errors when finding slope; some understanding of how to determine if the slopes of two segments on a line are the same.	Provide additional practice problems for determining whether slopes of two segments on a line are the same line. Have students review how to find and compare slopes.
3	Accurately determined whether the slopes of two segments on a line are the same line.	Assign the Lesson 5 Quiz.

LESSON 6 — Linear Equations with Rational Coefficients

PLUG IN — Interpreting Solutions of Equations

		OBJECTIVES	CONCEPTS AND SKILLS	VOCABULARY
FOUNDATIONAL UNDERSTANDING	**▶ PLUG IN** — Interpreting Solutions of Equations — Student Edition pp. 54–55	• Simplify equations to determine the number of solutions.	Give examples of linear equations with one solution, infinitely many solutions, or no solutions. Show which of these is the case by transforming the equation into simpler forms. **CCSS:** 8.EE.7.a	• **algebraic equation** • **variable** • **expressions**
	POWER UP — Linear Equations with Whole-Number Coefficients	• Apply the distributive property and combine like terms to find the solutions to an equation.	Solve linear equations with whole-number coefficients, including equations whose solutions require expanding expressions using the distributive property and collecting like terms. **CCSS:** 8.EE.7.b	• **distributive property** • **like terms** • **coefficients**
ON-LEVEL TARGET	**READY TO GO** — Linear Equations with Rational Coefficients	• Solve linear equations with rational coefficients.	Solve linear equations with rational coefficients, including equations whose solutions require expanding expressions using the distributive property and collecting like terms. **CCSS:** 8.EE.7.b	• **rational numbers** • **integers**

MATERIALS
- Index cards *(suggested)*
- Algebra tiles *(suggested)*
- Equation mats *(suggested)*

ENGLISH LANGUAGE LEARNERS
MP6 ELL students may need extra support in understanding the terms *no solution, one solution*, and *infinitely many solutions*. On an index card, have students write the terms and the definition in their own words. For example, *no solution* means no value for the variable makes the equation true; *one solution* means only one value for the variable makes the equation true; and *infinitely many solutions* means all values for the variable make the equation true.

Build Background
- Talk to students about the reasons to interpret solutions of equations in real life. For example, Maria paid $13 for a movie ticket, which was $3 more than twice the price of a drink at the movie theater. What was the price of the drink? Explain that this question can be answered by finding and interpreting the solution to an equation.
- **MP4** Have students discuss additional examples of real situations that involve interpreting the solutions to equations.

Introduce and Model
- **Introduce Concepts and Vocabulary** Emphasize that a solution is what makes an equation true and that when interpreting solutions, it is important to check the solutions by substituting the values back into the original equation.
- **Support Discussion** **MP3** Have partners discuss briefly before group discussion. As needed, remind students that an equation can have one solution, infinitely many solutions, and no solution.

> *Prompt:* How can you determine if Emma's reasoning is correct?
> *Sentence Starter:* I would tell Emma …

LESSON 6 Linear Equations with Rational Coefficients

PLUG IN Interpreting Solutions of Equations

The solution to an **algebraic equation** with one variable is any value of the variable that makes both sides equal.

This equation has one solution.

$x + 2 = 5$

$x = 3$

I see! The only number that can be added to 2 to get 5 is 3.

If the **expressions** on both sides of an equation are identical or proportional, the equation has infinitely many solutions.

This equation has infinitely many solutions.

$x + 2 = x + 2 \leftarrow$ always true

$3 + 2 = 3 + 2 \leftarrow x$ could be 3.

$0 + 2 = 0 + 2 \leftarrow x$ could be 0.

I get it! Any value of x makes the equation true.

If the expressions on both sides of an equation can never be equal, the equation has no solution.

This equation has no solutions.

$x + 2 = x - 2 \leftarrow$ never true

$3 + 2 \neq 3 - 2 \leftarrow x \neq 3$

$0 + 2 \neq 0 - 2 \leftarrow x \neq 0$

Right! $2 \neq -2$, so there is no value of x that will make the equation true.

Words to Know

algebraic equation	variable	expression
a number sentence with at least one variable and an equal sign	a letter or symbol used to stand for one or more numbers	a mathematical phrase containing numbers and/or variables and operations

DISCUSS Emma says that the variable n in an equation always stands for exactly one number. What can you tell Emma about her work?
Possible response: Emma is incorrect. Many equations have only one solution, but some have infinitely many solutions, and some have no solution.

A Simplify an equation to determine its number of solutions.

DO Solve for a: $5a = 20$

1. Identify the inverse operation to isolate the variable.
2. Use the same operation on both sides to make both sides equal.
3. Simplify to solve for a.
4. Interpret the solution.

Fractions are one way to show division.

The inverse of multiplication is __division__.

So divide $5a$ by __5__ to get a by itself.

$5a \div \underline{5} = 20 \div \underline{5}$

$a = \underline{4}$

The equation has __one__ solution(s).

B Simplify an equation to determine its number of solutions.

DO Solve for x: $x + 5 - 3 = x + 8$

1. Simplify the equation. Subtract 3 from 5.
2. Subtract x from both sides.
3. Compare the expressions on both sides of the simplified equation. Write = or ≠.
4. Interpret the solution.

To keep an equation balanced, I have to perform the same operation on both sides of an equation.

$x + 5 - 3 = x + 8$

$x + \underline{2} = x + 8$

$x - \underline{x} + 2 = x - \underline{x} + 8$

$2 \neq 8$

The equation has __no__ solution(s), because $2 = 8$ is __never__ true.

C Simplify an equation to determine its number of solutions.

DO Solve for n: $n - 4 = n - (8 \div 2)$

1. Simplify inside the parentheses.
2. Subtract n from both sides.
3. Compare the expressions on both sides of the equation using the = or ≠ symbol.
4. Interpret the solution.

$n - 4 = n - (8 \div 2)$

$n - 4 = n - \underline{4}$

$n - \underline{n} - 4 = n - \underline{n} - 4$

$-4 = -4$

The equation has __infinitely many__ solution(s), because the equation $-4 = -4$ is __always__ true.

DISCUSS Describe simplified equations that have one solution, infinitely many solutions, or no solution.
Possible response: A simplified equation with one solution has a variable equal to one number. A simplified equation with infinitely many solutions has same values on both sides of the equal sign. A simplified equation with no solution has different values on either side of the equal sign.

PRACTICE

State if each equation has no solution, one solution, or infinitely many solutions.

1. $g + 10 = g - 10$
   __no solution__

2. $2 + m = 3$
   __one solution__

3. $4b = 4b$
   __infinitely many solutions__

4. $3k = 6$
   __one solution__

Solve for x. If there are infinitely many solutions, write *infinitely many solutions*. If there is no solution, write *no solution*.

5. $\frac{x}{3} = 6$
   $x = \underline{18}$

6. $x - 4 = x - 5 + 1$
   $x = \underline{\text{infinitely many solutions}}$

7. $x - (8 - 3) = x - 11$
   $x = \underline{\text{no solution}}$

8. $x + (3 - 1) = 4$
   $x = \underline{2}$

• Model Application

DO **A** If needed, review inverse operations with students.

DO **B** Explain that an equation has no solution when the values on either side of the equal sign are not equal.

DO **C** Explain that an equation has infinitely many solutions when the values on either side of the equal sign are equal.

• **Support Discussion** MP6 Have partners discuss briefly before group discussion. As needed, have students review the different types of solutions to an equation.

> **Prompt:** What is the difference between an equation with no solution and an equation with one solution?
>
> **Sentence Starter:** A simplified equation with one solution…

Practice and Assess

• Ask students to complete practice items 1–8 on page 55 independently or in pairs. Monitor ongoing work.

• Observe whether students are correctly interpreting the solutions to an equation. Use the chart below as needed to address any difficulties.

Observation	Action
Students have difficulty solving equations.	If students struggle with solving the equations, have them use algebra tiles and equation mats to help model the equations.

SPOTLIGHT ON MATHEMATICAL PRACTICES

MP6 Attend to Precision.

Help students think about question by asking: *What are the characteristics of an equation? What does the simplified equation with one solution look like? How is that different from a simplified equation with no solution? with infinitely many solutions?*

Linear Equations with Whole-Number Coefficients

		OBJECTIVES	CONCEPTS AND SKILLS	VOCABULARY
FOUNDATIONAL UNDERSTANDING	**PLUG IN** **Interpreting Solutions of Equations**	• Simplify equations to determine the number of solutions.	Give examples of linear equations with one solution, infinitely many solutions, or no solutions. Show which of these is the case by transforming the equation into simpler forms. **CCSS:** 8.EE.7.a	• **algebraic equation** • **variable** • **expressions**
	▶ POWER UP **Linear Equations with Whole-Number Coefficients** Student Edition pp. 56–57	• Apply the distributive property and combine like terms to find the solutions to an equation.	Solve linear equations with whole-number coefficients, including equations whose solutions require expanding expressions using the distributive property and collecting like terms. **CCSS:** 8.EE.7.b	• **distributive property** • **like terms** • **coefficients**
ON-LEVEL TARGET	**READY TO GO** **Linear Equations with Rational Coefficients**	• Solve linear equations with rational coefficients.	Solve linear equations with rational coefficients, including equations whose solutions require expanding expressions using the distributive property and collecting like terms. **CCSS:** 8.EE.7.b	• **rational numbers** • **integers**

MATERIALS
• Index cards *(suggested)*

ENGLISH LANGUAGE LEARNERS

MP7 ELL students may need additional support in identifying *like terms*. Make flashcards for students to practice identifying like terms. On the front of an index card, write an expression that contains like terms. On the back of the card provide the answer. Have students work in pairs and take turns identifying the like terms.

Build Background

• Talk to students about reasons to use the distributive property and combine like terms when solving equations with whole-number coefficients. For example, four friends attend a baseball game. Each friend paid x dollars for a ticket and $18 for a souvenir T-shirt. They also paid $5 each for parking. If the friends spent a total of $245, what is the cost of one ticket? Explain that this question can be answered by using the distributive property and combining like terms when solving an equation.

• **MP4** Have students discuss additional examples of real situations in which they would solve an equation with whole-number coefficients by using the distributive property and combining like terms.

Introduce and Model

• **Introduce and Model** Emphasize that it is important to distribute the number outside the parentheses to both terms inside the parentheses. **MP6** Have students define the terms *distributive property, like terms,* and *coefficients* in their own words.

• **Support Discussion** **MP7** Have partners discuss briefly before group discussion. As needed, remind students of the definition of a variable.

> *Prompt: What is the difference between a constant and a variable?*
> *Sentence Starter: Like terms can only be combined …*

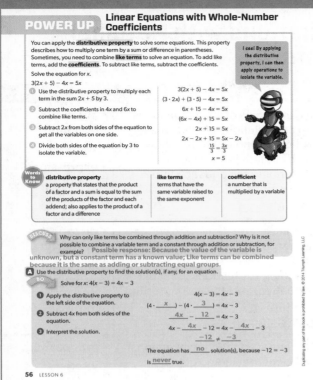

POWER UP Linear Equations with Whole-Number Coefficients

You can apply the **distributive property** to solve some equations. This property describes how to multiply one term by a sum or difference in parentheses. Sometimes, you need to combine **like terms** to solve an equation. To add like terms, add the **coefficients**. To subtract like terms, subtract the coefficients.

Solve the equation for x.

$3(2x + 5) - 4x = 5x$

I see! By applying the distributive property, I can then apply operations to isolate the variable.

① Use the distributive property to multiply each term in the sum $2x + 5$ by 3.

② Subtract the coefficients in 4x and 6x to combine like terms.

③ Subtract 2x from both sides of the equation to get all the variables on one side.

④ Divide both sides of the equation by 3 to isolate the variable.

$3(2x + 5) - 4x = 5x$
$(3 \cdot 2x) + (3 \cdot 5) - 4x = 5x$
$6x + 15 - 4x = 5x$
$(6x - 4x) + 15 = 5x$
$2x + 15 = 5x$
$2x - 2x + 15 = 5x - 2x$
$\frac{15}{3} = \frac{3x}{3}$
$x = 5$

Words to Know	distributive property	like terms	coefficient
	a property that states that the product of a factor and a sum is equal to the sum of the products of the factor and each addend; also applies to the product of a factor and a difference	terms that have the same variable raised to the same exponent	a number that is multiplied by a variable

DISCUSS Why can only like terms be combined through addition and subtraction? Why is it not possible to combine a variable term and a constant through addition or subtraction, for example? **Possible response: Because the value of the variable is unknown, but a constant term has a known value; Like terms can be combined because it is the same as adding or subtracting equal groups.**

A Use the distributive property to find the solution(s), if any, for an equation.

DO Solve for x: $4(x - 3) = 4x - 3$

① Apply the distributive property to the left side of the equation.

② Subtract 4x from both sides of the equation.

③ Interpret the solution.

$4(x - 3) = 4x - 3$
$(4 \cdot x) - (4 \cdot 3) = 4x - 3$
$4x - 12 = 4x - 3$
$4x - 4x - 12 = 4x - 4x - 3$
$-12 \neq -3$

The equation has _no_ solution(s), because $-12 = -3$ is _never_ true.

B Apply the distributive property and combine like terms to find the solution(s), if any, for an equation.

DO Solve for k: $3(k + 5) = 4k + 10 - k + 5$

① Apply the distributive property.

② Combine like terms and perform operations to isolate the variable.

③ Interpret the solution.

$3(k + 5) = 4k + 10 - k + 5$
$(3 \cdot k) + (3 \cdot 5) = 4k + 10 - k + 5$
$3k + 15 = 4k + 10 - k + 5$
$3k + 15 = 4k - k + 10 + 5$
$3k + 15 = 3k + 15$

The equation has _infinitely many_ solution(s) because $3k + 15 = 3k + 15$ will _always_ be true.

DISCUSS Kurt simplifies this equation and says it has no solution. What can you tell Kurt about his work?

$2(x - 7) = 2x - 14$
$2x - 7 = 2x - 14$
$-7 = -14$

Possible response: Kurt is incorrect. He did not distribute the 2 to both parts of the difference. The correct equation for the second step is $2x - 14 = 2x - 14$. Since both sides of the equation will always be equal, there are infinitely many solutions.

PRACTICE

Use the distributive property to solve for x. If there are infinitely many solutions, write *infinitely many solutions*. If there is no solution, write *no solution*.

1 $5(x + 1) = 10$
   $x =$ _1_

2 $8(x - 4) = 8x - 32$
   $x =$ _infinitely many solutions_

Combine like terms to solve for n. If there are infinitely many solutions, write *infinitely many solutions*. If there is no solution, write *no solution*.

3 $11n - 4 - 3n = 8n - 5$
   $n =$ _no solution_

4 $4n + 5 = 8n + 3$
   $n =$ _$\frac{1}{2}$_

Apply the distributive property and combine like terms to solve for b.

5 $5(b - 1) + 7 = 6b + 1$
   $b =$ _1_

6 $3(5b + 2) - b = 4(b + 9)$
   $b =$ _3_

56 LESSON 6

57

• Model Application

DO A Guide students as they use the distributive property to find the solution(s), if any, for an equation. Remind students of how to tell if an equation has no solution.

DO B Monitor students as they use the distributive property and combine like terms to find the solution(s), if any, for an equation. If needed, remind students of how to tell if an equation has infinitely many solutions.

• **Support Discussion MP3** Have partners discuss briefly before group discussion. Remind students of how to check the solution to an equation.

Prompt: How can you check Kurt's solution?
Sentence Starter: When you use the distributive property, you ...

Practice and Assess

• Ask students to complete practice items 1–6 on page 57 independently or in pairs. Monitor ongoing work.

• Observe whether students correctly use the distributive property and combine like terms when solving an equation with whole-number coefficients. Use the chart below as needed to address any difficulties.

Observation	Action
Students do not correctly use the distributive property when solving an equation.	Make two sets of index cards. On one set of cards, write expressions that require using the distributive property to simplify. On the other set of cards, write the expressions in simplified form. Ask students to match the expressions.

SPOTLIGHT ON MATHEMATICAL LANGUAGE

MP6 Support students in using mathematical language as they work:

■ *Why can you combine **like terms**?*

■ *Must terms have **coefficients** for them to be like terms?*

■ *If two different **variables** have the same coefficients, does this make them like terms?*

Linear Equations with Rational Coefficients

		OBJECTIVES	CONCEPTS AND SKILLS	VOCABULARY
FOUNDATIONAL UNDERSTANDING	**PLUG IN** Interpreting Solutions of Equations	• Simplify equations to determine the number of solutions.	Give examples of linear equations with one solution, infinitely many solutions, or no solutions. Show which of these is the case by transforming the equation into simpler forms. **CCSS:** 8.EE.7.a	• **algebraic equation** • **variable** • **expressions**
	POWER UP Linear Equations with Whole-Number Coefficients	• Apply the distributive property and combine like terms to find the solutions to an equation.	Solve linear equations with whole-number coefficients, including equations whose solutions require expanding expressions using the distributive property and collecting like terms. **CCSS:** 8.EE.7.b	• **distributive property** • **like terms** • **coefficients**
ON-LEVEL TARGET	**▶ READY TO GO** Linear Equations with Rational Coefficients Student Edition pp. 58–63	• Solve linear equations with rational coefficients.	Solve linear equations with rational coefficients, including equations whose solutions require expanding expressions using the distributive property and collecting like terms. **CCSS:** 8.EE.7.b	• **rational numbers** • **integers**

MATERIALS

- Lesson 6 Quiz, Assessment Manual pp. 14–15
- Lesson 6 Quiz Answer Key, Assessment Manual
- Math Tool: Properties of Multiplication, p. A5 (Student Edition p. 215)
- Math Tool: Fraction Strips, p. A14 (Student Edition p. 235)

ENGLISH LANGUAGE LEARNERS

MP6 ELL students may need additional support in understanding reciprocal fractions. Write fractions and their reciprocals on individual index cards. Keep the fractions in one pile and the reciprocals in another pile. Have students pick a fraction from one pile of cards and then find and identify its reciprocal from the other pile.

Build Background

- Talk to students about reasons to solve linear equations with rational coefficients. For example, the cost of renting a canoe is $12.50 for the first hour and $10.50 for each additional hour. If the total cost of renting a canoe was $44, for how many hours was the canoe rented? Explain that by solving a linear equation you can answer this question.

- **MP4** Have students discuss additional examples of real situations that require solving linear equations with rational coefficients.

- Tell students they will solve linear equations with rational coefficients.

Introduce and Model

- **Introduce Concepts and Vocabulary** Guide students through the information about solving equations with rational coefficients. Emphasize that it is important to pay attention to signs of numbers when solving equations. Use **Words to Know** to clarify their understanding of vocabulary. **MP6** Have students give examples of the terms *rational numbers* and *integers*.

- **Support Discussion** **MP8** Have partners discuss briefly before group discussion. If needed, recall how to solve an equation.

> *Prompt: What strategies do you use when solving an equation?*
> *Sentence Starter: When solving both types of equations …*

READY TO GO — Linear Equations with Rational Coefficients

Some algebraic equations have coefficients that include **rational numbers**, which include fractions, decimals, and negative **integers**.

Solve for x: $\frac{1}{3}(4x - 3) = \frac{2}{3}x - 5 + 2x$

1. Apply the distributive property.
2. Rename the whole number coefficient of a variable term to combine like terms.
3. Isolate the variable.
4. Solve for x.

I see! I can multiply both sides by the reciprocal of the coefficient. The reciprocal of a number is its multiplicative inverse.

$$\frac{1}{3}(4x - 3) = \frac{2}{3}x - 5 + 2x$$
$$\left(\frac{1}{3} \cdot 4x\right) - \left(\frac{1}{3} \cdot 3\right) = \frac{2}{3}x - 5 + 2x$$
$$\frac{4}{3}x - 1 = \frac{2}{3}x - 5 + 2x$$
$$\frac{4}{3}x - 1 = \frac{2}{3}x + 2x - 5$$
$$\frac{4}{3}x - 1 = \frac{2}{3}x + \frac{6}{3}x - 5$$
$$\frac{4}{3}x - 1 = \frac{8}{3}x - 5$$
$$\frac{4}{3}x - \frac{4}{3}x - 1 = \frac{8}{3}x - \frac{4}{3}x - 5$$
$$-1 = \frac{4}{3}x - 5$$
$$-1 + 5 = \frac{4}{3}x - 5 + 5$$
$$4 = \frac{4}{3}x$$
$$\frac{4}{1} \cdot \frac{3}{4} = \frac{4}{3}x \cdot \frac{3}{4}$$
$$3 = x$$

Words to Know

rational number a number that can be written as the ratio of two integers

integers counting numbers (1, 2, 3, …), their opposites (−1, −2, −3, …), and zero

DISCUSS How is solving an equation with rational coefficients like solving an equation with whole-number coefficients?
Possible response: In both types of equations, you can apply the distributive property, combine like terms, and isolate the variable to solve.

LESSON LINK

PLUG IN	POWER UP	GO!
You can simplify an equation to determine if it has no solution, one solution, or infinitely many solutions. $6x = 2$ $\frac{6x}{6} = \frac{2}{6}$ $x = \frac{1}{3}$ ← one solution	You can use the distributive property and combine like terms to solve equations with whole-number coefficients. $2(x - 1) - x = 4$ $2x - 2 - x = 4$ $x - 2 = 4$ $x = 6$	I get it! I can apply the same strategies for solving equations with whole number coefficients to solve equations with rational number coefficients.

WORK TOGETHER

$$1.5(2a + 4) = -6.5a - 3 + 0.5a$$
$$(1.5 \cdot 2a) + (1.5 \cdot 4) = -6.5a - 3 + 0.5a$$

Solve for a:
$$1.5(2a + 4) = -6.5a - 3 + 0.5a$$

- Apply the distributive property. $3a + 6 = -6.5a - 3 + 0.5a$
- Apply the commutative property. $3a + 6 = -6.5a + 0.5a - 3$
- Combine like terms. $3a + 6 = -6a - 3$
- Isolate the variable and solve for a. $3a - 3a + 6 = -6a - 3a - 3$
$$6 = -9a - 3$$
$$6 + 3 = -9a - 3 + 3$$
$$9 = -9a$$
$$\frac{9}{-9} = \frac{-9a}{-9}$$
$$-1 = a$$

$a = -1$

Properties of Multiplication can be found on p. 215

A Solve an equation with fractional coefficients.

I know a variable without a coefficient is the same as 1 times that variable. So I can rewrite the coefficient 1 as $\frac{5}{5}$.

DO Solve for c: $-\frac{1}{5}c + 2 + c = \frac{1}{5}(10c - 20)$

1. Apply the distributive property.
$$-\frac{1}{5}c + 2 + c = \left(\frac{1}{5} \cdot 10c\right) - \left(\frac{1}{5} \times 20\right)$$
$$-\frac{1}{5}c + 2 + c = 2c - 4$$
2. Use the commutative property and combine like terms.
$$-\frac{1}{5}c + c + 2 = 2c - 4$$
$$-\frac{1}{5}c + \frac{5}{5}c + 2 = 2c - 4$$
3. Isolate the variable.
$$\frac{4}{5}c + 2 = 2c - 4$$
4. Multiply both sides by the reciprocal of the coefficient to solve for c.
$$\frac{4}{5}c - \frac{4}{5} + 2 = \frac{10}{5}c - \frac{4}{5}c - 4$$
$$2 = \frac{6}{5}c - 4$$
$$2 + 4 = \frac{6}{5}c - 4 + 4$$
$$6 = \frac{6}{5}c$$
$$6 \cdot \frac{5}{6} = \frac{6}{5}c \cdot \frac{5}{6}$$
$$5 = c$$

I can rewrite 2c in the equivalent form of $\frac{10}{5}c$ to make subtraction easier.

DISCUSS How do you know when you are finished simplifying an equation with one variable?
Possible answer: You are finished when you have either isolated the variable or found an equality statement that is always or never true.

LESSON LINK

Connect to Foundational Understanding Skills learned in the **Plug In** and **Power Up** are referenced in the **Lesson Link**. Explain that an equation can have one solution, infinitely many solutions, or no solution. To solve equations with whole-number and rational coefficients you can use the distributive property and combine like terms.

- **Work Together** Explain that students will solve equations with rational coefficients.

DO **A** Monitor students as they solve equations with fractional coefficients. Remind students that the reciprocal of a number multiplied by the number equals 1.

- **Support Discussion** **MP7** Have partners discuss briefly before group discussion. As needed, have students explain what it means to solve an equation.

> *Prompt: What does it mean to isolate a variable?*
> *Sentence Starter: You are finished simplifying an equation when…*

FOCUS ON FLUENCY

MP5 Use **Math Tool: Fraction Strips** to have students model multiplying by rational coefficients. Ask students to model the following situation: *Alex does $\frac{3}{4}$ hour of math homework each night of the week. How many hours of math homework does Alex do in 5 nights?* To model the situation, students should show 5 fraction strips that each show 3 out of 4 sections shaded or colored. They should find that Alex does $3\frac{3}{4}$ hours of math homework in 5 nights.

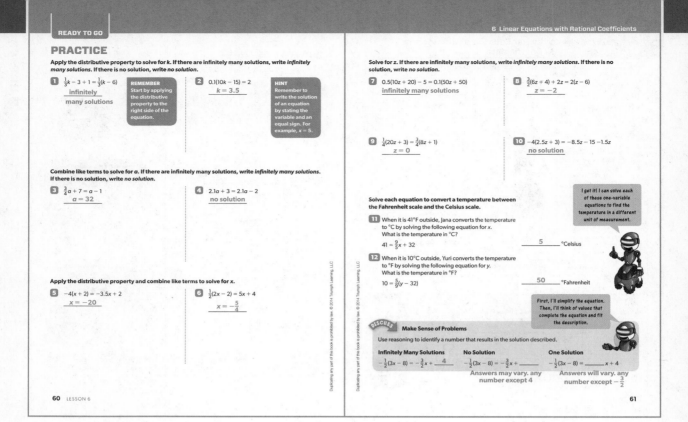

READY TO GO

PRACTICE

Apply the distributive property to solve for *k*. If there are infinitely many solutions, write *infinitely many solutions*. If there is no solution, write *no solution*.

1 $\frac{1}{3}k - 3 + 1 = \frac{1}{3}(k - 6)$
  <u>infinitely
  many solutions</u>

> **REMEMBER**
> Start by applying the distributive property to the right side of the equation.

2 $0.1(10k - 15) = 2$
  $k = 3.5$

> **HINT**
> Remember to write the solution of an equation by stating the variable and an equal sign. For example, *x* = 5.

Combine like terms to solve for *a*. If there are infinitely many solutions, write *infinitely many solutions*. If there is no solution, write *no solution*.

3 $\frac{3}{4}a + 7 = a - 1$
  $a = 32$

4 $2.1a + 3 = 2.1a - 2$
  <u>no solution</u>

Apply the distributive property and combine like terms to solve for *x*.

5 $-4(x + 2) = -3.5x + 2$
  $x = -20$

6 $\frac{1}{2}(2x - 2) = 5x + 4$
  $x = -\frac{5}{4}$

Solve for *z*. If there are infinitely many solutions, write *infinitely many solutions*. If there is no solution, write *no solution*.

7 $0.5(10z + 20) - 5 = 0.1(50z + 50)$
  <u>infinitely many solutions</u>

8 $\frac{3}{2}(6z + 4) + 2z = 2(z - 6)$
  $z = -2$

9 $\frac{1}{4}(20z + 3) = \frac{3}{4}(8z + 1)$
  $z = 0$

10 $-4(2.5z + 3) = -8.5z - 15 - 1.5z$
  <u>no solution</u>

Solve each equation to convert a temperature between the Fahrenheit scale and the Celsius scale.

11 When it is 41°F outside, Jana converts the temperature to °C by solving the following equation for *x*. What is the temperature in °C?
$41 = \frac{9}{5}x + 32$

  <u>   5   </u> °Celsius

> I get it! I can solve each of these one-variable equations to find the temperature in a different unit of measurement.

12 When it is 10°C outside, Yuri converts the temperature to °F by solving the following equation for *y*. What is the temperature in °F?
$10 = \frac{5}{9}(y - 32)$

  <u>   50   </u> °Fahrenheit

> First, I'll simplify the equation. Then, I'll think of values that complete the equation and fit the description.

DISCUSS **Make Sense of Problems**

Use reasoning to identify a number that results in the solution described.

Infinitely Many Solutions	No Solution	One Solution
$-\frac{1}{2}(3x - 8) = -\frac{3}{2}x + \underline{4}$	$-\frac{1}{2}(3x - 8) = -\frac{3}{2}x + \underline{\quad}$	$-\frac{1}{2}(3x - 8) = \underline{\quad}x + 4$
	Answers may vary. any number except 4	Answers will vary. any number except $-\frac{3}{2}$

60 LESSON 6

61

Additional Practice

Provide students with additional practice to model and solve:

> Solve for *x*. If there are infinitely many solutions, write "infinitely many solutions." If there is no solution, write "no solution."
>
> $0.2(40x + 10) = 0.1(80x + 20)$
>
> $\frac{1}{2}(14x + 6) + 4x = 14$
>
> $-2(1.25x + 1.5) = -4.25x - 7.5 + 1.75x$

SPOTLIGHT ON MATHEMATICAL PRACTICES

MP6 Make Sense of Problems

- Help students think about this problem by asking: *Is there more than one number that makes this equation true? Is there any number that makes this equation false?*

Support Independent Practice

1–6 Remind students to read the **HINT** and **REMEMBER**. If needed, ask: *Did you combine like terms correctly? Did you distribute the number to both terms inside the parentheses?*

7–10 *Did you double-check your solution to the equation?*

11–12 *What is the first step in converting the temperature?*

Support Discussion MP2 Have partners discuss briefly before group discussion. As needed, have students discuss the types of solutions to an equation.

> *Prompt: What is the first step in finding the number?*
> *Sentence Starter: The number that makes the equation true is …*

Problem Solving

- **Model the Four-Step Method MP1 MP4** Guide students through the four-step method using think-aloud strategies. Point out the clue words *the first mile costs*.

  Think Aloud To find the number of miles, I need to write and solve an equation.

- **Support Problem-Solving Practice** Have students use the Checklist as they complete each step.

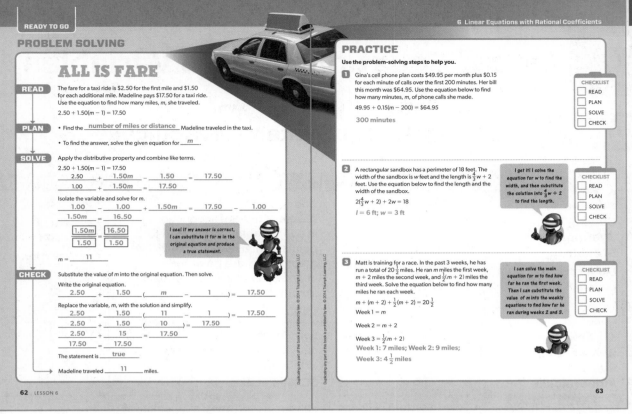

READY TO GO
PROBLEM SOLVING

ALL IS FARE

READ The fare for a taxi ride is $2.50 for the first mile and $1.50 for each additional mile. Madeline pays $17.50 for a taxi ride. Use the equation to find how many miles, m, she traveled.

$2.50 + 1.50(m − 1) = 17.50$

PLAN
• Find the ___number of miles or distance___ Madeline traveled in the taxi.

• To find the answer, solve the given equation for ___m___.

SOLVE Apply the distributive property and combine like terms.

$2.50 + 1.50(m − 1) = 17.50$

$\underline{2.50} + \underline{1.50m} − \underline{1.50} = \underline{17.50}$

$\underline{1.00} + \underline{1.50m} = \underline{17.50}$

Isolate the variable and solve for m.

$\underline{1.00} − \underline{1.00} + \underline{1.50m} = \underline{17.50} − \underline{1.00}$

$\underline{1.50m} = \underline{16.50}$

$\dfrac{\boxed{1.50m}}{\boxed{1.50}} = \dfrac{\boxed{16.50}}{\boxed{1.50}}$

$m = \underline{11}$

I see! If my answer is correct, I can substitute it for m in the original equation and produce a true statement.

CHECK Substitute the value of m into the original equation. Then solve.

Write the original equation.

$\underline{2.50} + \underline{1.50}(\underline{m} − \underline{1}) = \underline{17.50}$

Replace the variable, m, with the solution and simplify.

$\underline{2.50} + \underline{1.50}(\underline{11} − \underline{1}) = \underline{17.50}$

$\underline{2.50} + \underline{1.50}(\underline{10}) = \underline{17.50}$

$\underline{2.50} + \underline{15} = \underline{17.50}$

$\underline{17.50} = \underline{17.50}$

The statement is ___true___.

→ Madeline traveled ___11___ miles.

PRACTICE
Use the problem-solving steps to help you.

1 Gina's cell phone plan costs $49.95 per month plus $0.15 for each minute of calls over the first 200 minutes. Her bill this month was $64.95. Use the equation below to find how many minutes, m, of phone calls she made.

$49.95 + 0.15(m − 200) = \$64.95$

300 minutes

CHECKLIST
☐ READ
☐ PLAN
☐ SOLVE
☐ CHECK

2 A rectangular sandbox has a perimeter of 18 feet. The width of the sandbox is w feet and the length is $\frac{4}{3}w + 2$ feet. Use the equation below to find the length and the width of the sandbox.

$2(\frac{4}{3}w + 2) + 2w = 18$

$l = 6$ ft; $w = 3$ ft

I get it! I solve the equation for w to find the width, and then substitute the solution into $\frac{4}{3}w + 2$ to find the length.

CHECKLIST
☐ READ
☐ PLAN
☐ SOLVE
☐ CHECK

3 Matt is training for a race. In the past 3 weeks, he has run a total of $20\frac{1}{2}$ miles. He ran m miles the first week, $m + 2$ miles the second week, and $\frac{1}{2}(m + 2)$ miles the third week. Solve the equation below to find how many miles he ran each week.

$m + (m + 2) + \frac{1}{2}(m + 2) = 20\frac{1}{2}$

Week 1 = m

Week 2 = $m + 2$

Week 3 = $\frac{1}{2}(m + 2)$

Week 1: 7 miles; Week 2: 9 miles;
Week 3: $4\frac{1}{2}$ miles

I can solve the main equation for m to find how far he ran the first week. Then I can substitute the value of m into the weekly equations to find how far he ran during weeks 2 and 3.

CHECKLIST
☐ READ
☐ PLAN
☐ SOLVE
☐ CHECK

Prompt: What is the first step in solving the equation?
Prompt: How did you find the length of the sandbox?
Prompt: Did you double check that the number of miles he ran each week added up to $20\frac{1}{2}$?

• **Explore Student Thinking** **MP6** Invite students to explain how they solved their equation. Have partners compare their work on a problem and describe their results.

COMMON ERRORS
Students may think that all equations have only one value that makes the equation true. Remind students that some equations have no solution, one solution, or infinitely many solutions.

Assess

• Use the table below to address any difficulties.

	Observation	Action
1	Errors in solving equations with rational coefficients are frequent.	If students struggle with solving equations, have them review solving equations with whole numbers by using algebra tiles. If students struggle with rational operations, have them review operations with fractions, decimals, and integers.
2	Makes occasional errors when solving equations with rational coefficients.	Provide additional practice problems for solving equations with rational coefficients. Have students review how to use the distributive property and combine like terms.
3	Accurately solves equations with rational coefficients.	Assign the Lesson 6 Quiz.

Linear Equations in Two Variables

PLUG IN Solving Linear Systems Graphically

		OBJECTIVES	CONCEPTS AND SKILLS	VOCABULARY
FOUNDATIONAL UNDERSTANDING	**▶ PLUG IN** **Solving Linear Systems Graphically** Student Edition pp. 64–65	• Find the solution to a system of linear equations by finding their point of intersection.	Understand that solutions to a system of two linear equations in two variables correspond to points of intersection of their graphs, because points of intersection satisfy both equations simultaneously. **CCSS:** 8.EE.8.a	• **variable** • **system of equations** • **intersection**
	POWER UP **Solving Linear Systems Algebraically**	• Solve a system of linear equations algebraically.	Solve systems of two linear equations in two variables algebraically. **CCSS:** 8.EE.8.b	
ON-LEVEL TARGET	**READY TO GO** **Linear Equations in Two Variables**	• Solve a system of linear equations that represent real-life situations.	Solve real-world and mathematical problems leading to two linear equations in two variables. **CCSS:** 8.EE.8.c	

MATERIALS
• Math Tool: Grid paper, p. A11 (Student Edition, p. 229)

SPOTLIGHT ON MATHEMATICAL PRACTICES

MP4 Model with Mathematics

Model setting up a coordinate grid on graph paper. Encourage students to label the *x*- and *y*-axes. Explain that the scale, or the value of each grid line, is dependent on the solutions to the equations. To maintain proper perspective, however, the scale on both axes should be the same.

Build Background

■ Talk to students about when two linear equations might intersect. For example, two health clubs offer comparable memberships at different prices. At what point are the costs equal? At what points are the membership costs of one health club better or worse than the other?

■ **MP4** Have students discuss additional examples of real situations that involve price rate comparisons.

Introduce and Model

■ **Introduce Concepts and Vocabulary** Guide students through the information about graphing linear equations. Use **Words to Know** to clarify their understanding of vocabulary. **MP5** Have students demonstrate to a partner their understanding of *variables, system of equations,* and *intersection*.

■ **Support Discussion** **MP6** Have partners discuss briefly before group discussion. As needed, direct students to **Words to Know** and have them use the illustrations to explain the terms in their own words.

> *Prompt: How is the solution to a system of equations determined?*
> *Sentence Starter: The solution to a system of equations is …*

LESSON 7 — Linear Equations in Two Variables

PLUG IN · Solving Linear Systems Graphically

The graph of a linear equation with two **variables** x and y shows all pairs of x and y that make the equation true.

$$y = 3x - 2$$

A solution to a **system of equations** is a pair of x and y values that makes the equations true.

System of equations:

Equation 1:
$y = 3x - 2$

Equation 2:
$y = 2x + 1$

The **intersection** of lines on a graph is represented by a coordinate pair (x, y). This point is a solution to the system of equations.

Equation 1: $y = 3x - 2$

Equation 2: $y = 2x + 1$

If an equation is true, the left side of the equation equals the right side.

To find a solution to this system, I need to find a pair of x and y values that make both equations true.

The point (3, 7) is the intersection of both lines. So the solution to the system is (3, 7).

Words to Know

variable a letter or symbol used to stand for one or more numbers	**system of equations** two or more equations with the same variables	**intersection** the point or points where graphs of equations meet

DISCUSS Sam graphs two linear equations and sees the lines are parallel. He knows this means the lines never cross. If the lines never cross, does this system of equations have a solution?
Possible response: If two lines never cross, then there is no point (x, y) that makes both equations true. That means there is no solution to the system of equations.

A You can find the solution to a system of linear equations by finding their point of intersection.

DO What is the solution to the system $y = -x - 1$ and $y = 3x + 11$?

❶ Find several ordered pairs for each equation.
❷ Graph the system of equations.
❸ Check the solution.

$y = -x - 1$

x	y
−1	0
0	−1
1	−2
2	−3

$y = 3x + 11$

x	y
−1	8
0	11
1	14
−5	−4

When an ordered pair 'satisfies' an equation, that means substituting the values produces a true statement.

The graphs intersect at (−3, 2).

$y = -x - 1$

$2 = -(-3) - 1$

$2 = 3 - 1$

$2 = 2$

$y = 3x + 11$

$2 = 3(-3) + 11$

$2 = -9 + 11$

$2 = 2$

The ordered pair (−3, 2) satisfies both equations, so the solution is correct.

DISCUSS Julie graphs a system of linear equations twice. The first time, she draws it on a coordinate grid whose scale is from −10 to 10 for the x and y axes. The second time, she draws it on a coordinate grid whose scale is from −5 to 5 for the x and y axes. She sees the lines intersect on the first graph but not on the second graph. Does this system of equations have a solution? Explain. Possible response: Yes. Even if the point of intersection isn't shown because of the scale of the graph, that solution still satisfies both equations.

PRACTICE

Find the solution to the system of linear equations by graphing.

❶ $y = -5x - 10$
$y = -x + 2$

The solution is (−3, 5).

• Model Application

DO **A** Explain that the solution to the system can be checked by substituting the same x- and y-values into both equations. If both equations are true, the point is the solution to the system.

• Support Discussion **MP2** Have partners discuss briefly before group discussion. As needed, direct students to sketch an example using two graphs that have different scales.

> *Prompt:* How can you know whether a system of equations will have a solution if the lines do not intersect on the graph?
>
> *Sentence Starter:* The only time a system of equations will not have a solution is when …

Practice and Assess

• Ask students to complete practice item 1 on page 65 independently or in pairs. Monitor ongoing work.

• Observe whether students accurately graph each linear equation and correctly identify the solution.

Observation	Action
Students have difficulty graphing linear equations in two variables.	Remind students that only two points are necessary to identify a straight line. Often, one of the easiest values of x to use is 0. When choosing a second value of x, look at the equation and determine which value of x will be easiest to work with.

ENGLISH LANGUAGE LEARNERS

MP1 ELL students may need additional support in identifying ordered pairs. Remind them that an ordered pair identifies the location of a point on a coordinate grid by first identifying the location left or right (the x-coordinate), and then identifying the location up or down (the y-coordinate).

POWER UP — Solving Linear Systems Algebraically

		OBJECTIVES	CONCEPTS AND SKILLS	VOCABULARY
FOUNDATIONAL UNDERSTANDING	**PLUG IN** **Solving Linear Systems Graphically**	• Find the solution to a system of linear equations by finding their point of intersection.	Understand that solutions to a system of two linear equations in two variables correspond to points of intersection of their graphs, because points of intersection satisfy both equations simultaneously. **CCSS:** 8.EE.8.a	• **variable** • **system of equations** • **intersection**
	▶ POWER UP **Solving Linear Systems Algebraically** Student Edition pp. 66–67	• Solve a system of linear equations algebraically.	Solve systems of two linear equations in two variables algebraically. **CCSS:** 8.EE.8.b	
ON-LEVEL TARGET	**READY TO GO** **Linear Equations in Two Variables**	• Solve a system of linear equations that represent real-life situations.	Solve real-world and mathematical problems leading to two linear equations in two variables. **CCSS:** 8.EE.8.c	

Build Background

- Talk to students about reasons to solve systems of equations algebraically rather then by graphing. For example, when comparing the value of two health clubs memberships, it may not be feasible to graph the equations. The solution can be found algebraically.

- **MP4** Have students discuss additional examples of real situations in which it might be useful to solve a system of equations algebraically.

- Tell students they will use addition or subtraction to solve a system of equations algebraically.

Introduce and Model

- **Introduce Concepts** Guide students through the information about solving a system of equations algebraically. Emphasize that the objective is to eliminate one of the variables to find the value of the other variable. Then substitution is used to find the value of the eliminated variable.

- **Support Discussion** **MP3** Have partners discuss briefly before group discussion. Remind students to use what they know about additive inverse to support their reasoning.

> *Prompt:* Could Cora have multiplied the equations by other numbers and still successfully solved the system? Explain.
>
> *Sentence Starter:* To solve a system of equations, one variable must be …

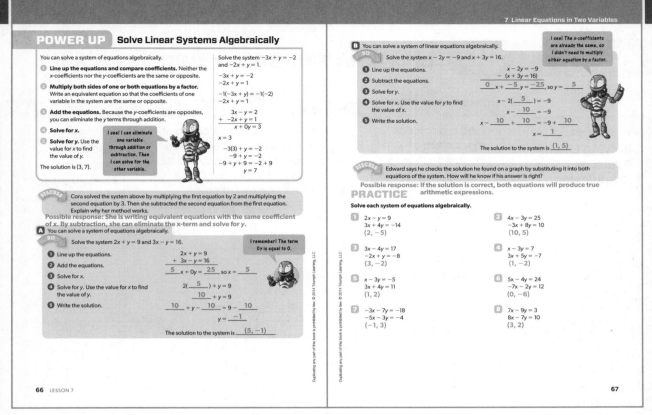

POWER UP Solve Linear Systems Algebraically

You can solve a system of equations algebraically.

① **Line up the equations and compare coefficients.** Neither the x-coefficients nor the y-coefficients are the same or opposite.

② **Multiply both sides of one or both equations by a factor.** Write an equivalent equation so that the coefficients of one variable in the system are the same or opposite.

③ **Add the equations.** Because the y-coefficients are opposites, you can eliminate the y terms through addition.

④ **Solve for x.**

⑤ **Solve for y.** Use the value for x to find the value of y.

The solution is (3, 7).

Solve the system $-3x + y = -2$ and $-2x + y = 1$.

$-3x + y = -2$
$-2x + y = 1$

$-1(-3x + y) = -1(-2)$
$-2x + y = 1$

$3x - y = 2$
$+ \ -2x + y = 1$
$\overline{\quad x + 0y = 3}$

$x = 3$

$-3(3) + y = -2$
$-9 + y = -2$
$-9 + y + 9 = -2 + 9$
$y = 7$

I see! I can eliminate one variable through addition or subtraction. Then I can solve for the other variable.

DISCUSS Cora solved the system above by multiplying the first equation by 2 and multiplying the second equation by 3. Then she subtracted the second equation from the first equation. Explain why her method works.
Possible response: She is writing equivalent equations with the same coefficient of x. By subtraction, she can eliminate the x-term and solve for y.

A You can solve a system of equations algebraically.

DO Solve the system $2x + y = 9$ and $3x - y = 16$.

① Line up the equations.

② Add the equations.

③ Solve for x.

④ Solve for y. Use the value for x to find the value of y.

⑤ Write the solution.

$2x + y = 9$
$+ \ 3x - y = 16$
$\overline{\underline{5}\ x + 0y = \underline{25}}$, so $x = \underline{5}$

$2(\underline{5}) + y = 9$
$\underline{10} + y = 9$
$\underline{10} + y - \underline{10} = 9 - \underline{10}$
$y = \underline{-1}$

The solution to the system is (5, −1)

I remember! The term 0y is equal to 0.

B You can solve a system of linear equations algebraically.

DO Solve the system $x - 2y = -9$ and $x + 3y = 16$.

① Line up the equations.

② Subtract the equations.

③ Solve for y.

④ Solve for x. Use the value for y to find the value of x.

⑤ Write the solution.

$x - 2y = -9$
$- \ (x + 3y = 16)$
$\overline{\underline{0}\ x + \underline{-5}\ y = \underline{-25}}$, so $y = \underline{5}$

$x - 2(\underline{5}) = -9$
$x - \underline{10} = -9$
$x - \underline{10} + \underline{10} = -9 + \underline{10}$
$x = \underline{1}$

The solution to the system is (1, 5)

I see! The x-coefficients are already the same, so I didn't need to multiply either equation by a factor.

DISCUSS Edward says he checks the solution he found on a graph by substituting it into both equations of the system. How will he know if his answer is right?
Possible response: If the solution is correct, both equations will produce true arithmetic expressions.

PRACTICE

Solve each system of equations algebraically.

1. $2x - y = 9$
$3x + 4y = -14$
(2, −5)

2. $4x - 3y = 25$
$-3x + 8y = 10$
(10, 5)

3. $3x - 4y = 17$
$-2x + y = -8$
(3, −2)

4. $x - 3y = 7$
$3x + 5y = -7$
(1, −2)

5. $x - 3y = -5$
$3x + 4y = 11$
(1, 2)

6. $5x - 4y = 24$
$-7x - 2y = 12$
(0, −6)

7. $-3x - 7y = -18$
$-5x - 3y = -4$
(−1, 3)

8. $7x - 9y = 3$
$8x - 7y = 10$
(3, 2)

66 LESSON 7

67

• Model Application

DO **A** Explain that because the y-values of the two equations are additive inverses, there is no need to use multiplication to change the values of the terms of either equation.

DO **B** Explain that because the x-values of the two equations are equivalent, subtracting x from x eliminates the variable.

• **Support Discussion** **MP5** Have partners discuss briefly before group discussion. Students may choose to use the solution to check the graphs of both equations on a coordinate grid.

> *Prompt:* Is it possible for Edward to use only one equation to check the solution to the system? Explain.
>
> *Sentence Starter:* In order for the solution to be true for the system of equations...

Practice and Assess

• Ask students to complete practice items 1–8 on page 67 independently or in pairs. Monitor ongoing work.

• Use the table below to address any difficulties.

Observation	Action
Students have difficulty algebraically eliminating a term from a system of equations.	Have students circle the pair of x terms. Ask students to brainstorm ways to make the terms either equivalent or inverses. Repeat with the y terms. Ask which term would be easiest to change.

		OBJECTIVES	CONCEPTS AND SKILLS	VOCABULARY
FOUNDATIONAL UNDERSTANDING	**PLUG IN** Solving Linear Systems Graphically	• Find the solution to a system of linear equations by finding their point of intersection.	Understand that solutions to a system of two linear equations in two variables correspond to points of intersection of their graphs, because points of intersection satisfy both equations simultaneously. **CCSS:** 8.EE.8.a	• **variable** • **system of equations** • **intersection**
	POWER UP Solving Linear Systems Algebraically	• Solve a system of linear equations algebraically.	Solve systems of two linear equations in two variables algebraically. **CCSS:** 8.EE.8.b	
ON-LEVEL TARGET	▶ **READY TO GO** Linear Equations in Two Variables Student Edition pp. 68–73	• Solve a system of linear equations that represent real-life situations.	Solve real-world and mathematical problems leading to two linear equations in two variables. **CCSS:** 8.EE.8.c	

MATERIALS

- Lesson 7 Quiz, Assessment Manual pp. 16–17
- Lesson 7 Quiz Answer Key, Assessment Manual
- Math Tool: Grid paper, p. A11 (Student Edition, p. 229)

COMMON ERRORS

Make sure students understand the meaning of the variables used in the equations. When writing and solving a system of equations, each variable must stand for the same unknown in each equation. Otherwise, the solution will not accurately represent a coordinate point that satisfies both equations.

Build Background

- Talk to students about reasons to solve systems of equations graphically and algebraically in real life. For example, a graph may be a better way for an advertiser to promote the value of a product. However, an algebraic solution may be more useful for marketers to monitor profit margins.
- **MP4** Have students discuss additional examples of real situations that involve graphic and algebraic systems of equations.
- Tell students they will graphically and algebraically solve real-world problems involving systems of equations.

Introduce and Model

- **Introduce Concepts** Guide students through the information about the relationship between different ways to solve systems of equations. Emphasize that sometimes graphing is more useful, and sometimes algebraic solutions are more useful.
- **Support Discussion** **MP2** Have partners discuss briefly before group discussion. If students have difficulty seeing the relationship between the graph and the equation, suggest they plot a few points for each equation on the corresponding line in the graph.

> *Prompt:* Are there limitations to graphing? Do those same limitations apply to algebraic equations? Explain.
> *Sentence Starter:* One of the limitations to graphing is …

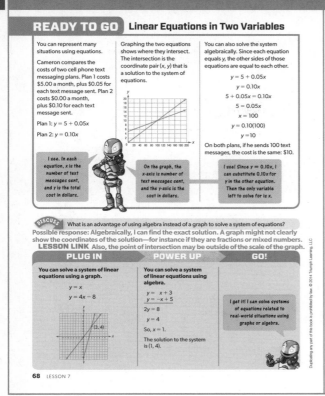

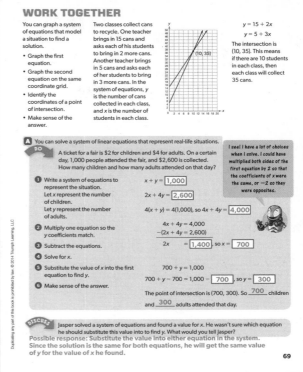

LESSON LINK

Connect to Foundational Understanding Skills learned in the **Plug In** and **Power Up** are referenced in the **Lesson Link**. Explain that solving systems of equations graphically and algebraically are both ways to represent the solution. These methods can be used to find the relationship between two related real situations.

- **Work Together** Explain that students will assign a variable to each unknown in a situation and write two separate equations. They will solve the system of equations graphically or algebraically.

DO ▸ A Monitor students as they write a system of equations to represent the situation. Encourage students to assign and identify the meaning of each variable so they are sure to apply it correctly in both equations.

- **Support Discussion** MP4 Have partners discuss briefly before group discussion. As needed, suggest students try substituting the value of x in both equations above and compare the values of y.

> **Prompt:** *What criteria might you use to determine which equation to use to find the value of the second variable?*
>
> **Sentence Starter:** *Since the value of the second variable will be the same regardless of which equation is used, I would consider…*

ENGLISH LANGUAGE LEARNERS

MP1 ELL students may need additional support in reading comprehension as they work to identify the meaning of the variables in the equations. Suggest they circle the unknowns in the question. Consider the question "How many children and how many adults attended on that day?" Students should circle the words *children* and *adults*, and then assign a variable to each.

FOCUS ON FLUENCY

MP4 Students may need additional practice writing algebraic expression to represent word problems. Often students can write equations that require one variable, but then two variables are needed, students struggle to find the relationship between them.

READY TO GO

PRACTICE

Solve.

1 A test has 20 questions worth a total of 100 points. The test has some true/false questions worth 3 points each. The rest are multiple-choice questions worth 11 points each. How many questions of each type are on the test?

Let *x* represent the number of true/false questions.

Let *y* represent the number of multiple-choice questions.

15 true-false questions, 5 multiple-choice questions

> **REMEMBER**
> Write one equation for the total number of questions and one equation for the number of points.

2 Catalina buys food and medicine for the dogs at a pet store. She spends 4 times as much on food as she spends on medicine. She spends a total of $400. How much did Catalina spend on food and on medicine?

Let *x* represent the amount spent on food.

Let *y* represent the amount spent on medication.

$320 on food and $80 on medicine

> **HINT**
> One equation for this situation is $y = 4x$.

3 Irene has a collection of 32 dolls that have either blue eyes or green eyes. She has 14 more green-eyed dolls than blue-eyed dolls. How many dolls of each type does Irene have?

Let *x* represent the number of green-eyed dolls.

Let *y* represent the number of blue-eyed dolls.

23 green-eyed dolls and 9 blue-eyed dolls

Solve.

4 Quinn and Derek bought office supplies together. Quinn bought 10 packs of paper and 12 boxes of pens for a total cost of $33. Derek bought 15 packs of paper and 7 boxes of pens for a total of $27.50. How much was one pack of paper? How much was one box of pens?
paper: $0.90; pens: $2.00

5 Diego ran a lemonade stand where he sold small cups of lemonade for $1 and large cups for $3.00. Diego sold a total of 75 cups of lemonade. If he collected a total of $125, how many cups of each size did Diego sell?
large: 25; small: 50

Solve.

6 Everyone at a park was either hiking or riding a bike. There were 24 more hikers than bike riders. If there were a total of 100 people at the park, how many were hiking? ___62___

7 Linda downloaded 4 movies and 3 TV shows for a total cost of $13. James downloaded 6 movies and 2 TV shows for a total of $17. How much did one movie download cost? ___$2.50___

> I know! I'll start by defining the variables. Then I can write equations using the given information.

DISCUSS **Model with Mathematics**

Jill's school can rent buses from one of two companies. The first company charges $500, plus $5 per student. The second company charges $800, plus $2 per student. Jill writes the following equations, where the cost is *y* and *x* is the number of students:

Company 1: $y = 500 + 5x$

Company 2: $y = 800 + 2x$

Jill wants to figure out the number of students for which both companies would charge the same amount. She sees *y* in both equations and says that both companies always charge the same amount. How would you explain her mistake to her?

> I can see Jill's equations are correct. So her mistake must be in her reasoning.

Possible response: The value of *y* changes with the value of *x*. To find the number of students for which both companies have the same cost, solve algebraically. So subtract Equation 2 from Equation 1, and solve for *x*. Substitute the value of *x* into either equation, and solve for *y*.

ADDITIONAL PRACTICE

Provide students with additional practice to model and solve:

$$x - 3y = -17 \qquad y + 4x = 15$$
$$y = -1 - x \qquad -9 + 8x = y$$
$$4x - 9 = 5y \qquad 2x - \frac{1}{4}y = 6$$
$$3y - 2x = 3 \qquad -3x + \frac{1}{2}y = -7$$

SPOTLIGHT ON MATHEMATICAL PRACTICES

MP1 Make Sense of Problems

Guide students to understand the relationship between the different parts of the problem. Remind students to evaluate the reasonableness of their solutions. If the solutions do not make sense, students should reassess their problem-solving strategy.

Support Independent Practice

1-3 Remind students to read the **HINT** and **REMEMBER**. If needed, ask: *What are the unknowns in the problem?*

4-5 *How can you use that information to write a system of equations?*

6-7 *Will your answer include the value of both variables? If not, explain.*

Support Discussion MP4 Have partners discuss whether graphing the equations or solving them algebraically would be a better strategy.

> *Prompt: What do the values in the equations represent?*
> *Sentence Starter: The $500 and $800 represent …*

Problem Solving

- **Model the Four-Step Method MP1 MP2** Guide student through the four-step method using think-aloud strategies. As needed, have students graph the equations. Suggest using multiples of 100 for the scale.

  Think Aloud *I need to find how many scoops of ice cream the students need to sell. I also need to find when the dollars in sales equals the dollars in costs. x = scoops; y = dollars*

- **Support Problem-Solving Practice** Have students use the Checklist as they complete each step.

> *Prompt: What is different about the rates Charlie and Mara charge?*
> *Prompt: What do the variables in the equations represent?*
> *Prompt: Which theater would be the better bargain if the class did not sell many tickets?*

PROBLEM SOLVING

ICE CREAM FUND-RAISER

READ Mrs. Foster's students hold an ice cream fund-raiser for charity. The cost for renting an ice cream truck is $300. The cost of the ice cream they sell is $0.50 per scoop. The students sell the ice cream for $2.00 per scoop. How many scoops of ice cream do Mrs. Foster's students need to sell so that their sales equal their costs?

PLAN • What is the problem asking you to do?

Find how many ___scoops___ must be sold for sales to equal costs.

• How can you solve this problem?

Write a system of equations.

SOLVE Solve the system algebraically.

$y = 300 + 0.5x$

$y = 2x$

Substitute $2x$ for y in the first equation. Solve for x.

$2x = 300 + 0.5x$

$2x - 0.5x = 300 + 0.5x - \boxed{0.5x}$

$1.5x = 300$, so $x = 300 \div 1.5 = \boxed{200}$

Substitute 200 for x to find y.

$y = 2(200) = \boxed{400}$

I see! In both equations, y is the amount of money in dollars. In the first equation, y is the cost. In the second equation, y is the sales.

CHECK Substitute the answers in each equation to check.

$y = 300 + 0.5x$ $y = 2x$

$\boxed{400} = 300 + 0.5(\boxed{200})$ $\boxed{400} = 2(\boxed{200})$

$\boxed{400} = 300 + \boxed{100}$ $\boxed{400} = \boxed{400}$

$\boxed{400} = \boxed{400}$

Both statements are true, so the answers check.

Mrs. Foster's students must sell ___200___ scoops of ice cream so that their total sales equal their costs, which are $___$400___.

PRACTICE

Use the problem-solving steps to help you.

1 Charlie and Mara are babysitters. Charlie charges $10 plus $6 per hour. Mara charges $8 per hour. For what number of hours will Charlie and Mara charge the same amount? How much would they charge for that number of hours?

5 hours; $40

CHECKLIST
☐ READ
☐ PLAN
☐ SOLVE
☐ CHECK

2 Oscar is offered jobs at two different dog-walking companies. At Company 1, he would earn $50 a day, plus $6 for each dog walked. At Company 2, he would earn $20 a day, plus $9 for each dog walked. How many dogs would Oscar have to walk to earn the same amount at both companies in a day? How much would he earn for walking that number of dogs?

10 dogs, $110

CHECKLIST
☐ READ
☐ PLAN
☐ SOLVE
☐ CHECK

3 Mrs. Keegan will rent one of two theaters for the school play. The first theater will cost $600, and tickets can be sold for $4 each. The second theater will cost $350, and the tickets can be sold for $3 each. How many tickets would the class need to sell for the money earned at each theater to be equal?

250 tickets

CHECKLIST
☐ READ
☐ PLAN
☐ SOLVE
☐ CHECK

I see I'll assign x as the number of tickets sold and y as the amount earned. So I'll write each equation as "the amount earned is equal to the ticket price times the number of tickets sold, less the cost of the theater."

• **Explore Student Thinking** **MP2** Ask students to consider whether the offer that is cheaper is always the better deal in the long run. Have students discuss other factors that might influence decisions based on solutions to systems of equations.

Assess

• Use the table below to observe whether students accurately write and solve systems of equations to answer the problems, and to address any difficulties as needed before the quiz.

• When all students are ready, assign the Lesson 7 Quiz.

SPOTLIGHT ON MATHEMATICAL LANGUAGE

MP3 Support students using mathematical language to reason about solutions.

• *Can any two linear equations represent a **system of equations**?*

• *What must be true of the **variables** used in both equations?*

	Observation	Action
1	Frequent errors in assigning variables and setting up equations; general confusion about how to solve systems of equations algebraically	Have students make a list of what they know and what they need to know based on the information given in the problem. The information they need to know should be assigned a variable. Provide graph paper for students to graph or sketch the system to check for reasonableness.
2	Occasional errors in assigning variables and setting up equations; basic understanding about how to solve systems of equations algebraically	Provide additional problems to model identifying and assigning variables. Present a variety of equations and support students looking for entry points and similarities in the way systems of equations are set up. Students may benefit from graphing the systems.
3	Accurately sets up and solves systems of equations algebraically.	Assign the Lesson 7 Quiz.

Modeling Relationships with Functions

PLUG IN Understanding Functions

		OBJECTIVES	CONCEPTS AND SKILLS	VOCABULARY
FOUNDATIONAL UNDERSTANDING	▶ **PLUG IN** **Understanding Functions** Student Edition pp. 74–75	• Use the graph to determine if a function is linear. • Use a table of values to determine if a function is linear. • Use an equation to determine if a function is linear.	Understand and define functions, linear functions, and nonlinear functions. Interpret the equation of a line in slope-intercept form as defining a linear function whose graph is a straight line. **CCSS:** 8.F.1, 8.F.3	• **function** • **linear function** • **nonlinear function**
	POWER UP **Graphing the Equation** $y = mx + b$	• Use the y-intercept and slope to graph a line. • Use an equation to find two points to graph a line.	Graph the equation $y = mx + b$. **CCSS:** 8.F.3	• **y-intercept** • **slope**
ON-LEVEL TARGET	**READY TO GO** **Modeling Relationships with Functions**	• Use two (x, y) values to find the rate of change and initial value of a function. • Use a description to find the rate of change and initial value of a function.	Determine the rate of change and initial value of the function from a description of a relationship or from two (x, y) values. **CCSS:** 8.F.4	• **rate of change** • **initial value**

MATERIALS
• Rulers *(suggested)*
• Math Tool: Coordinate Grid, p. A15 (Student Edition, p. 237)

ENGLISH LANGUAGE LEARNERS

MP1 Some ELL students may need additional support to differentiate between the terms *linear* and *nonlinear*. *Linear* is a form of the word *line*. Ask students to circle the root word *line* in the word *linear*. Explain that the prefix *non-* means "not"; therefore, *nonlinear* means not linear.

Build Background

● Talk to students about real-life examples of functions. For example, an hourly pay rate is a linear function. The amount of interest charged on a loan is a nonlinear function.

● MP4 Have students discuss additional examples of real situations that involve linear and nonlinear functions.

● Tell students they will identify linear and nonlinear functions.

Introduce and Model

● **Introduce Concepts and Vocabulary** Guide students through the information about functions. MP3 Have students demonstrate to a partner their understanding of a *linear function* and a *nonlinear function*.

● **Support Discussion** MP6 Have partners discuss briefly before group discussion. As needed, direct students to **Words to Know** and have them apply the definition of *linear function* to the problem.

> *Prompt: If all the negative input values were deleted, would the function be linear or nonlinear? How do you know?*
> *Sentence Starter: The graph of a linear function is …*

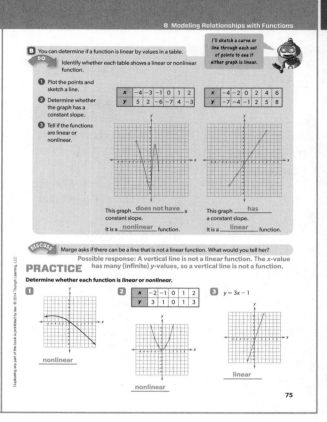

Lesson 8 — Modeling Relationships with Functions

PLUG IN — Understanding Functions

In this **function** table, the x-values are the input values, and the y-values are the output values.

x	1	4	7	5	2	8	9
y	2	5	0	5	6	1	3

I see! This table shows a function because each x-value has one, and only one, y-value.

A **linear function** is a function represented by a line. A linear function has a constant slope.

$y = -2x + 4$

This is a function because there is exactly one y-value for each x-value. And it's linear because it looks like a line!

A **nonlinear function** is a function whose graph is not a line.

$y = x^2$

A function that has an exponent is nonlinear. A nonlinear function does not have a constant slope.

Words to Know

function a rule that assigns exactly one output value to each input value

linear function a function whose graph is a straight line

nonlinear function a function whose graph is not a straight line

DISCUSS Wade says that $y = x^2 + 2$ is a linear function. What would you say to Wade about his statement? Possible response: His statement is incorrect because linear functions do not contain exponents.

A DO You can determine if a function is linear by its graph.

Identify whether each graph shows a linear or nonlinear function.

1. Look at the graph of the function.
2. Determine whether the graph has a constant slope.
3. Tell if the functions are linear or nonlinear.

Slope is constant. It is a linear function.

Slope is not constant. It is a nonlinear function.

74 LESSON 8

B DO You can determine if a function is linear by values in a table.

Identify whether each table shows a linear or nonlinear function.

1. Plot the points and sketch a line.
2. Determine whether the graph has a constant slope.
3. Tell if the functions are linear or nonlinear.

I'll sketch a curve or line through each set of points to see if either graph is linear.

x	−4	−3	−1	0	1	2
y	5	2	−6	−7	4	−3

x	−4	−2	0	2	4	6
y	−7	−4	−1	2	5	8

This graph __does not have__ a constant slope. It is a __nonlinear__ function.

This graph __has__ a constant slope. It is a __linear__ function.

DISCUSS Marge asks if there can be a line that is not a linear function. What would you tell her? Possible response: A vertical line is not a linear function. The x-value has many (infinite) y-values, so a vertical line is not a function.

PRACTICE

Determine whether each function is *linear* or *nonlinear*.

1. nonlinear

2.
x	−2	−1	0	1	2
y	3	1	0	1	3

nonlinear

3. $y = 3x − 1$

linear

75

• Model Application

DO **A** Guide students through evaluating graphs of linear and nonlinear functions. Remind students that the slope of a linear function is a constant. *Which two points could be used to show that the second graph does not model a linear function?*

DO **B** Explain that linear functions have a constant rate of change. In a linear function, each point is the same distance up or down on the y-axis and left or right on the x-axis as the previous point.

• **Support Discussion** **MP2** Have partners discuss briefly before group discussion. As needed, direct students to sketch a graph of a vertical and a horizontal line on a coordinate plane.

> *Prompt: Can a horizontal line represent a linear function? How do you know?*
> *Sentence Starter: For each x-value of a horizontal line …*

Practice and Assess

• Ask students to complete practice items 1–3 on page 75 independently or in pairs. Monitor ongoing work.

• Use the chart below as needed to address any difficulties.

Observation	Action
Students have difficulty distinguishing between linear and nonlinear functions.	Suggest students lay a ruler along the graph of each function. If any part of the graph is cut off by the edge of the ruler, the function is nonlinear. If all parts of the graph lie along the edge of the ruler, the function is linear.

SPOTLIGHT ON MATHEMATICAL LANGUAGE

MP3 Support students in using mathematical language as they work:

• *Can a line be curved?*
• *Can a line turn a corner?*
• *What does the graph of a* **linear function** *look like?*
• *What does the graph of a* **nonlinear function** *look like?*

		OBJECTIVES	CONCEPTS AND SKILLS	VOCABULARY
FOUNDATIONAL UNDERSTANDING	**PLUG IN** **Understanding Functions**	• Use the graph to determine if a function is linear. • Use a table of values to determine if a function is linear. • Use an equation to determine if a function is linear.	Understand and define functions, linear functions, and nonlinear functions. Interpret the equation of a line in slope-intercept form as defining a linear function whose graph is a straight line. **CCSS:** 8.F.1, 8.F.3	• **function** • **linear function** • **nonlinear function**
	▶ POWER UP **Graphing the Equation $y = mx + b$** Student Edition pp. 76–77	• Use the y-intercept and slope to graph a line. • Use an equation to find two points to graph a line.	Graph the equation $y = mx + b$. **CCSS:** 8.F.3	• **y-intercept** • **slope**
ON-LEVEL TARGET	**READY TO GO** **Modeling Relationships with Functions**	• Use two (x, y) values to find the rate of change and initial value of a function. • Use a description to find the rate of change and initial value of a function.	Determine the rate of change and initial value of the function from a description of a relationship or from two (x, y) values. **CCSS:** 8.F.4	• **rate of change** • **initial value**

MATERIALS

• Math Tool: Coordinate Grid, p. A15 (Student Edition, p. 237)

ENGLISH LANGUAGE LEARNERS

MP1 ELL students may not be familiar with the term *intercept*. Explain that intercept means to interrupt the progress. In football, the opposing team can *intercept* the football to interrupt the progress of their opponent. When graphing a line, the *y*-intercept is where the *y*-axis interrupts, or intersects, the progress of the line.

Build Background

● Talk to student about when it might be useful to write a linear function as an equation. For example, the band club sells popcorn at the football game to earn money for band camp. A linear equation can be used to show the amount of profit for any number of bags of popcorn sold.

● **MP4** Have students discuss additional examples of real situations in which linear equations could be useful.

● Tell students they will use an equation to determine the *y*-intercept and slope of a line, and then graph the line.

Introduce and Model

● **Introduce Concepts and Vocabulary** Emphasize that $y = mx + b$ is the slope-intercept form of the equation of a line. The slope is the coefficient of x, and the y-intercept is the constant.

● **Support Discussion** **MP5** Have partners discuss briefly before group discussion. Students can use a coordinate plane to model their reasoning.

> *Prompt: Slope is often referred to as "rise over run." Using the coordinate plane as a reference, how can this phrase be useful in locating a second point of a line?*
> *Sentence Starter: The vertical axis is represented by …*

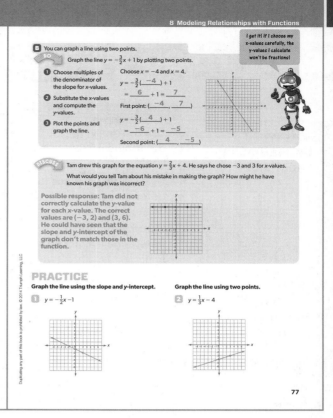

POWER UP Graphing the Equation $y = mx + b$

A linear function can be written as the equation $y = mx + b$.

The b in the equation is the **y-intercept**. This is the y-coordinate of the point where the line crosses the y-axis on a graph.

The m in the equation is the **slope** of the line. The value of m tells you the steepness and direction of the line.

$y = \frac{2}{3}x + 1$

To find points on a line, I can select x-values and calculate the corresponding y-values.

The y-intercept is 1.

I can use the y-intercept as a starting point when I graph a line.

$m = \frac{\text{change in } y}{\text{change in } x} = \frac{2}{3}$

I see! If the steepness of a line is constant, then its slope also has a constant value.

Words to Know

y-intercept the y-coordinate of the point at which a line crosses the y-axis

slope a ratio of the change in y-coordinates (rise) of a graph to the change in corresponding x-coordinates (run); the symbol for slope is m

DISCUSS Belinda has plotted one point of a linear function. She asks how she can use the slope to graph the rest of the line. How would you explain it to her?

Possible response: The slope tells her how many units to move in the y-direction for each move in the x-direction to plot another point. She can draw a line through the two points, or she can continue plotting points using the slope.

A You can use the y-intercept and slope to graph a line.

DO Graph the line $y = \frac{4}{5}x - 3$ using the slope and y-intercept.

1. Identify and plot the y-intercept.
2. Use the slope to plot another point.
3. Draw a line through the points.

The y-intercept is -3.

Find another point 4 units up and 5 units right.

The coordinate pair is (5 , 1).

B You can graph a line using two points.

DO Graph the line $y = -\frac{3}{2}x + 1$ by plotting two points.

1. Choose multiples of the denominator of the slope for x-values.
2. Substitute the x-values and compute the y-values.
3. Plot the points and graph the line.

Choose $x = -4$ and $x = 4$.

$y = -\frac{3}{2}(\underline{-4}) + 1$

$= \underline{6} + 1 = \underline{7}$

First point: (-4 , 7)

$y = -\frac{3}{2}(\underline{4}) + 1$

$= \underline{-6} + 1 = \underline{-5}$

Second point: (4 , -5)

I get it! If I choose my x-values carefully, the y-values I calculate won't be fractions!

DISCUSS Tam drew this graph for the equation $y = \frac{2}{3}x + 4$. He says he chose -3 and 3 for x-values. What would you tell Tam about his mistake in making the graph? How might he have known his graph was incorrect?

Possible response: Tam did not correctly calculate the y-value for each x-value. The correct values are $(-3, 2)$ and $(3, 6)$. He could have seen that the slope and y-intercept of the graph don't match those in the function.

PRACTICE

Graph the line using the slope and y-intercept.

1. $y = -\frac{1}{2}x - 1$

Graph the line using two points.

2. $y = \frac{1}{3}x - 4$

76 LESSON 8

77

• Model Application

DO **A** Since the value of x is always 0 at the y-intercept, model plotting the y-intercept first. Then use the slope to locate a second point on the line.

DO **B** Explain that since x is multiplied by the slope, substituting 0 for x will always result in the y-intercept.

• **Support Discussion** **MP3** Have partners discuss briefly before group discussion. As needed, direct students to sketch the graph using Tam's x-values.

> Prompt: What is the slope of the line Tam graphed?
> Sentence Starter: The slope of the line $y = \frac{2}{3}x + 4$ is …

Practice and Assess

• Ask students to complete practice items 1 and 2 on page 77 independently or in pairs. Monitor ongoing work.

• Observe whether students accurately graph equations of lines written in slope-intercept form. Use the chart below as needed to address any difficulties.

Observation	Action
Students have difficulty identifying two points that lie on the same line as represented by the equation.	Ask student to cover up the entire equation with the exception of operation symbol and the final number. Explain that this is the point on the y-axis. If the operation is addition, the point is positive. If the operation is subtraction, the point is negative. Guide students to plot the point. Then use the slope to find another point on the line.

COMMON ERRORS

Students may be intimidated by a fractional slope of a line. Remind students that substituting the value of the denominator for x will eliminate the fraction. The product of mx will be the numerator written as a whole number.

Modeling Relationships with Functions

		OBJECTIVES	CONCEPTS AND SKILLS	VOCABULARY
FOUNDATIONAL UNDERSTANDING	**PLUG IN** **Understanding Functions**	• Use the graph to determine if a function is linear. • Use a table of values to determine if a function is linear. • Use an equation to determine if a function is linear.	Understand and define functions, linear functions, and nonlinear functions. Interpret the equation of a line in slope-intercept form as defining a linear function whose graph is a straight line. **CCSS:** 8.F.1, 8.F.3	• **function** • **linear function** • **nonlinear function**
	POWER UP **Graphing the Equation** $y = mx + b$	• Use the y-intercept and slope to graph a line. • Use an equation to find two points to graph a line.	Graph the equation $y = mx + b$. **CCSS:** 8.F.3	• **y-intercept** • **slope**
ON-LEVEL TARGET	▶ **READY TO GO** **Modeling Relationships with Functions** Student Edition pp. 78–83	• Use two (x, y) values to find the rate of change and initial value of a function. • Use a description to find the rate of change and initial value of a function.	Determine the rate of change and initial value of the function from a description of a relationship or from two (x, y) values. **CCSS:** 8.F.4	• **rate of change** • **initial value**

MATERIALS

- Lesson 8 Quiz, Assessment Manual pp. 18–19
- Lesson 8 Quiz Answer Key, Assessment Manual
- Math Tool: Coordinate Grid, p. A16 (Student Edition, p. 239)

ENGLISH LANGUAGE LEARNERS

MP6 ELL students may not be familiar with the meaning of *initial value* in mathematical terms. Explain that a person's initials are the beginning letter of each name. It is the starting point. In mathematical terms, the initial value represents the starting point upon which all other values of a function are based.

Build Background

- Talk to students about real-life examples of functions that include initial values. For example, a plumber charges a base fee of $50 plus an hourly rate of $25.
- **MP4** Have students discuss additional examples of real situations that involve linear functions with initial values and constant rates of change.

Introduce and Model

- **Introduce Concepts and Vocabulary** Relate the initial value to the y-intercept and the rate of change to the slope of a line. **MP3** Have students explain to a partner how a change in the initial value changes the graph of a line.
- **Support Discussion** **MP2** Have partners discuss briefly before group discussion. If students are struggling, suggest they sketch the graph of an equation that has two different initial values.

> **Prompt:** What does the initial value represent in the equation of a line?
> **Sentence Starter:** The initial value is another name for the ...

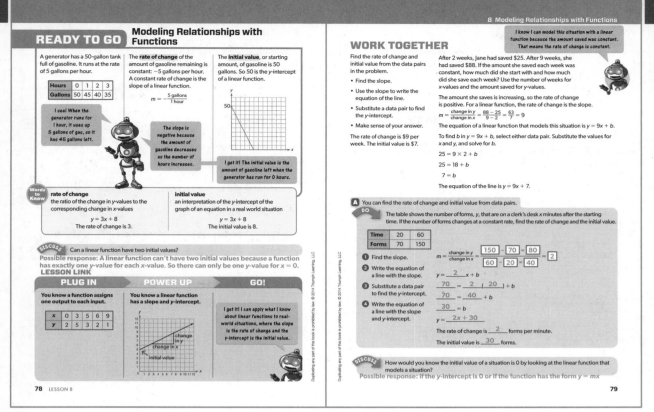

LESSON LINK

Connect to Foundational Understanding Skills learned in the **Plug In** and **Power Up** are referenced in the **Lesson Link**. Explain that functions can be linear or nonlinear. Linear functions are represented by the graph of a straight line. Every linear function has a slope and a *y*-intercept. Vertical lines do not represent functions because one *x*-value has an infinite number of *y*-values. Horizontal lines are functions where the slope is 0.

- **Work Together** Guide students to reason about how to find how much money Jane saves each week. *After 2 weeks, she had $25. Seven weeks later, she had saved an additional $63.* Divide to find how much Jane saved each week. This is the rate of change, or slope, *m*. *If Jane saves $9 each week, how much money had she saved after 2 weeks? How much money did she start with?* This is the initial value, or *y*-intercept, *b*.

DO A Monitor students as they work to identify the slope and initial value of linear equation from a data table. Guide students to set up equations to find the change in the *x*- and *y*-values: Forms (*y*): $70 + y = 150$; $y = 150 - 70$; $y = 80$; Time (*x*): $20 + x = 60$; $x = 60 - 20$; $x = 40$.

- **Support Discussion** MP4 Have partners discuss briefly before group discussion. As needed, have students sketch two lines, one with an initial value of 2, and the other with an initial value of 0.

> *Prompt: Which variable in the equation of a linear function represents the initial value? If the y-intercept is 0, how does the equation change?*
> *Sentence Starter: The initial value is represented by the variable …*

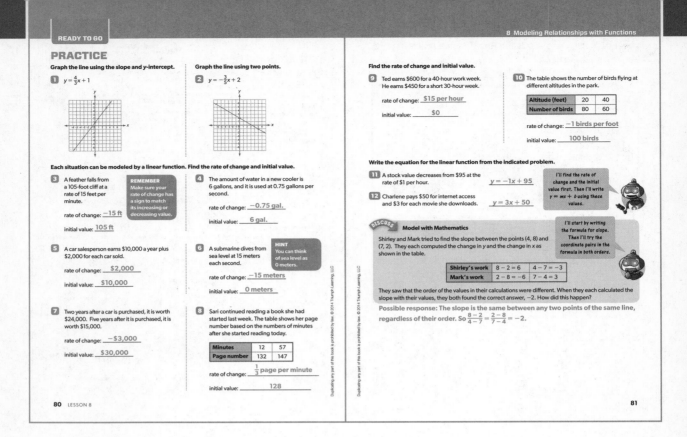

PRACTICE

Graph the line using the slope and y-intercept.

1 $y = \frac{4}{3}x + 1$

Graph the line using two points.

2 $y = -\frac{3}{5}x + 2$

Each situation can be modeled by a linear function. Find the rate of change and initial value.

3 A feather falls from a 105-foot cliff at a rate of 15 feet per minute.

> **REMEMBER** Make sure your rate of change has a sign to match its increasing or decreasing value.

rate of change: __−15 ft__

initial value: __105 ft__

4 The amount of water in a new cooler is 6 gallons, and it is used at 0.75 gallons per second.

rate of change: __−0.75 gal.__

initial value: __6 gal.__

5 A car salesperson earns $10,000 a year plus $2,000 for each car sold.

rate of change: __$2,000__

initial value: __$10,000__

6 A submarine dives from sea level at 15 meters each second.

> **HINT** You can think of sea level as 0 meters.

rate of change: __−15 meters__

initial value: __0 meters__

7 Two years after a car is purchased, it is worth $24,000. Five years after it is purchased, it is worth $15,000.

rate of change: __−$3,000__

initial value: __$30,000__

8 Sari continued reading a book she had started last week. The table shows her page number based on the numbers of minutes after she started reading today.

Minutes	12	57
Page number	132	147

rate of change: __$\frac{1}{3}$ page per minute__

initial value: __128__

Find the rate of change and initial value.

9 Ted earns $600 for a 40-hour work week. He earns $450 for a short 30-hour week.

rate of change: __$15 per hour__

initial value: __$0__

10 The table shows the number of birds flying at different altitudes in the park.

Altitude (feet)	20	40
Number of birds	80	60

rate of change: __−1 birds per foot__

initial value: __100 birds__

Write the equation for the linear function from the indicated problem.

11 A stock value decreases from $95 at the rate of $1 per hour. $\quad y = -1x + 95$

12 Charlene pays $50 for internet access and $3 for each movie she downloads. $\quad y = 3x + 50$

> I'll find the rate of change and the initial value first. Then I'll write $y = mx + b$ using these values.

DISCUSS **Model with Mathematics**

> I'll start by writing the formula for slope. Then I'll try the coordinate pairs in the formula in both orders.

Shirley and Mark tried to find the slope between the points (4, 8) and (7, 2). They each computed the change in y and the change in x as shown in the table.

Shirley's work	$8 - 2 = 6$	$4 - 7 = -3$
Mark's work	$2 - 8 = -6$	$7 - 4 = 3$

They saw that the order of the values in their calculations were different. When they each calculated the slope with their values, they both found the correct answer, −2. How did this happen?

Possible response: The slope is the same between any two points of the same line, regardless of their order. So $\frac{8-2}{4-7} = \frac{2-8}{7-4} = -2$.

Provide students with additional practice to model and solve:

Write the equation of a line in the form $y = mx + b$ that includes point (0, 4) and a slope of $\frac{5}{2}$.

Make a table of five ordered pairs that satisfy the equation $y = \frac{7}{3}x - 6$.

Graph the line of the equation $y = \frac{7}{3}x - 6$.

Rewrite the equation $x = 2(y - 7)$ so it is in the form $y = mx + b$.

Support Independent Practice

1–8 Remind students to read the **HINT** and **REMEMBER**. If needed, ask: *What is changing? How fast is it changing? Where did it start?*

9–10 *How can you set up an equation to find the change in amount over the change in hours?*

11–12 *Is the initial value positive or negative? Is the rate of change positive or negative?*

Support Discussion **MP3** Have partners discuss briefly before group discussion. As needed, ask students to use the graph of a line to model why either equation works.

> **Prompt:** Are the slopes $\frac{-2}{5}$ and $\frac{2}{-5}$ the same? How do you know?
>
> **Sentence Starter:** Slope is rise over run, so the first slope indicates that another point is found 2 units down on the y-axis and …

Problem Solving

- **Model the Four-Step Method** **MP2** **MP3** Guide students through the four-step method using think-aloud strategies. Guide students to identify the x- and y-values in the problem.

  Think Aloud *I can subtract to find the difference in cost: $140 − 65$. Then I can subtract to find the difference in the length of track: $200 − 50$.*

- **Support Problem-Solving Practice** Have students use the Checklist as they complete each step.

PROBLEM SOLVING

A MODEL TRAIN MODEL

READ

A model train set with a 50-inch track and train cars costs $65. A model train set with a 200-inch track and the same cars costs $140. If the cost can be modeled by a linear function, find the cost of the train cars and the cost of one inch of the track.

PLAN

• Find a linear function that models the situation.

• Find the _cost of the cars_, which is the initial value, and the _cost of the track_, which is the rate of change.

• Use two ordered pairs: (__50__, __65__) and (__200__, __140__).

> I see! The cost of the cars is the same for each set. That means that's the initial value of the equation!

SOLVE

Find the slope as a decimal.

$$m = \frac{\text{change in } y}{\text{change in } x} = \frac{\boxed{140} - \boxed{65}}{\boxed{200} - \boxed{50}} = \frac{\boxed{75}}{\boxed{150}} = \frac{\boxed{1}}{\boxed{2}} = \boxed{0.50}$$

$$y = \underline{0.50}\, x + b$$

Substitute an ordered pair into the equation to find the y-intercept.

$$\underline{65} = \underline{0.50}\,(\underline{50}) + b$$
$$\underline{65} = \underline{25} + b$$
$$\underline{40} = b$$

The slope of the line is __0.50__, and the y-intercept is __40__.
The equation of the line is __$y = 0.50x + 40$__.

> I can choose either ordered pair to find b. I'll get the same answer either way.

CHECK

To check the answer, substitute the other coordinate pair in the equation.

$$y = \underline{0.50}\, x + \underline{40}$$
$$\underline{140} = \underline{0.50}\,(\underline{200}) + \underline{40}$$
$$\underline{140} = \underline{100} + \underline{40}$$
$$\underline{140} = \underline{140}$$

The train cars cost __$40__ and the track is __$0.50 per inch__.

PRACTICE

Use the problem-solving steps to help you.

1 After saving newspapers for a project for 3 weeks, Jon had a stack that was 2 feet high. After 6 weeks, the stack was 4 feet high. How high was the stack when Jon started saving the papers? How much higher does the stack get each week?

The stack started when it was 0 feet high.
It gets $\frac{2}{3}$ foot higher each week.

CHECKLIST
☐ READ
☐ PLAN
☐ SOLVE
☐ CHECK

2 Lionel walks home from school. After walking 5 minutes, he is 4,000 feet from home, and after walking 15 minutes he is 2,000 feet from home. How many feet per minute does Lionel walk? How far is his school from his home? How far will he be from home after walking 20 minutes?

Lionel walks at the rate of 200 feet per minute, and he lives 5,000 feet from school. He will be 1,000 feet from home after 20 minutes.

> I see! After I find the equation, I can substitute a value for time to find how far he is from home at that time.

CHECKLIST
☐ READ
☐ PLAN
☐ SOLVE
☐ CHECK

3 After handing out flyers for 2 hours, Larry had 400 flyers left. After 10 hours, he had handed out all of the flyers. How many flyers did Larry start with, and how many did he give out each hour?

Larry started with 500 flyers and gave away 50 each hour.

CHECKLIST
☐ READ
☐ PLAN
☐ SOLVE
☐ CHECK

Prompt: *Identify the initial value and the rate of change for each problem.*

• **Explore Student Thinking** MP2 Invite students to describe the graph of each situation, including the *y*-intercept and the slope. Have partners explain their reasoning and how it applies to real-life situations.

SPOTLIGHT ON MATHEMATICAL PRACTICES

MP4 Model with Mathematics

Check student understanding by asking students to graph Problem 10. The scale for both axes should be tens. Ask: *If the rate of change is positive, in which position do you expect the graph of the equation to lie? If the initial value is positive, describe the position of the line in relation to the origin.*

Assess

• Use the table below to address any difficulties.

#	Observation	Action
1	Frequent errors in identifying the rate of change and the initial values of linear functions	Have students use a coordinate plane to graph the given points. Assist students in assigning the meaning of each axis. For example, in Problem 1, the x-axis is weeks, and the y-axis is feet of newspapers.
2	Occasional errors in identifying the rate of change and the initial values of linear functions	Remind students to consider the reasonableness of their solutions. For example, in Problem 2, if the distance, or rate of change, is decreasing, does it make sense that the initial value is 0?
3	Accurately identifies the rate of change and the initial values of linear functions.	Assign Lesson 8 Quiz.

PLUG IN Describing Functional Relationships from Graphs

		OBJECTIVES	CONCEPTS AND SKILLS	VOCABULARY
FOUNDATIONAL UNDERSTANDING	▶ **PLUG IN** **Describing Functional Relationships from Graphs** Student Edition pp. 84–85	• Use graphs to describe functional relationships.	Describe functional relationships from graphs. **CCSS:** 8.F.5	
	POWER UP **Sketching Graphs Using Verbal Descriptions**	• Sketch a graph using a verbal description.	Sketch a graph of a function that has been described verbally. **CCSS:** 8.F.5	
ON-LEVEL TARGET	**READY TO GO** **Comparing Functions**	• Compare the rates of change of functions. • Compare the properties of linear functions.	Compare the properties of two functions each represented in a different way. **CCSS:** 8.F.2	

MATERIALS
• Math Tool: Coordinate Grid, p. A16 (Student Edition p. 239)

COMMON ERRORS
Students may confuse the x- and y-intercepts when working in the coordinate plane. Remind them that the x-axis is the horizontal axis and the y-axis is the vertical axis. When writing coordinates, the x-coordinate is written first, and the y-coordinate is written second.

Build Background
- Talk to students about the reasons to interpret graphs in real life. For example, a marine biologist uses the function $y = 250x + 3$ to model the population growth for a harem of sea lions. Is the graph of the function linear or nonlinear? Explain that graphing the function is a way to solve this problem.
- **MP4** Have students discuss additional examples of real situations that involve interpreting graphs.
- Tell students they will describe functional relationships from graphs.

Introduce and Model
- **Introduce Concepts** Guide students through describing the functional relationship. Make sure students find the slope by dividing the difference of the y-coordinates by the difference of the x-coordinates.
- **Support Discussion** **MP7** Have partners discuss briefly before group discussion. Remind students that the first quadrant contains only positive numbers and zero.

> *Prompt: What types of numbers do you find in the first quadrant of a coordinate grid?*
> *Sentence Starter: Time cannot be less than . . .*

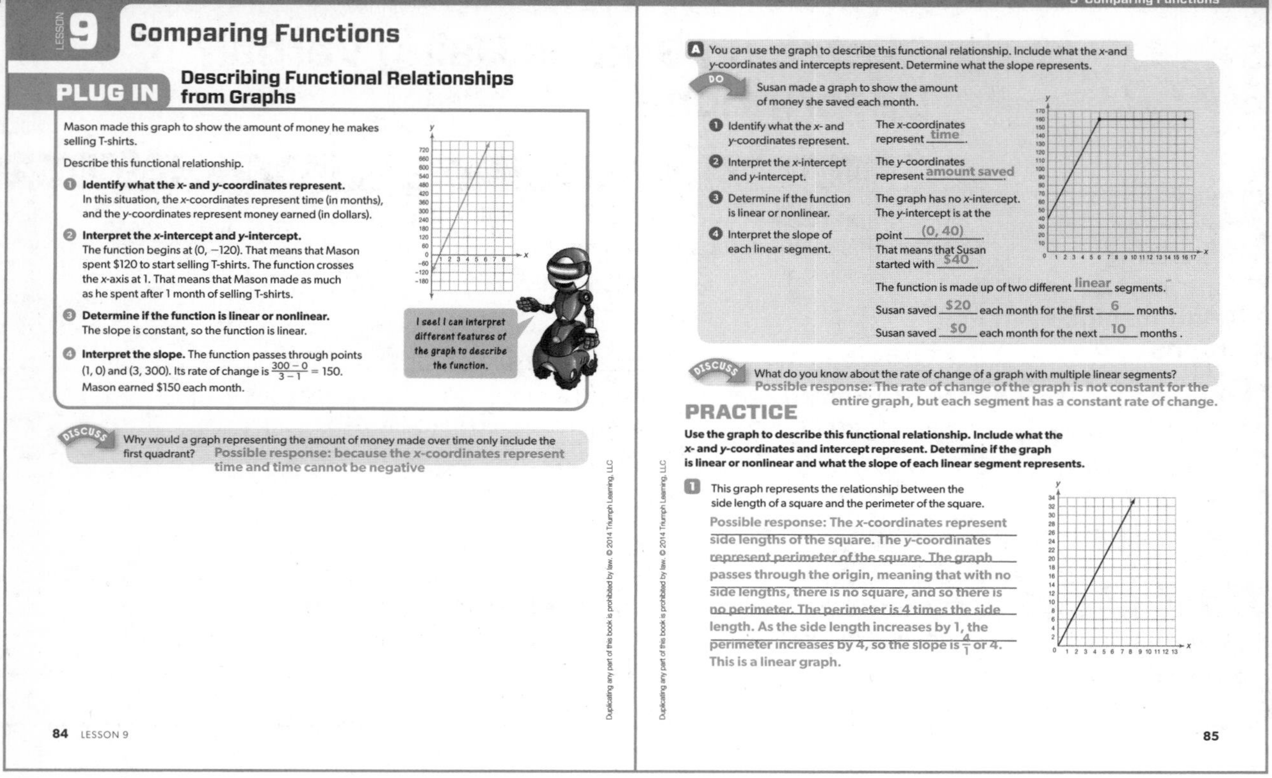

LESSON 9 Comparing Functions

PLUG IN Describing Functional Relationships from Graphs

Mason made this graph to show the amount of money he makes selling T-shirts.

Describe this functional relationship.

1 **Identify what the x- and y-coordinates represent.**
In this situation, the x-coordinates represent time (in months), and the y-coordinates represent money earned (in dollars).

2 **Interpret the x-intercept and y-intercept.**
The function begins at (0, −120). That means that Mason spent $120 to start selling T-shirts. The function crosses the x-axis at 1. That means that Mason made as much as he spent after 1 month of selling T-shirts.

3 **Determine if the function is linear or nonlinear.**
The slope is constant, so the function is linear.

4 **Interpret the slope.** The function passes through points (1, 0) and (3, 300). Its rate of change is $\frac{300-0}{3-1} = 150$. Mason earned $150 each month.

I see! I can interpret different features of the graph to describe the function.

DISCUSS Why would a graph representing the amount of money made over time only include the first quadrant? Possible response: because the x-coordinates represent time and time cannot be negative

---

A You can use the graph to describe this functional relationship. Include what the x-and y-coordinates and intercepts represent. Determine what the slope represents.

DO Susan made a graph to show the amount of money she saved each month.

1 Identify what the x- and y-coordinates represent.
The x-coordinates represent _time_.

2 Interpret the x-intercept and y-intercept.
The y-coordinates represent _amount saved_.

3 Determine if the function is linear or nonlinear.
The graph has no x-intercept. The y-intercept is at the point _(0, 40)_. That means that Susan started with _$40_.

4 Interpret the slope of each linear segment.
The function is made up of two different _linear_ segments.

Susan saved _$20_ each month for the first _6_ months.

Susan saved _$0_ each month for the next _10_ months.

DISCUSS What do you know about the rate of change of a graph with multiple linear segments? Possible response: The rate of change of the graph is not constant for the entire graph, but each segment has a constant rate of change.

PRACTICE

Use the graph to describe this functional relationship. Include what the x- and y-coordinates and intercept represent. Determine if the graph is linear or nonlinear and what the slope of each linear segment represents.

1 This graph represents the relationship between the side length of a square and the perimeter of the square.

Possible response: The x-coordinates represent side lengths of the square. The y-coordinates represent perimeter of the square. The graph passes through the origin, meaning that with no side lengths, there is no square, and so there is no perimeter. The perimeter is 4 times the side length. As the side length increases by 1, the perimeter increases by 4, so the slope is $\frac{4}{1}$ or 4. This is a linear graph.

• Model Application

DO A Guide students through using a graph to describe a functional relationship with a positive slope. Monitor that students correctly identify the x-axis as representing time and the y-axis as representing the amount saved.

• **Support Discussion** **MP2** Have partners discuss briefly before group discussion. Ask students to draw a graph with multiple linear segments to help them visualize the question.

> *Prompt: When would you have a constant rate of change?*
> *Sentence Starter: Each segment of the graph has . . .*

Practice and Assess

• Ask students to complete practice item 1 on page 85 independently or in pairs. Monitor ongoing work.

• Ensure that students correctly identify what each axis represents in the problem. Identifying these variables incorrectly can cause the rest of the problem to be wrong. Use the chart below as needed to address any difficulties.

Observation	Action
Students have difficulty describing functional relationships from graphs.	Provide students with blank coordinate grids to model their own problem with. Have students work in pairs to write and graph an equation that represents a situation. Have students identify what the x- and y-coordinates and intercepts represent, as well as what the slope represents.

ENGLISH LANGUAGE LEARNERS

MP5 ELL students may need additional support formulating sentences to answer the practice problems. Supplying sentence stems, such as "The x-coordinates represent _____" and "The y-coordinates represent _____" will be helpful.

POWER UP   Sketching Graphs Using Verbal Descriptions

		OBJECTIVES	CONCEPTS AND SKILLS	VOCABULARY
FOUNDATIONAL UNDERSTANDING	**PLUG IN** **Describing Functional Relationships from Graphs**	• Use graphs to describe functional relationships.	Describe functional relationships from graphs. **CCSS:** 8.F.5	
	▶ POWER UP **Sketching Graphs Using Verbal Descriptions** Student Edition pp. 86–87	• Sketch a graph using a verbal description.	Sketch a graph of a function that has been described verbally. **CCSS:** 8.F.5	
ON-LEVEL TARGET	**READY TO GO** **Comparing Functions**	• Compare the rates of change of functions. • Compare the properties of linear functions.	Compare the properties of two functions each represented in a different way. **CCSS:** 8.F.2	

MATERIALS

- Math Tool: Coordinate Grid, p. A13 (Student Edition p. 233)
- Graphing calculator (*suggested*)

ENGLISH LANGUAGE LEARNERS

MP4 ELL students may not realize that the slope is given in the problem statement. Remind students that *4 miles an hour* is a unit rate, which means that for every hour Lesley runs, she runs 4 miles. This can be interpreted in a graph as having a slope of 4. Have students show this on a coordinate grid by moving 1 unit to the left and 4 units up.

Build Background

- Talk to students about reasons to graph relationships in real life. For example, Lenny found that his company made $50,000 in 2011 and $80,000 in 2013. At this rate, what prediction could he make about his company's profits in 2015? Explain that using the two given points to graph the function and find the rate of change is a method to solving this problem.
- **MP4** Have students discuss additional examples of real situations that involve sketching graphs.
- Tell students they will work on sketching graphs based on verbal descriptions.

Introduce and Model

- **Introduce Concepts** Guide students through the information about sketching graphs. Help students understand that a point and a slope, or two points, are needed to graph a situation.
- **Support Discussion** **MP1** Have partners discuss briefly before group discussion. Have students sketch a graph of the situation and compare it to the previous question.

> *Prompt: What is Patrick's rate of change for the second part of the run?*
> *Sentence Starter: Patrick ran at two different speeds . . .*

68 LESSON 9

© 2014 Triumph Learning, LLC

POWER UP — Sketching Graphs Using Verbal Descriptions

Lesley is training for a walkathon. She calculated her walking rate is 4 miles an hour.

Sketch a graph that represents this functional relationship.

1. **Define what the x- and y-coordinates represent.** In this situation, the x-coordinates represent time (in hours), and the y-coordinates represent distance (in miles).

2. **Determine the initial value.** When $x = 0$, the distance is 0. The initial value is plotted as (0, 0).

3. **Determine if the function is linear.** The rate of change is constant: 4 miles an hour. So the function is linear.

4. **Determine the slope.** For each hour Lesley walks, she travels a distance of 4 miles. The slope is $\frac{4}{1}$ or 4.

Sketch a graph of a line that passes through (0, 0) with a slope of 4.

I get it! I can use the initial value and the slope to sketch the graph.

DISCUSS Lesley's friend Patrick trains with her. He walks 4 miles an hour for the first four hours. Then he starts walking 3 miles an hour. How would his graph be different from Lesley's graph?

I see! I can graph a situation that has more than one linear segment.

Possible Response: The graphs would be the same from 0 hours to 4 hours. Then Patrick's graph would have another linear segment starting at (4, 16), with a slope of 3.

A You can sketch a graph based on a verbal description.

DO Marco starts to fill an empty 20 liter aquarium with water. The amount of water in the aquarium increases by 1 liter per minute. Sketch a graph that represents this functional relationship.

1. Define what the x- and y-coordinates represent.
2. Determine the initial value.
3. If the function is linear, determine the slope.

The x-coordinate represents the **time in minutes**.

The y-coordinate represents the **liters** of water.

The aquarium starts empty, so at time 0, it holds 0 liters.

The initial value is (0, 0).

The slope is **1**.

B You can sketch a graph based on a verbal description.

I see! The graph has a different rate after the first 8 hours. So I'll need two linear segments!

The temperature decreased by 3 degrees Fahrenheit each hour. Then, after 8 hours, the temperature stayed the same for the rest of the day. If the temperature started at 45°F, sketch a graph that represents this functional relationship.

1. Define what the x- and y-coordinates represent.
2. Determine the initial value.
3. Determine the slope for each linear segment.

The x-coordinate represents the time in minutes.

The y-coordinate represents the temperature in °F.

The initial value is 45°F. So the y-intercept is (0, 45).

For the first segment, the slope is **−3**.

After 8 hours, the temperature stays the same.

For the next segment, the slope is **0**.

DISCUSS How will the values in a table of coordinate pairs for a linear function show that the slope of your graph will be positive or negative? Possible response: If the y-values increase as the corresponding x-values increase, then the slope will be positive. If the y-values decrease as the corresponding x-values increase, then the slope will be negative.

PRACTICE

Sketch a graph that represents each functional relationship.

1. Ray starts a savings account with $30. He deposits $30 each month for six months. Then he doesn't deposit any more money for the next ten months.

2. Mathias earns $9 an hour for babysitting.

86   LESSON 9

87

Model Application

DO A Make sure students understand that starting with an empty aquarium means the graph will start at (0, 0).

DO B Make sure students realize that since the temperature started at 45°F, their graph will begin at (0, 45)

Support Discussion MP4 Have partners discuss briefly before group discussion. Direct students to sketch graphs of both scenarios and make two tables of values.

> *Prompt: Can you look at a linear graph and tell whether the slope is positive or negative? How do you know?*
>
> *Sentence Starter: The slope of a line tells me . . .*

Practice and Assess

- Ask students to complete practice items 1 and 2 on page 87 independently or in pairs. Monitor ongoing work.
- Use the table below to address any difficulties.

Observation	Action
Students have difficulty determining what the x- and y-coordinates represent.	Have students use colored pencils or markers to circle each of the variables in the problems. The dependent variable (y-coordinates) are plotted on the y-axis. The independent variables (x-coordinates) are plotted on the x-axis.

SPOTLIGHT ON MATHEMATICAL PRACTICES

MP3 Critiquing Other's Reasoning

Pair students together to work out a solution to the problem. Working in pairs or groups often incites thoughtful discussion about how to approach a problem. In this case, the group should agree that Patrick's graph would have 2 linear segments.

COMMON ERRORS

Students may not be able to identify that the second linear segment will have a lesser slope than the first linear segment of Patrick's run. Have students use their graphing calculators to graph the lines $y = 4x$ and $y = 3x$ and have them compare the slopes of the lines.

		OBJECTIVES	CONCEPTS AND SKILLS	VOCABULARY
FOUNDATIONAL UNDERSTANDING	**PLUG IN** Describing Functional Relationships from Graphs	• Use graphs to describe functional relationships.	Describe functional relationships from graphs. **CCSS:** 8.F.5	
	POWER UP Sketching Graphs Using Verbal Descriptions	• Sketch a graph using a verbal description.	Sketch a graph of a function that has been described verbally. **CCSS:** 8.F.5	
ON-LEVEL TARGET	▶ **READY TO GO** Comparing Functions Student Edition pp. 88–93	• Compare the rates of change of functions. • Compare the properties of linear functions.	Compare the properties of two functions each represented in a different way. **CCSS:** 8.F.2	

MATERIALS

- Lesson 9 Quiz, Assessment Manual pp. 20–21
- Lesson 9 Quiz Answer Key, Assessment Manual
- Math Tool: Coordinate Grid, p. A16 (Student Edition p. 239)

ENGLISH LANGUAGE LEARNERS

MP2 Since it is a relatively new concept, ELL students may have difficulty comparing rates of change. Emphasize that they are only comparing two numbers. Draw the greater than and less than symbols on the board. Have students call out numbers to write on both sides of the inequality symbols to make the inequality true.

Build Background

- Talk to students about reasons to compare functions in real life. For example, at a presentation, Cailey made a graph and a table to show her sales predictions for each month next year. Cailey's graph has slope 5. As each x-value in the table increases, by how much do the y-values change?
- **MP4** Have students discuss additional examples of real situations that involve comparing functions.
- Tell students they will compare the rates of change and the properties of functions.

Introduce and Model

- **Introduce Concepts** Guide students through the information about comparing functions. Emphasize that the information in the problem could have been shown in either a table or a graph.
- **Support Discussion** **MP7** Have partners discuss briefly before group discussion. If students are struggling, suggest they model the graphs in the problem situation on a piece of paper.

> **Prompt:** How do you compare the slopes of two linear functions?
> **Sentence Starter:** The greater the slope, the . . .

READY TO GO Comparing Functions

The table and graph represent two different linear functions. Which function has a greater rate of change?

x	−3	−1	0	1	3
y	−5	−1	1	3	7

① Determine the rate of change for the function in the table.

Select any two ordered pairs from the table.

Using (3, 7) and (1, 3):

$\frac{\text{change in } y\text{-values}}{\text{change in } x\text{-values}} = \frac{7 - 3}{3 - 1} = \frac{4}{2} = 2.$

② Determine the rate of change for the function in the graph.

Select any two points from the graph.

Using (0, −1) and (2, 5):

$\frac{\text{change in } y\text{-values}}{\text{change in } x\text{-values}} = \frac{5 - (-1)}{2 - 0} = \frac{6}{2} = 3.$

③ Compare the rates of change. Since 3 > 2, the rate of change is greater for the function represented by the graph.

> I see! I can compare slopes to compare the rates of change of linear functions.

DISCUSS Dominic is comparing the rates of change of two positive linear functions by their graphs. How can he use the steepness of the lines to compare them? Explain.
Possible response: The function with the greater slope will be steeper. So the steeper line will have the greater rate of change.

LESSON LINK

PLUG IN	POWER UP	GO!
You can describe functional relationships from graphs.	You can sketch a graph of a functional relationship given a verbal description.	

PLUG IN: $y = 5x + 5$

POWER UP: Sally earns $10 an hour as a math tutor.

GO!: I get it! I can compare functional relationships given a verbal description, a graph, a table, or an equation.

WORK TOGETHER

Use coordinate grids to show which function has a greater y-intercept.

- Plot the points for each function.
- Draw the line for each function.
- Compare the y-intercepts.

The second function has a greater y-intercept.

x	3	6	8	9
y	−1	2	4	5

x	3	6	8	9
y	3	9	13	15

> If I'm comparing linear functions written as equations, I can always look at the value of b in y = mx + b.

The y-intercept of the first function is −4.
The y-intercept of the second function is −3.
−4 < −3

Ⓐ You can compare the rates of change of functions.

DO Determine which function has a greater rate of change.

$y = 5x − 10$

① Determine the rate of change from the graph.

② Determine the rate of change from the equation.

③ Compare the rates of change.

Use two coordinate pairs from the graph: (0, −4) and (2, 2).

$\frac{\text{change in } y\text{-values}}{\text{change in } x\text{-values}} = \frac{2 - (-4)}{2 - 0} = \frac{6}{2} = 3$

In the equation, y = 5x − 10, the rate of change is _5_.

Since _5_ > _3_, the _equation_ has the greater rate of change.

DISCUSS Marjorie asks how she could compare linear functions whose graphs are horizontal lines. What would you tell her? Possible response: The lines have the same slope and rates of change: 0. The functions can also be compared by their y-intercepts, which may be different.

LESSON LINK

Connect to Foundational Understanding Skills learned in the **Plug In** and **Power Up** are referenced in the **Lesson Link**. Explain that graphs can be used to describe linear functions, compare the rates of change of linear functions, and compare the properties of linear functions. Functional relationships can be compared given a verbal description, a graph, a table, or an equation.

- **Work Together** Explain that students will use coordinate grids to show which of two functions has a greater *y*-intercept. Begin by setting up students' coordinate grids to graph the values in the tables. If needed, suggest students label the *y*-axis from −5 to 15.

DO **Ⓐ** Monitor students as they compare the rates of change of two functions represented in different ways. Have students use two points in the first quadrant to determine the slope, since this will eliminate some possible confusion with negative numbers.

- **Support Discussion** **MP** Have partners discuss briefly before group discussion. As needed, ask students to write down all of the ways in which two graphs can be compared.

> *Prompt: What is the slope of a horizontal line?*
> *Sentence Starter: When the rate of change equals zero . . .*

SPOTLIGHT ON MATHEMATICAL LANGUAGE

MP6 Support students in using mathematical language as they work:

- *What is a **y-intercept**?*
- *Do both graphs have a positive or negative **slope**?*

PRACTICE

Determine which function has a greater rate of change.

1 Function 1:

x	−2	−1	2	5
y	−6	−3	6	15

Rate of change for Function 1: ___3___

Function 2:

(graph)

Rate of change for Function 2: $\frac{1}{2}$

Function ___1___ has a greater rate of change.

2 Function 1:

x	−3	0	3	6
y	−3	0	3	6

Rate of change for Function 1: ___1___

Function ___1___ has a greater rate of change.

Function 2:

$y = \frac{1}{3}x + 2$

Rate of change for Function 2: $\frac{1}{3}$

3 Function 1:

The output of this function is equal to the input multiplied by 10.

Rate of change for Function 1: ___10___

Function ___2___ has a greater rate of change.

Function 2:

$y = 15x − 25$

Rate of change for Function 2: ___15___

Determine which function has a greater y-intercept.

4 Function 1:

x	−2	0	1	3
y	−11	−5	−2	4

y-intercept for Function 1: ___−5___

Function 2:

The output of this function is equal to 3 less than the product of the input and 2.

y-intercept for Function 2: ___−3___

Function ___2___ has a greater y-intercept.

Compare functions based on their descriptions.

5 Which function has a greater rate of change?

Function 1: The output of this function is equal to 6 more than the product of the input and five.

Function 2: The output of this function is equal to 6 less than the product of the input and three.

Function 1

That's right! The rate of change is the number being multiplied by the input.

6 Which function has a greater y-intercept?

Function 1: The output of this function is equal to 12 less than the product of the input and five.

Function 2: The output of this function is equal to 12 more than the product of the input and three.

Function 2

DISCUSS

Reason quantitatively.

Sonya says that the graph has a greater rate of change than the table because $4 > 3$.

(graph)

x	−3	0	2	4
y	−9	0	6	12

I need to make sure I calculate the slope of a line correctly from a graph to know its rate of change.

Do you agree with Sonya? Explain.

Possible response: No, because the rate of change of the graph is −4. The rate of change of the table is 3. $3 > −4$, So the table has a greater rate of change.

ADDITIONAL PRACTICE

Provide students with additional practice to model and solve:

Sketch a graph that represents the functional relationship.

Jo raises $60 per week for the first five weeks of a fundraiser. Then she raises $40 per week for the next 2 weeks. Then she stops raising money.

Determine which function has a greater rate of change.

$y = −2x + 5$
$y = −5x + 2$

Support Independent Practice

1–3 Remind students to read the **REMEMBER**. If needed, ask: *How do you find the rate of change for a function?*

4 *What does the y-intercept tell you about the graph of a function?*

5–6 *How do you graph a function for which you are only given a description?*

- **Support Discussion** **MP2** Have partners discuss briefly before group discussion. If needed, have students choose their own pair of points from the graph to find the slope.

> *Prompt: Is the slope of the first graph positive or negative? What about the second graph?*
> *Sentence Starter: Sonya's reasoning is . . .*

Problem Solving

- **Model the Four-Step Method** **MP** **MP** Guide students through the four-step method using think-aloud strategies.

Think Aloud I need to find the rate of change of the values in the table for Allen. The rate of change will tell me how much he earned per hour.

PROBLEM SOLVING

SUMMER JOBS

READ Patricia and Allen each worked jobs during the summer. Patricia was paid $8 an hour. Allen created this table showing the number of hours he worked and the amount he was paid. Who was paid at a greater rate?

x	5	15	20	25	30
y	40.50	121.50	162.00	202.50	243.00

PLAN
- What is the problem asking you to find?
  You need to find who was paid at a ___greater___ rate.

- What do you need to solve the problem?
  Patricia's pay rate: $8 per hour
  Calculate Allen's pay rate by using the values in the table.

- How can you find Allen's pay rate?
  By calculating the ___rate of change___

SOLVE Write an equation for Patricia's pay rate.

$y = $ __8__ x

The rate of change is __8__.

Find Allen's pay rate.

I remember! I can find the rate of change by choosing two ordered pairs and then finding the ratio of the change in y to the corresponding change in x!

$$\frac{121.50 - 40.50}{15 - 5} = \frac{81.00}{10} = 8.1 \quad \text{Possible answers shown.}$$

The rate of change is $8.10.

CHECK Multiply Allen's pay rate by some of the hours he worked to check your answer.

$8.10 \times 20 = $ __162__

$8.10 \times 30 = $ __243__

Patricia earned $ __8__ an hour. Allen earned $ __8.10__ an hour.

___Allen___ was paid at a greater rate.

PRACTICE

Use the problem-solving steps to help you.

1. Eli jogged at a rate of 3 miles per hour. Taylor recorded his own distances and times in a table.

x	3	6	9	12
y	10.5	21	31.5	42

Who jogged at a faster rate?
Taylor

CHECKLIST
- [ ] READ
- [ ] PLAN
- [ ] SOLVE
- [ ] CHECK

2. Macie completed 10 multiplication problems a minute. Alexis made a graph showing the relationship between the number of multiplication problems she solved and how long it took her in minutes.

Who completed the problems at a faster rate? **Alexis**

CHECKLIST
- [ ] READ
- [ ] PLAN
- [ ] SOLVE
- [ ] CHECK

3. Alec deposits the same amount of money each month into his savings account. He uses this equation to calculate the amount of money he has in his savings account:
$y = 50x + 200$, after x months.

Shaelyn started her savings account with $250 and deposits $30 each month into her savings account.

Who saves money at a faster rate?
Alec

I can write an equation from a verbal description. Then it'll be easier to identify the slope!

CHECKLIST
- [ ] READ
- [ ] PLAN
- [ ] SOLVE
- [ ] CHECK

- **Support Problem-Solving Practice** Have students use the Checklist as they complete each step.

> *Prompt: How can you compare the rates of change?*
> *Prompt: In the graph, what does y equal when the x equals 1?*
> *Prompt: What equation can you write for Shaelyn's plan?*

- **Explore Student Thinking** MP3 Have students share which representation they prefer to work with: equation, graph, or description. Have partners compare their work on a particular problem and discuss their results.

SPOTLIGHT ON MATHEMATICAL PRACTICES

MP1 Some students may be more comfortable working with graphs rather than equations, and others may be more comfortable working with equations. Emphasize that comparing the functions using the same type of representation may make it easier to tell which rate of change is greater.

Assess

- Use the table below to address any difficulties.

	Observation	Action
1	Errors in describing, sketching, and comparing functional relationships	Distribute extra copies of the coordinate grid. Have students model each problem on a grid, even if a graph is already provided. Practicing in the coordinate grid will prove invaluable in future lessons.
2	Makes occasional errors when sketching and comparing functional relationships.	Provide additional practice problems for graphing. Have students use the coordinate grid for the foundation of their graphs. Ensure they assign the correct values to the *x*- and *y*-axes.
3	Describes, sketches, and compares functional relationships accurately.	Assign the Lesson 9 Quiz

10 Translations on a Coordinate Grid

PLUG IN Understanding Translations

		OBJECTIVES	CONCEPTS AND SKILLS	VOCABULARY
FOUNDATIONAL UNDERSTANDING	**▶ PLUG IN** **Understanding Translations** Student Edition pp. 94–95	• Determine if transformations of a figure are translations. • Translate segments. • Translate angles.	Perform a single translation of line segments and angles. **CCSS:** 8.G.1	• **rigid motion** • **image** • **translation**
	POWER UP **Translations and Congruence**	• Find a translation that shows two figures are congruent. • Show that two figures are not congruent.	Understand congruency of a single translation of a figure. **CCSS:** 8.G.2	• **congruent** • **corresponding sides** • **corresponding angles**
ON-LEVEL TARGET	**READY TO GO** **Translations on a Coordinate Grid**	• Use a rule to translate a figure. • Write a rule for a translation.	Describe the effect of translations on two-dimensional figures using coordinates. **CCSS:** 8.G.3	

MATERIALS

• Cardboard *(suggested)*
• Scissors *(suggested)*

ENGLISH LANGUAGE LEARNERS

MP6 ELL students may need additional support in understanding the mathematical term *translation*, since they may confuse it with translating languages. Ask students their understanding of the term *translation*, and then explain that they will be learning the mathematical meaning of the term in this lesson.

Build Background

▪ Discuss with students reasons to use translations in real life. For example, architects may translate a figure when it is used multiple times in a technical drawing. Explain that a translated figure is an exact copy of the original figure.

▪ MP6 Have students describe other uses for translations.

▪ Tell students that they will be exploring the translations of angles and line segments.

Introduce and Model

▪ **Introduce Concepts and Vocabulary** Cut two congruent triangles from cardboard. Using the same orientation, label one triangle "Original" and label the other "Image." Place one triangle onto the other to show that the corresponding angles have the same measure and the corresponding sides have the same lengths. MP6 Have students demonstrate to a partner their understanding of *rigid motion* and *translation*.

▪ **Support Discussion** MP6 Have partners discuss briefly before group discussion. As needed, direct students to **Words to Know** and have them demonstrate their understanding of translations by drawing an angle and its translated image.

> *Prompt: How can you tell if an image is a translation of a 60° angle?*
> *Sentence Starter: The image of an angle will …*

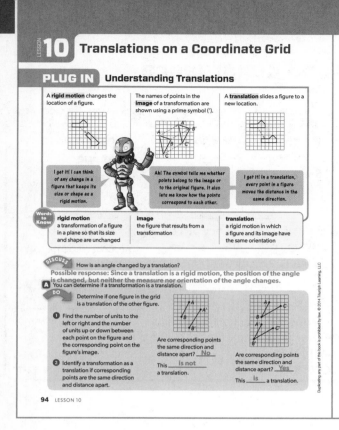

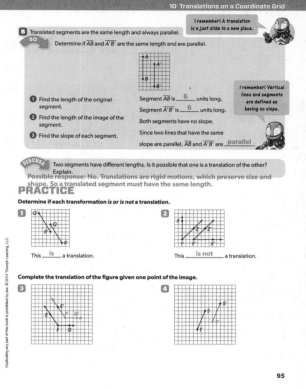

• Model Application

DO **A** Monitor students' work, making sure they write horizontal and vertical distances in the same order for each pair of corresponding points.

DO **B** Ask students whether a translated line segment will have the same length as the original line segment. Have them justify their answer. Monitor as students determine the slope of the vertical lines.

• **Support Discussion** **MP3** Have partners discuss briefly before group discussion. As needed, direct students to **Words to Know** and have them draw line segments in a coordinate plane to justify their answer.

> *Prompt: If you know two line segments are related by a rigid motion, what do you know about their size?*
>
> *Sentence Starter: The original segment and its image must be …*

Practice and Assess

• Ask students to complete items 1–4 on page 95 independently or in pairs. Monitor ongoing work.

• Observe whether students accurately identify translations.

Observation	Action
Students do not accurately identify if a change in position is a translation.	Have students draw another image for a segment or angle using a rigid motion. Ask them to explain why their figure is a translation. Based on their responses, review any missed problems.

MP7 **MP6** Support students in using mathematical language as they work:

• *Is the move from the first figure to the second a **rigid motion**?*

• *Which figure is the **image**?*

• *Is the move a **translation**?*

Translations and Congruence

		OBJECTIVES	CONCEPTS AND SKILLS	VOCABULARY
FOUNDATIONAL UNDERSTANDING	**PLUG IN** **Understanding Translations**	• Determine if transformations of a figure are translations. • Translate segments. • Translate angles.	Perform a single translation of line segments and angles. **CCSS:** 8.G.1	• **rigid motion** • **image** • **translation**
	▶ *POWER UP* **Translations and Congruence** Student Edition pp. 96–97	• Find a translation that shows two figures are congruent. • Show that two figures are not congruent.	Understand congruency of a single translation of a figure. **CCSS:** 8.G.2	• **congruent** • **corresponding sides** • **corresponding angles**
ON-LEVEL TARGET	**READY TO GO** **Translations on a Coordinate Grid**	• Use a rule to translate a figure. • Write a rule for a translation.	Describe the effect of translations on two-dimensional figures using coordinates. **CCSS:** 8.G.3	

MATERIALS

- Math Tool: Grids, p. A17 (Student Edition, p. 241)
- Cardboard (*suggested*)
- Scissors (*suggested*)

COMMON ERRORS

Students may have difficulty applying *congruence* to a figure that does not have line segments or angles. Discuss how the shape of every circle is the same. Then focus on size. Help students determine how they can describe the difference in size using radius or circumference.

Build Background

- Talk to students about where they see congruent figures in everyday life. For example, the windows in the classroom or a set of textbooks on a shelf.

- **MP3** Have students discuss additional examples of congruent figures and justify their reasoning.

- Tell students that they will use translations to determine whether a figure and its image are congruent.

Introduce and Model

- **Introduce Concepts and Vocabulary** Guide students to understand the connection between a figure and its translated image and two figures that are congruent. Use **Words to Know** to clarify their understanding of vocabulary. **MP6** Have students demonstrate to a partner that they understand the meaning of *congruence*.

- **Support Discussion** **MP6** Have partners discuss briefly before group discussion. Cut circles of varying sizes from cardboard, including some that have the same size. As needed, have students pair the congruent circles.

> *Prompt: How can you tell if two circles have the same size?*
> *Sentence Starter: To show that two circles have the same size, I need to …*

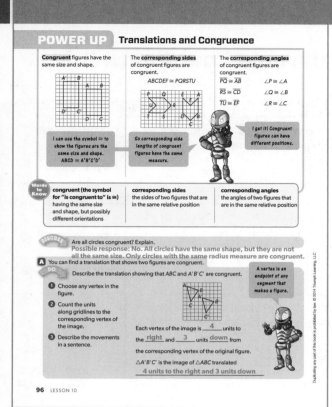

POWER UP Translations and Congruence

Congruent figures have the same size and shape.

The **corresponding sides** of congruent figures are congruent.

ABCDEF ≅ PQRSTU

$\overline{PQ} \cong \overline{AB}$

$\overline{RS} \cong \overline{CD}$

$\overline{TU} \cong \overline{EF}$

The **corresponding angles** of congruent figures are congruent.

∠P ≅ ∠A

∠Q ≅ ∠B

∠R ≅ ∠C

I can use the symbol ≅ to show the figures are the same size and shape. ABCD ≅ A'B'C'D'

So corresponding side lengths of congruent figures have the same measure.

I get it! Congruent figures can have different positions.

Words to Know

congruent (the symbol for "is congruent to" is ≅) having the same size and shape, but possibly different orientations

corresponding sides the sides of two figures that are in the same relative position

corresponding angles the angles of two figures that are in the same relative position

DISCUSS Are all circles congruent? Explain.
Possible response: No. All circles have the same shape, but they are not all the same size. Only circles with the same radius measure are congruent.

A You can find a translation that shows two figures are congruent.

DO Describe the translation showing that ABC and A'B'C' are congruent.

1. Choose any vertex in the figure.
2. Count the units along gridlines to the corresponding vertex of the image.
3. Describe the movements in a sentence.

A vertex is an endpoint of any segment that makes a figure.

Each vertex of the image is ___4___ units to the _right_ and __3__ units _down_ from the corresponding vertex of the original figure.

△A'B'C' is the image of △ABC translated _4 units to the right and 3 units down_

96 LESSON 10

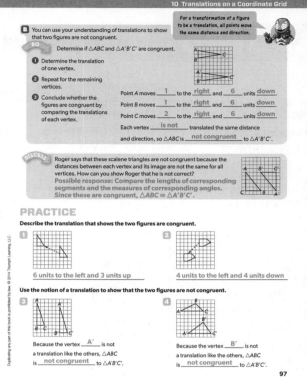

B You can use your understanding of translations to show that two figures are not congruent.

For a transformation of a figure to be a translation, all points move the same distance and direction.

DO Determine if △ABC and △A'B'C' are congruent.

1. Determine the translation of one vertex.
2. Repeat for the remaining vertices.
3. Conclude whether the figures are congruent by comparing the translations of each vertex.

Point A moves __1__ to the _right_ and __6__ units _down_

Point B moves __1__ to the _right_ and __6__ units _down_

Point C moves __2__ to the _right_ and __6__ units _down_

Each vertex _is not_ translated the same distance and direction, so △ABC is _not congruent_ to △A'B'C'.

DISCUSS Roger says that these scalene triangles are not congruent because the distances between each vertex and its image are not the same for all vertices. How can you show Roger that he is not correct?
Possible response: Compare the lengths of corresponding segments and the measures of corresponding angles. Since these are congruent, △ABC ≅ △A'B'C'.

PRACTICE

Describe the translation that shows the two figures are congruent.

1. 6 units to the left and 3 units up

2. 4 units to the left and 4 units down

Use the notion of a translation to show that the two figures are not congruent.

3. Because the vertex ___A'___ is not a translation like the others, △ABC is _not congruent_ to △A'B'C'.

4. Because the vertex ___B'___ is not a translation like the others, △ABC is _not congruent_ to △A'B'C'.

97

● Model Application

DO ▶ A Help students understand that a translation results in two figures that are congruent. If students are able to confirm that an image is a translation of the original figure, then the original figure and the image are congruent.

DO ▶ B Students may see that the two triangles do not appear to have the same exact shape. They should find that the change in position for A and B is the same but the change in position for C is different. This will lead them to show that all parts of the image are not the same, so the image is not a translation and the figures are not congruent.

● **Support Discussion MP3** Have partners discuss briefly before group discussion. If students do not think that the figures are congruent, ask them to trace the original figure and use their copy to check for congruence.

Prompt: Could you measure the side lengths of each image?
Sentence Starter: If two triangles are the same size and shape, I know …

Practice and Assess

● Ask students to complete practice items 1–4 on page 97 independently or in pairs. Monitor ongoing work.

● Use the table below to address any difficulties.

Observation	Action
Students have difficulty explaining why figures are or are not congruent.	Ask students to draw a line segment and its translated image. Ask them to explain their step aloud. Have students apply this understanding to explain why the two segments are congruent.

Translations on a Coordinate Grid

		OBJECTIVES	CONCEPTS AND SKILLS	VOCABULARY
FOUNDATIONAL UNDERSTANDING	**PLUG IN** **Understanding Translations**	• Determine if transformations of a figure are translations. • Translate segments. Translate angles.	Perform a single translation of line segments and angles. **CCSS:** 8.G.1	• **rigid motion** • **image** • **translation**
	POWER UP **Translations and Congruence**	• Find a translation that shows two figures are congruent. • Show that two figures are not congruent.	Understand congruency of a single translation of a figure. **CCSS:** 8.G.2	• **congruent** • **corresponding sides** • **corresponding angles**
ON-LEVEL TARGET	▶ **READY TO GO** **Translations on a Coordinate Grid** Student Edition pp. 98–103	• Use a rule to translate a figure. • Write a rule for a translation.	Describe the effect of translations on two-dimensional figures using coordinates. **CCSS:** 8.G.3	

MATERIALS

• Lesson 10 Quiz, Assessment Manual pp. 22–23
• Lesson 10 Quiz Answer Key, Assessment Manual
• Math Tool: Coordinate Grid, p. A15 (Student Edition p. 237)

SPOTLIGHT ON
MATHEMATICAL PRACTICES

MP7 Look for Structure

Help students make the connection between describing a translation in words, as in left 6 and up 2, to writing a rule for the translation, as in $(x, y) \rightarrow (x - 6, y + 2)$. Ask: *How does the rule for a translation keep every point in the original figure and the image the same distance apart?*

Build Background

• Discuss with students how a rule in mathematics is related to other kinds of rules, for instant a rule in a game.

• **MP7** Have students discuss examples of mathematical rules.

• Tell students that they will use rules to translate figures and will also write rules to describe translations.

Introduce and Model

• **Introduce and Model** Guide students in understanding the rule for translating any point (x, y) showing how to find new points using a rule and then graphing the image. **MP1** Encourage students to pay attention to detail as they find and graph the coordinates of the image.

• **Support Discussion MP3** Have partners discuss briefly before group discussion. Ask students to draw a segment and use one rule to move an endpoint and another rule to move the other endpoint. Ask students to explain their results.

> *Prompt: If you use the same rule to find the image of a figure, what do you know about the change in position for the corresponding points?*
>
> *Sentence Starter: To translate a figure using a rule, I …*

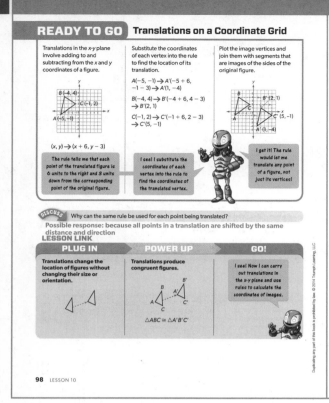

READY TO GO Translations on a Coordinate Grid

Translations in the *x-y* plane involve adding to and subtracting from the *x* and *y* coordinates of a figure.

Substitute the coordinates of each vertex into the rule to find the location of its translation.

$A(-5, -1) \rightarrow A'(-5 + 6, -1 - 3) \rightarrow A'(1, -4)$

$B(-4, 4) \rightarrow B'(-4 + 6, 4 - 3) \rightarrow B'(2, 1)$

$C(-1, 2) \rightarrow C'(-1 + 6, 2 - 3) \rightarrow C'(5, -1)$

Plot the image vertices and join them with segments that are images of the sides of the original figure.

$(x, y) \rightarrow (x + 6, y - 3)$

The rule tells me that each point of the translated figure is 6 units to the right and 3 units down from the corresponding point of the original figure.

I see! I substitute the coordinates of each vertex into the rule to find the coordinates of the translated vertex.

I get it! The rule would let me translate any point of a figure, not just its vertices!

DISCUSS Why can the same rule be used for each point being translated?
Possible response: because all points in a translation are shifted by the same distance and direction

LESSON LINK

PLUG IN	POWER UP	GO!
Translations change the location of figures without changing their size or orientation.	Translations produce congruent figures.	I see! Now I can carry out translations in the *x-y* plane and use rules to calculate the coordinates of images.

$\triangle ABC \cong \triangle A'B'C'$

98 LESSON 10

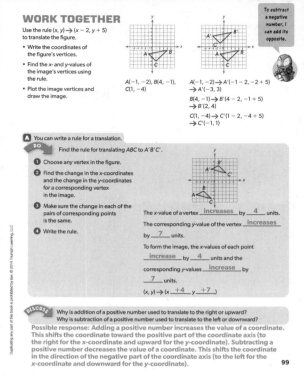

WORK TOGETHER
Use the rule $(x, y) \rightarrow (x - 2, y + 5)$ to translate the figure.

- Write the coordinates of the figure's vertices.
- Find the *x*- and *y*-values of the image's vertices using the rule.
- Plot the image vertices and draw the image.

To subtract a negative number, I can add its opposite.

$A(-1, -2)$, $B(4, -1)$, $C(1, -4)$

$A(-1, -2) \rightarrow A'(-1 - 2, -2 + 5) \rightarrow A'(-3, 3)$

$B(4, -1) \rightarrow B'(4 - 2, -1 + 5) \rightarrow B'(2, 4)$

$C(1, -4) \rightarrow C'(1 - 2, -4 + 5) \rightarrow C'(-1, 1)$

A You can write a rule for a translation.

DO Find the rule for translating *ABC* to *A'B'C'*.

1. Choose any vertex in the figure.
2. Find the change in the *x*-coordinates and the change in the *y*-coordinates for a corresponding vertex in the image.
3. Make sure the change in each of the pairs of corresponding points is the same.
4. Write the rule.

The *x*-value of a vertex increases by 4 units. The corresponding *y*-value of the vertex increases by 7 units.

To form the image, the *x*-values of each point increase by 4 units and the corresponding *y*-values increase by 7 units.

$(x, y) \rightarrow (x +4, y +7)$

DISCUSS Why is addition of a positive number used to translate to the right or upward? Why is subtraction of a positive number used to translate to the left or downward?
Possible response: Adding a positive number increases the value of a coordinate. This shifts the coordinate toward the positive part of the coordinate axis (to the right for the *x*-coordinate and upward for the *y*-coordinate). Subtracting a positive number decreases the value of a coordinate. This shifts the coordinate in the direction of the negative part of the coordinate axis (to the left for the *x*-coordinate and downward for the *y*-coordinate).

99

LESSON LINK

Connect to Foundational Understanding Skills learned in the **Plug In** and **Power Up** are referenced in the **Lesson Link**. Explain that understanding how to describe a translation in words helps in writing the rule for a translation.

- **Work Together** Explain that students will use addition and subtraction to identify the vertices of a figure's image.

DO **A** Monitor students as they write a rule for a translation. After they write the rule based on the rigid motion of one vertex, have the students check their rule using the other vertices.

- **Support Discussion** **MP3** Have partners discuss briefly before group discussion. If necessary, have students use their coordinate grids to explain the location of the points $(2, 2)$ and $(-2, -2)$ using the origin as a starting point.

> *Prompt: Where are the positive numbers located on a coordinate grid?*
>
> *Sentence Starter: To translate a figure four units right and three units down, the rule would be …*

COMMON ERRORS

MP1 Students may confuse the coordinates of the original figure. Be sure they accurately find and use the *x*-value and *y*-value of a vertex of the original figure as they find the coordinates of its image.

SPOTLIGHT ON MATHEMATICAL LANGUAGE

MP6 Support students in using mathematical language as they work:

- *Which is the original figure and which is the **image**?*
- *Is the image **congruent** to the original figure? How do you know?*

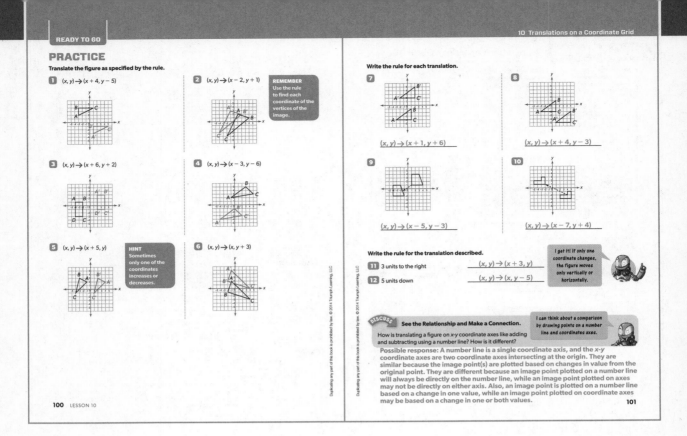

ADDITIONAL PRACTICE

Provide students with additional practice to model and solve: For the triangle with vertices $A(0, 3)$, $B(-2, 1)$, and $C(3, 0)$, state the vertices of the image for each translation.

$(x, y) \rightarrow (x + 3, y + 2)$
$(x, y) \rightarrow (x + 3, y - 2)$

$(x, y) \rightarrow (x - 3, y + 2)$
$(x, y) \rightarrow (x - 3, y - 2)$

Support Independent Practice

1–6 Remind students to read the **HINT** and **REMEMBER**. If needed, have students draw line segments showing how a vertex is to move. Ask: *How can you describe the translation?*

7–10 *How is the original figure being translated?*

11–12 *What is the horizontal change? What is the vertical change?*

• **Support Discussion** **MP7** Have partners translate a point on a number line and compare this to translating a point on coordinate axes.

> **Prompt:** *What kind of figure can you translate on a number line? What kind of figure can you translate on a coordinate plane?*
>
> **Sentence Starter:** *Graphing on a number line is like graphing on a coordinate plane because ...*

Problem Solving

• **Model the Four-Step Method** **MP7** Guide students through the four-step method using Think Aloud strategies. Discuss the diagram and how it shows the change in the position of the desk.

Think Aloud *The blue shape is the image. The point at the lower right of the original figure moves left 6 units and up 5 units.*

READY TO GO

PROBLEM SOLVING

FURNITURE ARRANGEMENT

READ

Jim draws a diagram on a grid to show how he moved the desk in his office. Write a translation rule to describe how he moved his desk.

1 square = 1 square foot.

PLAN

• What are you asked to do? Describe how he moved his ___desk___.

• What information do you need? The location of his desk ___before___ and ___after___ the move.

• How do you solve the problem? Find the ___change___ in the x- and y-values of the ___corresponding___ vertices of the desk.

SOLVE

Find the coordinates of a vertex of the original position of the desk.
The coordinates of the bottom right vertex are (___12___, ___0___).

Find the coordinates of the corresponding vertex of the new position of the desk.
The corresponding coordinates are (___6___, ___5___).

The x-coordinate ___decreases___ by ___6___.
The y-coordinate ___increases___ by ___5___.
Jim moved the desk ___6___ feet to the left and ___5___ feet up.

CHECK

Find the change in the other vertices. Make sure the changes in the x- and y-values for the remaining corresponding vertices are the same.

(8, 0) → (___2___, ___5___)
(12, 5) → (___6___, ___10___)
(10, 5) → (___4___, ___10___)
(10, 2) → (___4___, ___7___)
(8, 2) → (___2___, ___7___)

The scale tells me that 1 square on the graph is equal to one square foot. That means the side of each square is equal to one foot.

The rule for the change in the location of the desk is $(x, y) \rightarrow (x$ ___−6___ $, y$ ___+5___ $)$.

102 LESSON 10

PRACTICE

A quick sketch can help you understand the translation.

Use the problem-solving steps to help you.

1 Jason drew a diagram of his room on a grid. Each square on the grid is equal to one square foot. His desk is 11 squares down and 6 squares to the right of the window. Write a translation rule for moving the desk to the window.

$(x, y) \rightarrow (x + 6, y - 11)$

CHECKLIST
☐ READ
☐ PLAN
☐ SOLVE
☐ CHECK

2 Triangle *QRS* is drawn on a coordinate grid where *Q*(−3, 2), *R*(6, 1), and *S*(3, −4). Michelle draws its image, △*Q'R'S'*, on the same coordinate grid using the translation rule $(x, y) \rightarrow (x − 6, y + 1)$. What are the coordinates of △*Q'R'S'*?

$Q'(−9, 3), R'(0, 2), S'(−3, −3)$

CHECKLIST
☐ READ
☐ PLAN
☐ SOLVE
☐ CHECK

3 Maxine drew a map on a coordinate grid. Maxine's house is located at (7, 12). The distance on the map between Maxine's house and her friend's house can be described by the translation rule $(x, y) \rightarrow (x − 3, y + 2)$. What are the coordinates on the map of Maxine's friend's house?

(4, 14)

CHECKLIST
☐ READ
☐ PLAN
☐ SOLVE
☐ CHECK

4 Jorge noticed a bug walking on a coordinate grid he drew on a piece of graph paper. He first sees the bug when it is at (7, 3). The bug crawls in a straight line to (1, −2). Write the bug's path as a translation rule.

$(x, y) \rightarrow (x − 6, y − 5)$

CHECKLIST
☐ READ
☐ PLAN
☐ SOLVE
☐ CHECK

103

• **Support Problem-Solving Practice** Have students use the Checklist as they complete each step.

> *Prompt: Can you draw each situation?*

• **Explore Student Thinking MP3** Invite students to describe the process they use to analyze a translation. Have partners compare their work and discuss their results.

SPOTLIGHT ON MATHEMATICAL PRACTICES

MP2 Help students make sense of the real-world situation in terms of points on a coordinate plane. Encourage them to relate their answers to the original situation. In Problem 1, ask: *What does your translation rule tell about what happens to Jason's desk?*

Assess

• Use the table below to address any difficulties.

• When all students are ready, assign the Lesson 10 Quiz.

	Observation	Action
1	Errors in writing or using translation rules are frequent or irregular; general confusion about how to solve a problem.	Have students graph each situation on a coordinate grid and explain each step. Determine if the challenge is in translating the words of the problem to a mathematical situation or in understanding translations.
2	Makes occasional errors when writing or using a translation rule.	Provide additional practice to assure that students' approach to their work is consistent.
3	Writes and uses translation rules accurately.	Assign the Lesson 10 quiz.

11 Reflections on a Coordinate Grid

PLUG IN Understanding Reflections

		OBJECTIVES	CONCEPTS AND SKILLS	VOCABULARY
FOUNDATIONAL UNDERSTANDING	▶ **PLUG IN** **Understanding Reflections** Student Edition pp. 104–105	• Reflect a line segment or angle across a line. • Draw a line of reflection for two line segments or angles.	Perform a single reflection of line segments and angles across a line. **CCSS:** 8.G.1	• **reflection** • **line of reflection**
	POWER UP **Reflections and Congruence**	• Use a reflection to show that two triangles are congruent. • Reflect a figure across a line to form a congruent figure.	Understand congruency of a single reflection of a figure. **CCSS:** 8.G.2	
ON-LEVEL TARGET	**READY TO GO** **Reflections on a Coordinate Grid**	• Graph a reflection of a figure and give the coordinates of its vertices. • Describe the sequence of reflections that makes two figures congruent.	Describe the effect of reflections on two-dimensional figures using coordinates. **CCSS:** 8.G.3	

MATERIALS
• Small rectangular mirrors (*suggested*)
• Tracing paper (*suggested*)

ENGLISH LANGUAGE LEARNERS

MP5 **MP6** ELL students may need extra support for understanding the term *reflection*. Have students hold the edge of a small rectangular mirror along the line of reflection to see an actual reflection of the figure. Explain that the reflected figures they draw are models of the mirror image.

Build Background

■ Talk to students about reasons to reflect line segments and angles in real life. For example, when you draw a star, how do you make sure that it looks the same on the right and left sides? Explain that reflecting each line segment and angle on one side over a vertical line that bisects the star is one way to keep the star symmetrical.

■ **MP4** Have students discuss additional examples of real situations that involve reflection of line segments and angles.

■ Tell students they will work on reflecting line segments and angles and on drawing lines of reflection.

Introduce and Model

■ **Introduce Concepts and Vocabulary** Guide students through the reflection of a line segment and an angle. Use **Words to Know** to clarify their understanding of vocabulary. **MP6** Have students point to a *reflection* and a *line of reflection* in the text.

■ **Support Discussion** **MP2** Have partners discuss briefly before group discussion. As needed, direct students to **Words to Know** and have students sketch each step of the problem.

LESSON 11 — Reflections on a Coordinate Grid

PLUG IN — Understanding Reflections

A **reflection** is a flip of a figure over line.

The grid shows a segment and its reflection. If you fold the grid along the **line of reflection**, the two line segments will match exactly.

I see! When the paper is folded, the blue line segment aligns with the red line segment.

∠PQR is reflected over a line to form an image. The image of the reflection of point P is named with a prime symbol, P'.

Each point and its reflection are the same distance from the line of reflection.

2 units 2 units

I get it! Points P and P' are each 2 units from the line of reflection.

Words to Know

reflection — a flip of a figure over a line

line of reflection — the line over which a figure is reflected

line of reflection

DISCUSS Segment CD is reflected over a vertical line to form $\overline{C'D'}$. If you reflect $\overline{C'D'}$ over the same line, what will the image look like? Explain. Possible response: The image of $\overline{C'D'}$ will look like CD. Reflecting CD over the line resulted in C'D'. So reflecting $\overline{C'D'}$ over the same line of reflection will reflect it back onto the original figure, CD.

A You can reflect a segment over a line by finding the distance from each endpoint to the line.

DO Reflect $\overline{MN}$ over the dashed line to form $\overline{M'N'}$.

1. Reflect point M over the line.
2. Reflect point N over the line.
3. Connect the points to form the reflected image, $\overline{M'N'}$.

Point M is __2__ units to the __right__ of the line of reflection.
So plot point M' __2__ units to the __left__ of the line of reflection.
Point N is __4__ units to the __right__ of the line of reflection.
So plot point N' __4__ units to the __left__ of the line of reflection.
$\overline{M'N'}$ is the reflection of $\overline{MN}$.

B You can reflect an angle over a line by finding the distance from each labeled point to the line.

DO Reflect ∠XYZ over the dashed line.

1. Reflect point X over the line.
2. Reflect point Y over the line.
3. Reflect point Z over the line.
4. Draw $\overline{Y'X'}$ and $\overline{Y'Z'}$ to form the image, ∠X'Y'Z'.

Point X is __1__ unit(s) __above__ the line of reflection. So plot point X' __1__ unit(s) __below__ the line of reflection.
Point Y is __1__ unit(s) __above__ the line of reflection. So plot point Y' __1__ unit(s) __below__ the line of reflection.
Point Z is __3__ unit(s) __above__ the line of reflection. So plot point Z' __3__ unit(s) __below__ the line of reflection.
∠X'Y'Z' is the reflection of ∠XYZ.

C You can draw a line of reflection to show how figures can be reflected.

DO Draw a line that could be used to reflect blue line segment $\overline{LM}$ so it aligns with the red segment $\overline{JK}$.

I know my line is correct because I could fold the grid over the line and the segments would match up.

1. Find the distances between the corresponding endpoints.
2. Draw a line of reflection halfway between the corresponding endpoints.

The distance between J and L is __2__ unit(s).
The distance between K and M is __4__ unit(s).
One half of 2 is __1__. So start a line that is __1__ unit(s) above L.
One half of 4 is __2__. So continue the line so that it is __2__ unit(s) above M.

PRACTICE

Reflect the figure across the line.
1. Reflect $\overline{FG}$ to form $\overline{F'G'}$.

Draw a line of reflection.
2.

Prompt: What happens when you reflect a segment?
Sentence Starter: If I reflect $\overline{C'D'}$ …

Model Application

DO A Guide students through reflecting a line segment. Monitor that students reflect both endpoints correctly.

DO B Explain that reflecting an angle is similar to reflecting a line segment. Monitor that students reflect all labeled points correctly.

DO C Have students draw a line of reflection for the two segments. Monitor that students are drawing a line that is the same distance from the two segments.

Practice and Assess

- Ask students to complete practice items 1 and 2 on page 105 independently or in pairs. Monitor ongoing work.
- Observe whether students are correctly reflecting segments and angles and drawing lines of reflection. Use the chart below as needed to address any difficulties.

Observation	Action
Students incorrectly reflect one or more points of a figure or draw an incorrect line of reflection.	Have students trace the figure and line of reflection on tracing paper and draw the reflected figure. They could also trace the figures and draw the line of reflection. Have them fold the paper along the line of reflection and check if the two figures match up.

SPOTLIGHT ON MATHEMATICAL LANGUAGE

MP6 Support students in using mathematical language as they work:
- What is the **reflection** of the segment over the line?
- Draw a **line of reflection** between the two angles.

		OBJECTIVES	CONCEPTS AND SKILLS	VOCABULARY
FOUNDATIONAL UNDERSTANDING	**PLUG IN** **Understanding Reflections**	• Reflect a line segment or angle across a line. • Draw a line of reflection for two line segments or angles.	Perform a single reflection of line segments and angles across a line. **CCSS:** 8.G.1	• **reflection** • **line of reflection**
	▶ **POWER UP** **Reflections and Congruence** Student Edition pp. 106–107	• Use a reflection to show that two triangles are congruent. • Reflect a figure across a line to form a congruent figure.	Understand congruency of a single reflection of a figure. **CCSS:** 8.G.2	
ON-LEVEL TARGET	**READY TO GO** **Reflections on a Coordinate Grid**	• Graph a reflection of a figure and give the coordinates of its vertices. • Describe the sequence of reflections that makes two figures congruent.	Describe the effect of reflections on two-dimensional figures using coordinates. **CCSS:** 8.G.3	

MATERIALS
• Construction paper *(suggested)*

ENGLISH LANGUAGE LEARNERS
MP5 Cut out a polygon and its reflection from construction paper and label their vertices. Have students compare the polygons and verify that corresponding angles and sides are equal and therefore congruent.

Build Background
■ Talk to students about reasons to recognize the congruence of reflected figures in real life. For example, how do you find the glove that matches the one you're wearing? Explain that the matching glove is the congruent reflection of the one you're wearing.

■ **MP4** Have students discuss additional examples of real situations that involve congruence of reflected figures.

■ Tell students they will work on drawing lines of reflection and reflecting triangles and other figures.

Introduce and Model
■ **Introduce Concepts** Guide students through the information about the congruency of reflected figures. Emphasize that reflecting a figure is the same as reflecting a series of line segments and angles.

■ **Support Discussion** **MP2** Have partners discuss briefly before group discussion. As needed, direct students to the descriptions of congruence on the page for support.

> *Prompt: What does congruence mean?*
> *Sentence Starter: A triangle is congruent to another if …*

■ **Model Application**

DO ▶ **A** Explain that if two polygons are reflections of each other, then a line of reflection can be drawn that shows their congruence. Monitor that students draw the line of reflection between the figures correctly.

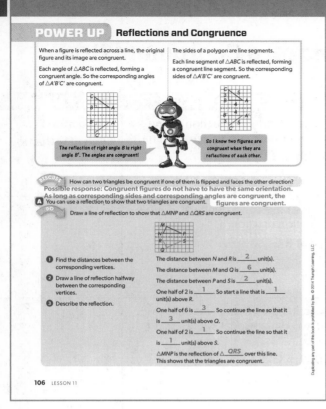

POWER UP Reflections and Congruence

When a figure is reflected across a line, the original figure and its image are congruent.

Each angle of △ABC is reflected, forming a congruent angle. So the corresponding angles of △A'B'C' are congruent.

The sides of a polygon are line segments.

Each line segment of △ABC is reflected, forming a congruent line segment. So the corresponding sides of △A'B'C' are congruent.

The reflection of right angle B is right angle B'. The angles are congruent!

So I know two figures are congruent when they are reflections of each other.

DISCUSS How can two triangles be congruent if one of them is flipped and faces the other direction? Possible response: Congruent figures do not have to have the same orientation. As long as corresponding sides and corresponding angles are congruent, the figures are congruent.

A You can use a reflection to show that two triangles are congruent.

DO Draw a line of reflection to show that △MNP and △QRS are congruent.

1 Find the distances between the corresponding vertices.
2 Draw a line of reflection halfway between the corresponding vertices.
3 Describe the reflection.

The distance between N and R is 2 unit(s).
The distance between M and Q is 6 unit(s).
The distance between P and S is 2 unit(s).
One half of 2 is 1. So start a line that is 1 unit(s) above R.
One half of 6 is 3. So continue the line so that it is 3 unit(s) above Q.
One half of 2 is 1. So continue the line so that it is 1 unit(s) above S.
△MNP is the reflection of △ QRS over this line. This shows that the triangles are congruent.

106 LESSON 11

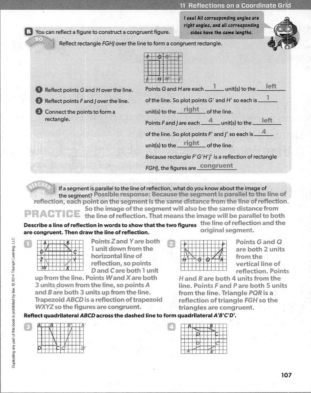

B You can reflect a figure to construct a congruent figure.

I see! All corresponding angles are right angles, and all corresponding sides have the same lengths.

DO Reflect rectangle FGHJ over the line to form a congruent rectangle.

1 Reflect points G and H over the line.
2 Reflect points F and J over the line.
3 Connect the points to form a rectangle.

Points G and H are each 1 unit(s) to the left of the line. So plot points G' and H' so each is 1 unit(s) to the right of the line.
Points F and J are each 4 unit(s) to the left of the line. So plot points F' and J' so each is 4 unit(s) to the right of the line.
Because rectangle F'G'H'J' is a reflection of rectangle FGHJ, the figures are congruent.

DISCUSS If a segment is parallel to the line of reflection, what do you know about the image of the segment? Possible response: Because the segment is parallel to the line of reflection, each point on the segment is the same distance from the line of reflection. So the image of the segment will also be the same distance from the line of reflection. That means the image will be parallel to both the line of reflection and the original segment.

PRACTICE Describe a line of reflection in words to show that the two figures are congruent. Then draw the line of reflection.

1 Points Z and Y are both 1 unit down from the horizontal line of reflection, so points D and C are both 1 unit up from the line. Points W and X are both 3 units down from the line, so points A and B are both 3 units up from the line. Trapezoid ABCD is a reflection of trapezoid WXYZ so the figures are congruent.

2 Points G and Q are both 2 units from the vertical line of reflection. Points H and R are both 4 units from the line. Points F and P are both 5 units from the line. Triangle PQR is a reflection of triangle FGH so the triangles are congruent.

Reflect quadrilateral ABCD across the dashed line to form quadrilateral A'B'C'D'.

3

4

107

DO B Guide students through the reflection of a plane figure. Monitor that students reflect all sides and vertices correctly.

- **Support Discussion** MP2 MP7 Have partners discuss briefly before group discussion. As needed, have students draw the segment and its image to model the problem.

> *Prompt: What will the image of the segment look like?*
> *Sentence Starter: The segment is parallel to...*

Practice and Assess

- Ask students to complete practice items 1–4 on page 107 independently or in pairs. Monitor ongoing work.

- Observe whether students are correctly drawing lines of reflection and reflecting figures. Use the chart below as needed to address any difficulties.

Observation	Action
Students incorrectly reflect one or more points of a figure.	Have students draw guide lines from each vertex of the polygon to the other side of the line of reflection to make sure that they place their reflected points correctly. Have them say aloud how far each vertex is from the line of reflection as they draw the guide lines. For example: *Point A is 5 units away from the line of reflection, so point A' will be 5 units away on the other side.*

COMMON ERRORS

Students may translate a figure over a line rather than reflect it. Have students write the distance from each vertex of the figure and its image to the line of reflection. Have them check that the distances from corresponding vertices are equal.

		OBJECTIVES	CONCEPTS AND SKILLS	VOCABULARY
FOUNDATIONAL UNDERSTANDING	**PLUG IN** **Understanding Reflections**	• Reflect a line segment or angle across a line. • Draw a line of reflection for two line segments or angles.	Perform a single reflection of line segments and angles across a line. **CCSS:** 8.G.1	• **reflection** • **line of reflection**
	POWER UP **Reflections and Congruence**	• Use a reflection to show that two triangles are congruent. • Reflect a figure across a line to form a congruent figure.	Understand congruency of a single reflection of a figure. **CCSS:** 8.G.2	
ON-LEVEL TARGET	**▶ READY TO GO** **Reflections on a Coordinate Grid** Student Edition pp. 108–113	• Graph a reflection of a figure and give the coordinates of its vertices. • Describe the sequence of reflections that makes two figures congruent.	Describe the effect of reflections on two-dimensional figures using coordinates. **CCSS:** 8.G.3	

MATERIALS

- Lesson 11 Quiz, Assessment Manual p. 24–25
- Lesson 11 Quiz Answer Key, Assessment Manual
- Math Tool: Coordinate grid, p. A15 (Student Edition p. 237)
- Small mirror *(suggested)*

Build Background

- Talk to students about reasons to identify the coordinates of reflection vertices in real life. For example, an architect wants the left and right halves of a building to be mirror images of each other. She designs the left half first. How will she know where to put the windows on each side? Explain that reflecting the left-side windows and finding the coordinates of their vertices is one way to answer that question.

- **MP4** Have students discuss additional examples of real situations that involve identifying the coordinates of reflected vertices.

- Tell students they will work on reflecting figures and finding their coordinates, as well as on describing the series of reflections used to create congruent figures.

Introduce and Model

- **Introduce Concepts** Guide students through graphing a reflection and finding its coordinates. Emphasize that this is the same reflection process that they have been using, except that now they are labeling the vertices with coordinates.

- **Support Discussion** **MP2** **MP7** Have partners discuss briefly before group discussion. As needed, direct students to draw reflections over the x- and y-axis to model.

> *Prompt: When you reflect a point, what happens to it?*
> *Sentence Starter: If I start with a point at (0, 0) …*

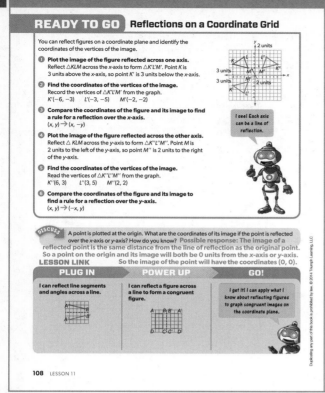

READY TO GO — Reflections on a Coordinate Grid

You can reflect figures on a coordinate plane and identify the coordinates of the vertices of the image.

1. **Plot the image of the figure reflected across one axis.**
Reflect △KLM across the x-axis to form △K'L'M'. Point K is 3 units above the x-axis, so point K' is 3 units below the x-axis.

2. **Find the coordinates of the vertices of the image.**
Record the vertices of △K'L'M' from the graph.
K'(−6, −3)   L'(−3, −5)   M'(−2, −2)

3. **Compare the coordinates of the figure and its image to find a rule for a reflection over the x-axis.**
(x, y) → (x, −y)

4. **Plot the image of the figure reflected across the other axis.**
Reflect △ KLM across the y-axis to form △K''L''M''. Point M is 2 units to the left of the y-axis, so point M'' is 2 units to the right of the y-axis.

5. **Find the coordinates of the vertices of the image.**
Read the vertices of △K''L''M'' from the graph.
K''(6, 3)   L''(3, 5)   M''(2, 2)

6. **Compare the coordinates of the figure and its image to find a rule for a reflection over the y-axis.**
(x, y) → (−x, y)

I see! Each axis can be a line of reflection.

DISCUSS A point is plotted at the origin. What are the coordinates of its image if the point is reflected over the x-axis or y-axis? How do you know? Possible response: The image of a reflected point is the same distance from the line of reflection as the original point. So a point on the origin and its image will both be 0 units from the x-axis or y-axis. So the image of the point will have the coordinates (0, 0).

LESSON LINK

PLUG IN	POWER UP	GO!
I can reflect line segments and angles across a line.	I can reflect a figure across a line to form a congruent figure.	I get it! I can apply what I know about reflecting figures to graph congruent images on the coordinate plane.

108 LESSON 11

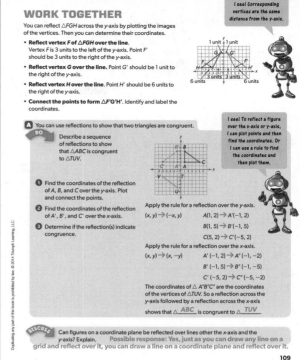

WORK TOGETHER

You can reflect △FGH across the y-axis by plotting the images of the vertices. Then you can determine their coordinates.

- **Reflect vertex F of △FGH over the line.**
Vertex F is 3 units to the left of the y-axis. Point F' should be 3 units to the right of the y-axis.

- **Reflect vertex G over the line.** Point G' should be 1 unit to the right of the y-axis.

- **Reflect vertex H over the line.** Point H' should be 6 units to the right of the y-axis.

- **Connect the points to form △F'G'H'.** Identify and label the coordinates.

I see! Corresponding vertices are the same distance from the y-axis.

DO **A** You can use reflections to show that two triangles are congruent.

Describe a sequence of reflections to show that △ABC is congruent to △TUV.

1. Find the coordinates of the reflection of A, B, and C over the y-axis. Plot and connect the points.

2. Find the coordinates of the reflection of A', B', and C' over the x-axis.

3. Determine if the reflection(s) indicate congruence.

I see! To reflect a figure over the x-axis or y-axis, I can plot points and then find the coordinates. Or I can use a rule to find the coordinates and then plot them.

Apply the rule for a reflection over the y-axis.
(x, y) → (−x, y)   A(1, 2) → A'(−1, 2)
B(1, 5) → B'(−1, 5)
C(5, 2) → C'(−5, 2)

Apply the rule for a reflection over the x-axis.
(x, y) → (x, −y)   A' (−1, 2) → A'' (−1, −2)
B' (−1, 5) → B'' (−1, −5)
C' (−5, 2) → C'' (−5, −2)

The coordinates of △ A''B''C'' are the coordinates of the vertices of △TUV. So a reflection across the y-axis followed by a reflection across the x-axis shows that △ __ABC__ is congruent to △ __TUV__.

DISCUSS Can figures on a coordinate plane be reflected over lines other than the x-axis and the y-axis? Explain. Possible response: Yes, just as you can draw any line on a grid and reflect over it, you can draw a line on a coordinate plane and reflect over it.

109

LESSON LINK

Connect to Foundational Understanding Skills learned in the **Plug In** and **Power Up** are referenced in the **Lesson Link**. Explain that because an image is congruent to its figure and is the same distance from the line of reflection, you can find the coordinates of the image and the series of reflections that created it.

- **Work Together** Explain that students will reflect a triangle on the coordinate plane and identify the coordinates of the vertices of the image. As needed, remind students that the y-axis is the line of reflection and to use the coordinate grid to help them find the coordinates of the vertices.

DO **A** Guide students as they identify the sequence of reflections that shows the congruence of △ABC to △TUV. Draw the first reflection on the board as a model if needed.

- **Support Discussion** **MP2** Have partners discuss briefly before group discussion. As needed, direct students to sketch a model on the coordinate plane.

> *Prompt: What kinds of lines can you reflect a figure over?*
> *Sentence Starter: If I draw a line on a coordinate plane…*

READY TO GO

PRACTICE

Graph each reflection. Give the coordinates of the vertices of the image.

1 Reflect △ABC over the x-axis to form △A'B'C'.

> **REMEMBER**
> The distance from corresponding vertices to the x-axis should be the same.

Coordinates: A'(−4 , −6), B'(−3 , −4), C'(−5 , −1)

2 Reflect △DEF over the y-axis to form △D'E'F'.

Coordinates: D'(−1 , −2), E'(−3 , −2), F'(−3 , −5)

3 Reflect trapezoid JKLM over the x-axis to form trapezoid J'K'L'M'.

Coordinates: J'(−4 , 4), K'(−2 , 4), L'(−2 , 6), M'(−5 , 6)

4 Reflect triangle STV over the line x = 6 to form triangle S'T'V'.

> **HINT**
> Find the distance from each vertex to x = 6. Then plot the image the same distance on the other side of the line.

Coordinates: S'(10 , 10), T'(7 , 8), V'(9 , 5)

Describe a reflection or a sequence of reflections that could be used to show that quadrilateral ABCD is congruent to quadrilateral MNPQ.

5

Possible response: reflection across the x-axis, then reflection of the image across the y-axis

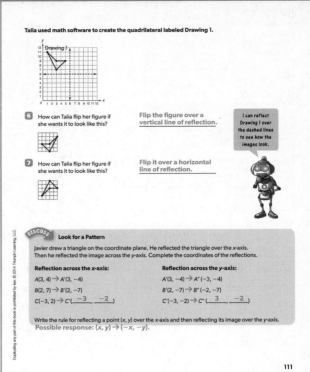

Talia used math software to create the quadrilateral labeled Drawing 1.

6 How can Talia flip her figure if she wants it to look like this?

Flip the figure over a vertical line of reflection.

7 How can Talia flip her figure if she wants it to look like this?

Flip it over a horizontal line of reflection.

> I can reflect Drawing 1 over the dashed lines to see how the images look.

DISCUSS

Look for a Pattern

Javier drew a triangle on the coordinate plane. He reflected the triangle over the x-axis. Then he reflected the image across the y-axis. Complete the coordinates of the reflections.

Reflection across the x-axis:

A(3, 4) → A'(3, −4)
B(2, 7) → B'(2, −7)
C(−3, 2) → C'(−3 , −2)

Reflection across the y-axis:

A'(3, −4) → A''(−3, −4)
B'(2, −7) → B''(−2, −7)
C'(−3, −2) → C''(3 , −2)

Write the rule for reflecting a point (x, y) over the x-axis and then reflecting its image over the y-axis.
Possible response: (x, y) → (−x, −y).

ADDITIONAL PRACTICE

Provide students with additional practice to model and solve:

Describe a sequence of reflections that could be used to show that △FGH is congruent to △F''G''H''. Coordinates: F(−4, 1), G(−1, 5), H(−1, 1) and F''(6, −1), G''(3, −5), H''(3, −1)

SPOTLIGHT ON MATHEMATICAL PRACTICES

MP7 Look for Patterns

Help students think of a general rule for reflecting across an axis: *What is changing about the x- and y-coordinates when you reflect across the x-axis? when you reflect across the y-axis?*

Support Independent Practice

1–4 Remind students to read the **HINT** and **REMEMBER**. If needed, have students describe the location of each vertex aloud: *Point A is 4 units to the left of the x-axis, so point A' is 4 units to the right.*

5 *How many reflections does it take to make the two figures congruent?*

6–7 *Did you try flipping the figure over the dashed lines?*

• **Support Discussion** **MP7** Have partners discuss briefly before group discussion. As needed, have students draw the reflections on a coordinate plane to model the problem.

> *Prompt:* How are the coordinates of Point A related to point A'? What about Point B and point B'? Point C and point C'?
> *Sentence Starter:* The x-coordinate of point A …

Problem Solving

• **Model the Four-Step Method** **MP1** **MP5** Guide students through the four-step method using think-aloud strategies. Point out the reflection clue words *reflection, line,* and *image*.

> *Think Aloud* To make an X from the letter V, I need to reflect it. The line where I hold the mirror will be the line of reflection.

• **Support Problem-Solving Practice** Have students use the Checklist as they complete each step.

PROBLEM SOLVING

READY TO GO

MIRROR, MIRROR

READ

Rosa created this letter V on a coordinate grid. She wants to hold a mirror against the grid so the letter and its reflection look like the letter X. Draw a line to show where she should hold the mirror on the grid to create the letter X. Draw the image.

PLAN

- Find the location of the line of reflection over which V could be flipped so that the letter and its image create the letter ___X___.

- Use the drawing of the ___V___ on the coordinate plane to help solve the problem.

- Use trial and error to determine the horizontal or ___vertical___ line of reflection.

SOLVE

Try drawing a vertical line of reflection along the line $x = 5$.

Reflect the V over that line. Does it look like an X? ___no___

Try drawing a horizontal line of reflection along the line $y = 7$.

Reflect the V over that line. Does it look like an X? ___yes___

CHECK

To check your answer, compare the distances of each vertex with its image.

(1, 12) and (___1___, ___2___) are both ___5___ units from $y = 7$.
(2, 7) and (___2___, ___7___) are both ___0___ units from $y = 7$.
(4, 7) and (___4___, ___7___) are both ___0___ units from $y = 7$.
(5, 12) and (___5___, ___2___) are both ___5___ units from $y = 7$.
(4, 12) and (___4___, ___2___) are both ___5___ units from $y = 7$.
(3, 8) and (___3___, ___6___) are both ___1___ units from $y = 7$.
(2, 12) and (___2___, ___2___) are both ___5___ units from $y = 7$.

Corresponding vertices are the same ___distance___ from the ___line of reflection___ so the image is the reflection of the original figure.

If the mirror is placed along the line ___$y = 7$___, the original figure and its reflection will form an X.

PRACTICE

Use the problem-solving steps to help you.

1 Ian created this letter L on grid paper. He wants to hold his letter up against a mirror so that it looks like the letter U. Draw a line to show how he should hold the mirror against the letter to create a U shape. Draw the image.

CHECKLIST
- [ ] READ
- [ ] PLAN
- [ ] SOLVE
- [ ] CHECK

2 Keitaro draws a diagram to decide where to move furniture in his house. The diagram shows the location of a rug in a living room. He wants to flip the rug over so it is in the new location shown. Draw the line of reflection he could use.

Living Room
current   new

CHECKLIST
- [ ] READ
- [ ] PLAN
- [ ] SOLVE
- [ ] CHECK

3 Stella is using drawing software to make a product logo. The design uses a figure and its reflection as shown. Draw a line of reflection between the figure and its reflection.

Stella's Designs   original
new

CHECKLIST
- [ ] READ
- [ ] PLAN
- [ ] SOLVE
- [ ] CHECK

Prompt: Will the line of reflection be vertical or horizontal?

Prompt: Can you point to where you think the line of reflection should be?

Prompt: How far is the reflection from the line of reflection?

- **Explore Student Thinking** [MP1] [MP7] Invite students to explain why they drew each line of reflection. Have partners compare their work on a problem and describe their results.

COMMON ERRORS

Students may describe the sequence of reflections in the incorrect order. Have students draw the image after every reflection to keep track of each step.

Assess

- Use the table below to observe whether students accurately graph and describe reflections, and to address any difficulties before the quiz.

- When all students are ready, assign the Lesson 11 Quiz.

	Observation	Action
1	Errors in graphing or describing reflections are frequent or irregular; general confusion about reflections.	Have students hold a mirror along the line of reflection to check their work. Provide extra coordinate grids so that they can test out different reflection sequences for a figure.
2	Makes occasional errors in graphing or describing reflections; some understanding of reflections.	Provide additional practice problems for graphing or describing reflections. Encourage students to model reflections on coordinate grids.
3	Writes, models, and solves problems involving graphing or describing reflections accurately.	Assign the Lesson 11 Quiz.

PLUG IN Understanding Rotations

<table>
<tr><th></th><th></th><th>OBJECTIVES</th><th>CONCEPTS AND SKILLS</th><th>VOCABULARY</th></tr>
<tr>
<td rowspan="2">FOUNDATIONAL UNDERSTANDING</td>
<td>▶ PLUG IN
Understanding Rotations
Student Edition pp. 114–115</td>
<td>• Rotate segments around a center of rotation, or a point.
• Rotate angles around a point.</td>
<td>Perform a single rotation of line segments and angles.
CCSS: 8.G.1</td>
<td>• **rotation**
• **center of rotation**</td>
</tr>
<tr>
<td>POWER UP
Rotations and Congruence</td>
<td>• Create a congruent figure by rotation.
• Use a rotation to determine if two figures are congruent.</td>
<td>Understand the congruency of a single rotation of a figure.
CCSS: 8.G.2</td>
<td>• **congruent**</td>
</tr>
<tr>
<td>ON-LEVEL TARGET</td>
<td>READY TO GO
Rotations on a Coordinate Grid</td>
<td>• Rotate a figure around the origin to create a congruent figure.</td>
<td>Describe the effect of reflections on two-dimensional figures using coordinates.
CCSS: 8.G.3</td>
<td>• **quadrant**</td>
</tr>
</table>

MATERIALS
• Protractor *(suggested)*
• Paper *(suggested)*
• Pencils *(suggested)*

Build Background

■ Talk to students about real world examples where line segments and angles are rotated. For example, the minute hand on an analog clock is a line segment that rotates around the clock face.

■ **MP4** Have students discuss additional examples of real situations that involve rotating line segments and angles.

■ Tell students they will rotate line segments and angles.

Introduce and Model

■ **Introduce Concepts and Vocabulary** Guide students through the process of rotating a line segment and an angle. Use **Words to Know** to clarify their understanding of vocabulary. **MP7** Have students identify the *center of rotation* in the examples.

■ **Support Discussion** **MP3** **MP5** Have partners discuss briefly before group discussion. Remind students what a translation is.

> *Prompt: What are the properties of a translation?*
> *Sentence Starter: A rotation and translation are different because …*

ENGLISH LANGUAGE LEARNERS

MP4 ELL students may have difficulty understanding the concept of rotation. Have students draw a point on a piece of paper and then trace a circle around that point, so that the point is in the center. Place a pencil on the circle facing any direction. Encourage students to experiment with rotations, by moving the pencil along the circle, without changing its orientation.

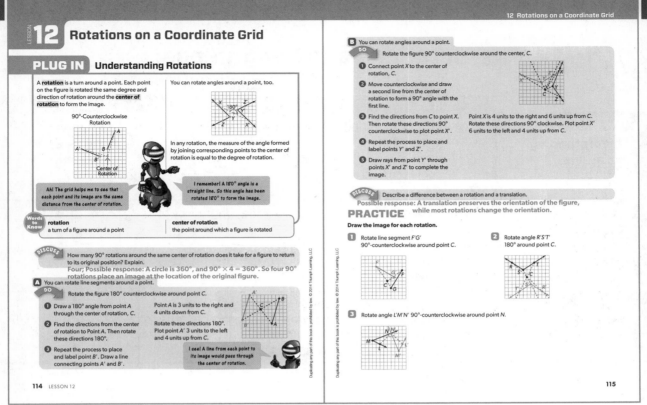

• Model Application

DO ▶ A Guide students through the process of rotating the line segment clockwise around a point. Remind students what *clockwise* means. Be sure that students understand that the center of rotation is not one of the endpoints of the line segment.

DO ▶ B Guide students through the process of rotating an angle. Remind students what *counterclockwise* means. Point out that because an angle is being rotated, three points will need to be plotted. As needed, have students refer to the **Words to Know** to clarify the symbols or terms.

Practice and Assess

- Ask students to complete practice items 1–3 on page 115 independently or in pairs. Monitor ongoing work.

- Make sure that students are not confusing the point of rotation with any points on the figures and are using protractors correctly. Use the chart below as needed to address any difficulties.

Observation	Action
Students have difficulty positioning the protractors.	Review with students how to use a protractor to draw a 90° angle. Give students additional practice with this skill, if necessary.

COMMON ERRORS

MP5 Students may use the protractor incorrectly, by placing an edge of the protractor—rather than the center—on the endpoint or vertex of the figure being rotated. Review how to use a protractor. If necessary, provide students with practice in using a protractor to draw 90° angles.

		OBJECTIVES	CONCEPTS AND SKILLS	VOCABULARY
FOUNDATIONAL UNDERSTANDING	**PLUG IN** **Understanding Rotations**	• Rotate segments around a center of rotation, or a point. • Rotate angles around a point.	Perform a single rotation of line segments and angles. **CCSS:** 8.G.1	• **rotation** • **center of rotation**
	▶ **POWER UP** **Rotations and Congruence** Student Edition pp. 116–117	• Create a congruent figure by rotation. • Use a rotation to determine if two figures are congruent.	Understand the congruency of a single rotation of a figure. **CCSS:** 8.G.2	• **congruent**
ON-LEVEL TARGET	**READY TO GO** **Rotations on a Coordinate Grid**	• Rotate a figure around the origin to create a congruent figure.	Describe the effect of reflections on two-dimensional figures using coordinates. **CCSS:** 8.G.3	• **quadrant**

MATERIALS

- Rulers *(suggested)*
- Grid paper *(suggested)*
- Scissors *(suggested)*
- Paper *(suggested)*
- Pencils *(suggested)*
- Colored markers *(suggested)*

ENGLISH LANGUAGE LEARNERS

MP4 Clockwise and counterclockwise may be difficult concepts for ELL students to understand. Have students draw an analog clock face on a piece of paper. Ask students to trace with their fingers the direction in which the hour, minute, and second hands move. Then have them trace with their fingers the opposite direction. Use arrows of two different colors to label "clockwise" and "counterclockwise" on their clock faces. Encourage students to refer to these if they don't remember the difference.

Build Background

- Talk to students about reasons to rotate figures and why it's important to know that rotated figures are congruent. For example, interior designers often make scale drawings of rooms. To see how everything fits, they may cut out figures that represent the furniture. The designer can rotate these figures to different places in the room. The size and orientation of the figures do not change, but their location does.

- **MP4** Have students discuss additional examples of real situations that involve rotations and congruent figures.

Introduce and Model

- **Introduce Concepts and Vocabulary** Show students how rotated figures are congruent. Use **Words to Know** to clarify their understanding of vocabulary. **MP4** In pairs and using rulers, have students draw and identify congruent triangles with different orientations. Encourage them to describe why the triangles are congruent or not.

- **Support Discussion** **MP3** Have partners discuss briefly before group discussion. Encourage students to draw a triangle on a grid and then rotate it.

> *Prompt: How do you rotate a figure?*
> *Sentence Starter: The properties of a rotation are …*

- **Model Application**

  DO ▶ A Guide students through creating a congruent figure by rotation. Be sure that students are rotating all three vertices of the triangle.

  DO ▶ B Explain that you can use a rotation to determine if two figures are congruent. Monitor students to be sure that they are correctly identifying the corresponding parts of each figure.

POWER UP — Rotations and Congruence

Two figures are **congruent** if they are the same size and shape.

Rotating a figure does not change the size or shape of the original figure.

The distance between two points of the figure is equal to the distance between two corresponding points of the image. So rotated figures are congruent.

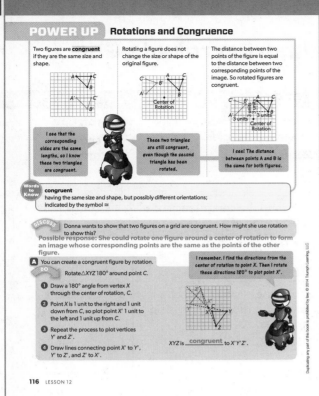

I see that the corresponding sides are the same lengths, so I know these two triangles are congruent.

These two triangles are still congruent, even though the second triangle has been rotated.

I see! The distance between points A and B is the same for both figures.

Words to Know — **congruent** — having the same size and shape, but possibly different orientations; indicated by the symbol ≅

DISCUSS Donna wants to show that two figures on a grid are congruent. How might she use rotation to show this?
Possible response: She could rotate one figure around a center of rotation to form an image whose corresponding points are the same as the points of the other figure.

A You can create a congruent figure by rotation.

I remember. I find the directions from the center of rotation to point X. Then I rotate these directions 180° to plot point X'.

DO Rotate △XYZ 180° around point C.

1. Draw a 180° angle from vertex X through the center of rotation, C.
2. Point X is 1 unit to the right and 1 unit down from C, so plot point X' 1 unit to the left and 1 unit up from C.
3. Repeat the process to plot vertices Y' and Z'.
4. Draw lines connecting point X' to Y', Y' to Z', and Z' to X'.

XYZ is ___congruent___ to X'Y'Z'.

116 LESSON 12

B You can use a rotation to determine if two figures are congruent.

DO Use rotation to show that figure JKLM is congruent to figure QRST.

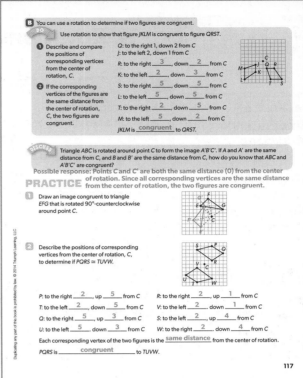

1. Describe and compare the positions of corresponding vertices from the center of rotation, C.

   Q: to the right 1, down 2 from C
   J: to the left 2, down 1 from C
   R: to the right __3__, down __2__ from C
   K: to the left __2__, down __3__ from C

2. If the corresponding vertices of the figures are the same distance from the center of rotation, C, the two figures are congruent.

   S: to the right __5__, down __5__ from C
   L: to the left __5__, down __5__ from C
   T: to the right __2__, down __5__ from C
   M: to the left __5__, down __2__ from C

   JKLM is ___congruent___ to QRST.

DISCUSS Triangle ABC is rotated around point C to form the image A'B'C'. If A and A' are the same distance from C, and B and B' are the same distance from C, how do you know that ABC and A'B'C' are congruent?
Possible response: Points C and C' are both the same distance (0) from the center of rotation. Since all corresponding vertices are the same distance from the center of rotation, the two figures are congruent.

PRACTICE

1. Draw an image congruent to triangle EFG that is rotated 90°-counterclockwise around point C.

2. Describe the positions of corresponding vertices from the center of rotation, C, to determine if PQRS ≅ TUVW.

   P: to the right __2__, up __5__ from C
   T: to the left __2__, down __5__ from C
   Q: to the right __5__, up __3__ from C
   U: to the left __5__, down __3__ from C

   R: to the right __2__, up __1__ from C
   V: to the left __2__, down __1__ from C
   S: to the left __2__, up __4__ from C
   W: to the right __2__, down __4__ from C

   Each corresponding vertex of the two figures is the ___same distance___ from the center of rotation.
   PQRS is ___congruent___ to TUVW.

117

- **Support Discussion** MP4 MP6 Have partners discuss briefly before group discussion. Encourage students to draw a picture of both triangles and identify corresponding parts.

> *Prompt: What are the corresponding vertices of the triangles?*
> *Sentence Starter: Rotated figures are …*

Practice and Assess

- Ask students to complete practice items 1 and 2 on page 117 independently or in pairs. Monitor ongoing work.

- Monitor students to be sure that they are correctly identifying the corresponding vertices. Use the chart below to address any difficulties.

Observation	Action
Students may have difficulty correctly identifying corresponding vertices.	Have students cut out a paper triangle and mark each vertex with a different color. Then ask students to trace the triangle on a piece of grid paper, marking the vertices of the traced triangle with the colors that correspond to those on the cut out triangle. Next, have students rotate the cut out triangle and trace it, marking the vertices of the second triangle with the corresponding colors. Ask students to identify the corresponding vertices of the two triangles.

SPOTLIGHT ON MATHEMATICAL PRACTICES

MP7 Make Use of Structure

Help students notice patterns in naming figures by asking probing questions: *What is the name of the original figure? What is the name of the rotated figure? Why do you think the figures were named in this way? What can the names of these figures help you identify?*

		OBJECTIVES	CONCEPTS AND SKILLS	VOCABULARY
FOUNDATIONAL UNDERSTANDING	**PLUG IN** **Understanding Rotations**	• Rotate segments around a center of rotation, or a point. • Rotate angles around a point.	Perform a single rotation of line segments and angles. **CCSS:** 8.G.1	• **rotation** • **center of rotation**
	POWER UP **Rotations and Congruence**	• Create a congruent figure by rotation. • Use a rotation to determine if two figures are congruent.	Understand the congruency of a single rotation of a figure. **CCSS:** 8.G.2	• **congruent**
ON-LEVEL TARGET	▶ **READY TO GO** **Rotations on a Coordinate Grid** Student Edition pp. 118–123	• Rotate a figure around the origin to create a congruent figure.	Describe the effect of reflections on two-dimensional figures using coordinates. **CCSS:** 8.G.3	• **quadrant**

MATERIALS

• Lesson 12 Quiz, Assessment Manual pp. 26–27
• Lesson 12 Quiz Answer Key, Assessment Manual
• Math Tool: Coordinate Grid, p. A13 (Student Edition p. 233)
• Protractors (suggested)

ENGLISH LANGUAGE LEARNERS

MP2 ELL students may have difficulty with the word *quadrant*. Help them break it down, noting that *quad* means "four." A quadrilateral has four sides and the coordinate plane has four quadrants.

Build Background

■ Talk to students about reasons to rotate figures on a coordinate plane. For example, many quilt designs are based on rotated figures. Quilters may create their designs on a coordinate plane before cutting out the fabric to make their designs.

■ **MP4** Have students discuss additional examples of real situations that involve rotating figures on a coordinate plane.

■ Tell students they will rotate figures on a coordinate plane by identifying the coordinates of the vertices of the rotated figure.

Introduce and Model

■ **Introduce Concepts and Vocabulary** Guide students through the process of rotating a figure around the origin on a coordinate plane. Introduce the rules for special rotations and paraphrase them. Use **Words to Know** to clarify their understanding of vocabulary. **MP4** Give students an ordered pair and its rotation. Referencing a blank coordinate plane, ask students to restate the rule that applies.

■ **Support Discussion** **MP2** **MP3** Have partners discuss briefly before group discussion. If necessary, encourage the students to sketch the triangle on a coordinate plane, choosing points that correspond to the description.

> *Prompt: Which of the three rules applies to this rotation?*
> *Sentence Starter: When I rotate a point 90° counterclockwise, its x and y values are …*

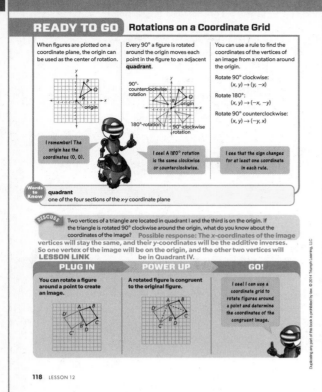

READY TO GO Rotations on a Coordinate Grid

When figures are plotted on a coordinate plane, the origin can be used as the center of rotation.

Every 90° a figure is rotated around the origin moves each point in the figure to an adjacent **quadrant**.

You can use a rule to find the coordinates of the vertices of an image from a rotation around the origin.

Rotate 90° clockwise:
$(x, y) \rightarrow (y, -x)$

Rotate 180°:
$(x, y) \rightarrow (-x, -y)$

Rotate 90° counterclockwise:
$(x, y) \rightarrow (-y, x)$

90°-counterclockwise rotation

180°-rotation   90°-clockwise rotation

I remember! The origin has the coordinates (0, 0).

I see! A 180° rotation is the same clockwise or counterclockwise.

I see that the sign changes for at least one coordinate in each rule.

Words to Know quadrant
one of the four sections of the x-y coordinate plane

DISCUSS Two vertices of a triangle are located in quadrant I and the third is on the origin. If the triangle is rotated 90° clockwise around the origin, what do you know about the coordinates of the image? **Possible response: The x-coordinates of the image vertices will stay the same, and their y-coordinates will be the additive inverses. So one vertex of the image will be on the origin, and the other two vertices will be in Quadrant IV.**

LESSON LINK

PLUG IN	POWER UP	GO!
You can rotate a figure around a point to create an image.	A rotated figure is congruent to the original figure.	I see! I can use a coordinate grid to rotate figures around a point and determine the coordinates of the congruent image.

118 LESSON 12

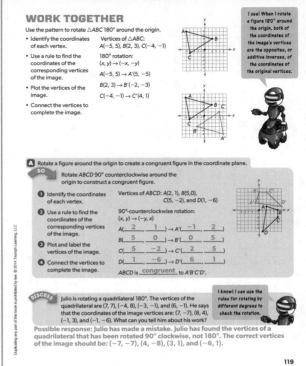

WORK TOGETHER

Use the pattern to rotate △ABC 180° around the origin.

• Identify the coordinates of each vertex.

• Use a rule to find the coordinates of the corresponding vertices of the image.

• Plot the vertices of the image.

• Connect the vertices to complete the image.

Vertices of △ABC:
A(−5, 5), B(2, 3), C(−4, −1)

180° rotation:
$(x, y) \rightarrow (-x, -y)$

A(−5, 5) → A′(5, −5)

B(2, 3) → B′(−2, −3)

C(−4, −1) → C′(4, 1)

I see! When I rotate a figure 180° around the origin, both of the coordinates of the image's vertices are the opposites, or additive inverses, of the coordinates of the original vertices.

A Rotate a figure around the origin to create a congruent figure in the coordinate plane.

DO Rotate ABCD 90° counterclockwise around the origin to construct a congruent figure.

① Identify the coordinates of each vertex.

② Use a rule to find the coordinates of the corresponding vertices of the image.

③ Plot and label the vertices of the image.

④ Connect the vertices to complete the image.

Vertices of ABCD: A(2, 1), B(5,0), C(5, −2), and D(1, −6)

90°-counterclockwise rotation:
$(x, y) \rightarrow (-y, x)$

A(2 , 1) → A′(−1 , 2)

B(5 , 0) → B′(0 , 5)

C(5 , −2) → C′(2 , 5)

D(1 , −6) → D′(6 , 1)

ABCD is __congruent__ to A′B′C′D′.

DISCUSS Julio is rotating a quadrilateral 180°. The vertices of the quadrilateral are (7, 7), (−4, 8), (−3, −1), and (6, −1). He says that the coordinates of the image vertices are: (7, −7), (8, 4), (−1, 3), and (−1, −6). What can you tell him about his work?

I know! I can use the rules for rotating by different degrees to check the rotation.

Possible response: Julio has made a mistake. Julio has found the vertices of a quadrilateral that has been rotated 90° clockwise, not 180°. The correct vertices of the image should be: (−7, −7), (4, −8), (3, 1), and (−6, 1).

119

LESSON LINK

Connect to Foundational Understanding Skills learned in the **Plug In** and **Power Up** are referenced in the **Lesson Link**. Explain that because ABCD was rotated to form A′B′C′D′, the two figures are congruent even though the new coordinates are different.

• **Work Together** Explain that students will rotate a triangle around the origin 180°. Begin by identifying the vertices of the triangle. Then apply the pattern to find the vertices of the rotated triangle. Monitor students to be sure they are following each step in order.

DO **A** Monitor students as they rotate the triangle 90° counterclockwise. Check to be sure that students are not rotating the quadrilateral 180° or rotating the triangle 90° clockwise.

• **Support Discussion** **MP3** **MP4** Have partners discuss briefly before group discussion. As needed, suggest that students sketch the original quadrilateral on a coordinate plane.

> **Prompt:** In what quadrants should Julio's rotated quadrilateral be?
>
> **Sentence Starter:** Julio can solve this problem by …

SPOTLIGHT ON MATHEMATICAL PRACTICES

MP6 Attend to Precision

Help students remember the order of the quadrants in a coordinate plane by asking probing questions. *What are the signs of the coordinates in quadrant I? From quadrant I, in what direction are the quadrants named?*

SPOTLIGHT ON MATHEMATICAL LANGUAGE

MP6 Support students in using mathematical language as they work:

• *(2, −3) is in which **quadrant**?*

• *The rotated figure is **congruent** to the original figure.*

• *The **center of rotation** is the origin.*

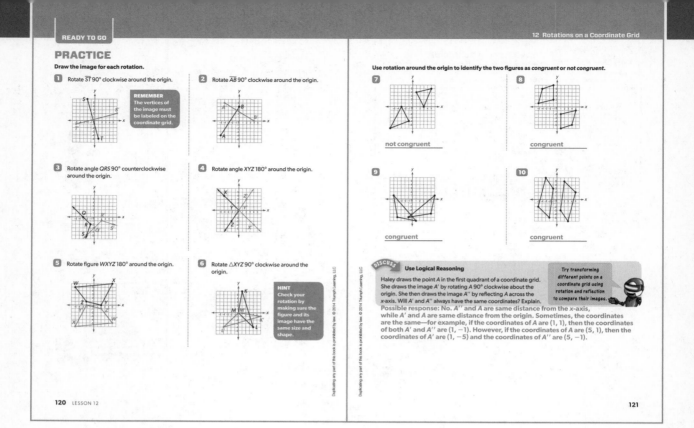

Support Independent Practice

1-6 Remind students to read the **HINT** and **REMEMBER**. If needed, encourage students to plot the points of the rotated figures on the coordinate plane.

7-10 *What does it mean for two figures to be congruent? If the figures have been rotated, are they congruent?*

- **Support Discussion MP3 MP2** Have partners discuss before group discussion. If necessary, suggest that students plot A, its rotation, and its reflection on a coordinate plane.

> *Prompt: How are reflections and rotations different?*
> *Sentence Starter: When Haley rotates and reflects the point …*

Problem Solving

- **Model the Four-Step Method MP1 MP6** Guide students through the four-step method using think-aloud strategies. Ask students to identify the rule that is used for this problem.

  Think Aloud The landscaper is rotating the square 90° counterclockwise around the origin. So, he needs to switch the y- and x-values and change the sign of the new y value.

- **Support Problem-Solving Practice** Have students use the Checklist as they complete each step.

> *Prompt: Which rule applies to this problem?*
> *Prompt: What happens to the coordinates of the figure once it is rotated?*

ADDITIONAL PRACTICE

Provide students with additional practice to model and solve:

A triangle with vertices at (1, 1), (7, 3) and (−2, 5) is rotated 90° counterclockwise. In which quadrants are the vertices of the rotated triangle?

A triangle with vertices at (−4, 3), (3, 3) and (2, −5) is rotated 180°. What are the coordinates of the vertices of the rotated triangle?

FOCUS ON FLUENCY

MP7 Use **Math Tool: Coordinate Grid** to have students practice identifying the quadrants of a coordinate plane and the rules of rotation. Play a game challenging students to quickly identify the quadrants on a blank coordinate grid. Do the same with rotation rules and their coordinates.

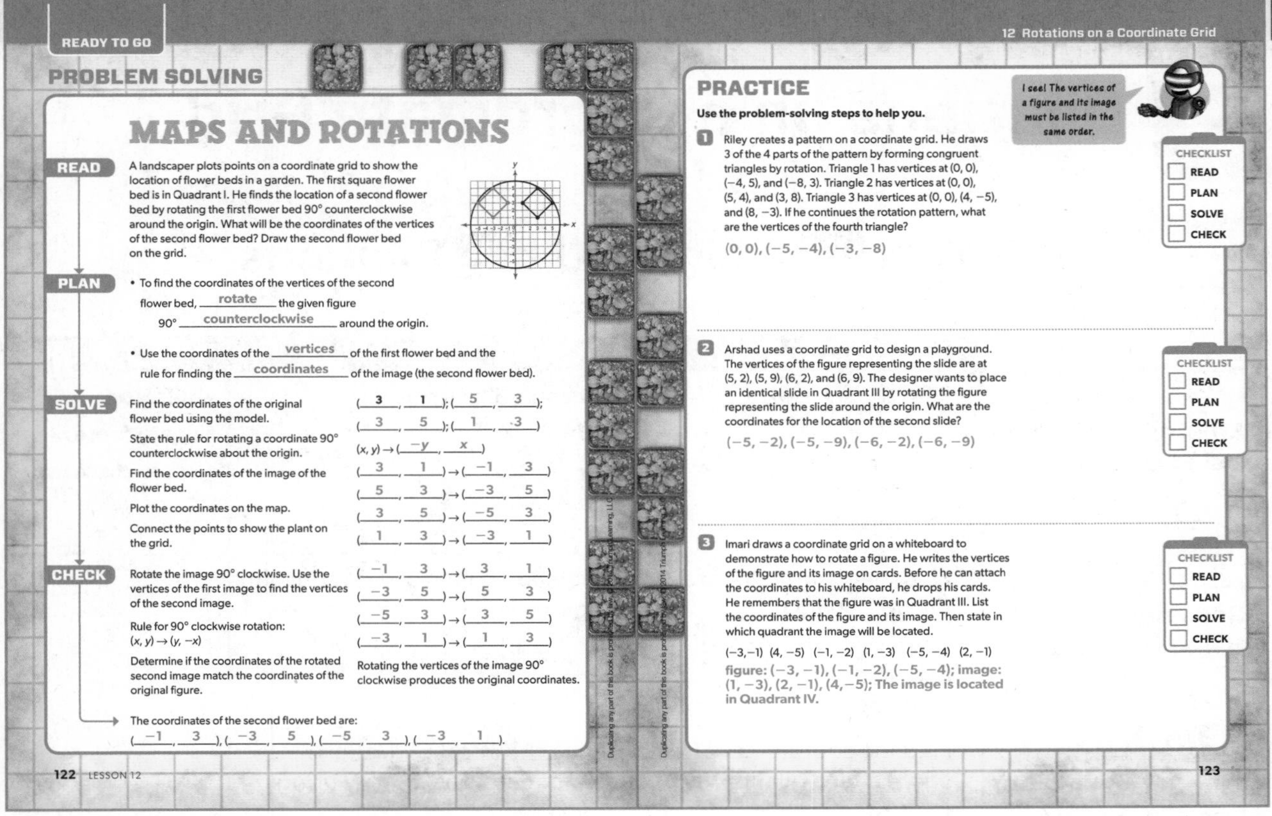

PROBLEM SOLVING

MAPS AND ROTATIONS

READ
A landscaper plots points on a coordinate grid to show the location of flower beds in a garden. The first square flower bed is in Quadrant I. He finds the location of a second flower bed by rotating the first flower bed 90° counterclockwise around the origin. What will be the coordinates of the vertices of the second flower bed? Draw the second flower bed on the grid.

PLAN
• To find the coordinates of the vertices of the second flower bed, __rotate__ the given figure 90° __counterclockwise__ around the origin.

• Use the coordinates of the __vertices__ of the first flower bed and the rule for finding the __coordinates__ of the image (the second flower bed).

SOLVE
Find the coordinates of the original flower bed using the model.

(__3__ , __1__); (__5__ , __3__);
(__3__ , __5__); (__1__ , __-3__)

State the rule for rotating a coordinate 90° counterclockwise about the origin.
$(x, y) \rightarrow ($ __−y__ , __x__ $)$

Find the coordinates of the image of the flower bed.
(__3__ , __1__) → (__−1__ , __3__)
(__5__ , __3__) → (__−3__ , __5__)
(__3__ , __5__) → (__−5__ , __3__)
(__1__ , __3__) → (__−3__ , __1__)

Plot the coordinates on the map.
Connect the points to show the plant on the grid.

CHECK
Rotate the image 90° clockwise. Use the vertices of the first image to find the vertices of the second image.
(__−1__ , __3__) → (__3__ , __1__)
(__−3__ , __5__) → (__5__ , __3__)
(__−5__ , __3__) → (__3__ , __5__)
(__−3__ , __1__) → (__1__ , __3__)

Rule for 90° clockwise rotation:
$(x, y) \rightarrow (y, -x)$

Determine if the coordinates of the rotated second image match the coordinates of the original figure.

Rotating the vertices of the image 90° clockwise produces the original coordinates.

The coordinates of the second flower bed are:
(__−1__ , __3__), (__−3__ , __5__), (__−5__ , __3__), (__−3__ , __1__).

122 | LESSON 12

PRACTICE

Use the problem-solving steps to help you.

I see! The vertices of a figure and its image must be listed in the same order.

1 Riley creates a pattern on a coordinate grid. He draws 3 of the 4 parts of the pattern by forming congruent triangles by rotation. Triangle 1 has vertices at (0, 0), (−4, 5), and (−8, 3). Triangle 2 has vertices at (0, 0), (5, 4), and (3, 8). Triangle 3 has vertices at (0, 0), (4, −5), and (8, −3). If he continues the rotation pattern, what are the vertices of the fourth triangle?

(0, 0), (−5, −4), (−3, −8)

CHECKLIST
☐ READ
☐ PLAN
☐ SOLVE
☐ CHECK

2 Arshad uses a coordinate grid to design a playground. The vertices of the figure representing the slide are at (5, 2), (5, 9), (6, 2), and (6, 9). The designer wants to place an identical slide in Quadrant III by rotating the figure representing the slide around the origin. What are the coordinates for the location of the second slide?

(−5, −2), (−5, −9), (−6, −2), (−6, −9)

CHECKLIST
☐ READ
☐ PLAN
☐ SOLVE
☐ CHECK

3 Imari draws a coordinate grid on a whiteboard to demonstrate how to rotate a figure. He writes the vertices of the figure and its image on cards. Before he can attach the coordinates to his whiteboard, he drops his cards. He remembers that the figure was in Quadrant III. List the coordinates of the figure and its image. Then state in which quadrant the image will be located.

(−3,−1) (4, −5) (−1, −2) (1, −3) (−5, −4) (2, −1)
figure: (−3, −1), (−1, −2), (−5, −4); image: (1, −3), (2, −1), (4, −5); The image is located in Quadrant IV.

CHECKLIST
☐ READ
☐ PLAN
☐ SOLVE
☐ CHECK

123

• **Explore Student Thinking** MP6 Ask students how the rules for rotation help the landscaper rotate the square correctly. Ask them to describe each rule in their own words.

Assess

• Use the table below to observe whether students accurately identify the coordinates of the vertices of the rotated figures.

• When all students are ready, assign the Lesson 12 Quiz.

	Observation	Action
1	Errors in finding the coordinates of the vertices of rotated figures are frequent or irregular; general confusion about rotating figures.	Guide students through the process of deriving the rules. For example, using a protractor, ask students to rotate several different figures 90° counterclockwise on a coordinate plane. Encourage them to notice the patterns in the original coordinates and the rotated coordinates. Do the same for other rotations.
2	Makes occasional errors when rotating figures on a coordinate plane; some understanding of rotating figures.	Provide additional practice problems. For each one, ask students to write down the rule that applies to the rotation described.
3	Rotates figures on a coordinate plane accurately.	Assign the Lesson 12 Quiz

13 Dilations on a Coordinate Grid

PLUG IN — Enlarging a Figure Using Dilations

		OBJECTIVES	CONCEPTS AND SKILLS	VOCABULARY
FOUNDATIONAL UNDERSTANDING	► PLUG IN **Enlarging a Figure Using Dilations** Student Edition pp. 124–125	• Find the scale factor of a dilation (enlargement). • Use a scale drawing to find actual lengths or measurements.	Understand dilation as the enlargement of a figure. **CCSS:** 7.G.1	• **dilation** • **scale factor** • **scale drawing**
	POWER UP **Reducing a Figure Using Dilations**	• Find the scale factor of a dilation (reduction). • Use a scale drawing to find actual lengths or measurements.	Understand dilation as the reduction of a figure. **CCSS:** 7.G.1	
ON-LEVEL TARGET	READY TO GO **Dilations on a Coordinate Grid**	• Find the coordinates of a figure after a dilation. • Find the scale factor of a dilation on a coordinate grid.	Describe the effect of dilations on two-dimensional figures using coordinates. **CCSS:** 8.G.3	

MATERIALS
• Magnifying glass (*suggested*)
• Highlighters, two different colors per student (*suggested*)

ENGLISH LANGUAGE LEARNERS

MP6 ELL students may need extra support to understand the terms used to describe dilations. If students know the word *large*, explain that *enlarge* means making an object larger. Provide students with a magnifying glass and allow them to use it to *enlarge* figures or photos. Explain that the magnifying glass *enlarges* the photo by a certain *scale factor* depending on how it is held. Students may notice that the magnifying glass changes the size, but not the shape, of the original figure. Explain that a *dilation* does the same thing.

Build Background

• Talk to students about reasons to enlarge objects or drawings. For example, you want to make a large print of your favorite photo to hang on the wall. How could you do this? Explain that you can decide how much you need to enlarge the photo using a scale factor.

• MP4 Have students discuss additional examples of real situations in which they might enlarge a figure or object.

Introduce and Model

• **Introduce Concepts and Vocabulary** Guide students through the information about dilations. Emphasize that the lengths of the sides of an original figure and its dilated image are in the same proportion. Use **Words to Know** to clarify their understanding of vocabulary. MP6 Have students explain to a partner the difference between a *scale drawing* and a *scale factor*.

• **Support Discussion** MP3 Have partners discuss briefly before group discussion. Remind students they can use **Words to Know** to help them explain.

Prompt: What does it mean to enlarge a figure by a scale factor of 2? A scale factor of 4?
Sentence Starter: The copy with the greater width was enlarged by ...

LESSON 13 Dilations on a Coordinate Grid

PLUG IN Enlarging a Figure Using Dilations

A **dilation** is a transformation that changes the size of a figure.

After a dilation, the measures of the corresponding sides of the figure and its image are proportional. When the **scale factor** is greater than 1, the dilation is an enlargement.

$$\frac{6 \text{ cm}}{3 \text{ cm}} = 2$$

$$\frac{2 \text{ cm}}{1 \text{ cm}} = 2$$

The scale factor of this dilation is 2, so the image is larger than the figure.

I see! In a dilation, the shape doesn't change, but the size does.

Scale drawings are used in construction, engineering, and architecture to represent much larger or smaller things.

Bathroom Closet
Bedroom Living Room Kitchen

Scale: 0.5 cm = 1 m

I get it! The actual rooms are much larger than they are in this scale drawing.

Words to Know

dilation a transformation that changes the size of a figure

scale factor the ratio of the lengths of corresponding sides of a dilation

scale drawing a drawing of a real object that has been enlarged or reduced by a scale factor

DISCUSS Diane has a 4-inch by 6-inch photo. She prints two larger copies of the photo. One copy has a scale factor of 2. The other copy has a scale factor of 4. Which copy has a greater width? Explain.

the second copy that used a scale factor of 4 because a greater scale factor results in larger dimensions for each side

124 LESSON 13

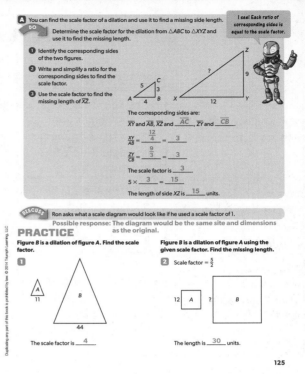

A You can find the scale factor of a dilation and use it to find a missing side length.

DO Determine the scale factor for the dilation from △ABC to △XYZ and use it to find the missing length.

❶ Identify the corresponding sides of the two figures.

❷ Write and simplify a ratio for the corresponding sides to find the scale factor.

❸ Use the scale factor to find the missing length of $\overline{XZ}$.

I see! Each ratio of corresponding sides is equal to the scale factor.

The corresponding sides are:

$\overline{XY}$ and $\overline{AB}$, $\overline{XZ}$ and $\overline{AC}$, $\overline{ZY}$ and $\overline{CB}$

$\frac{XY}{AB} = \frac{12}{4} = \underline{}3$

$\frac{ZY}{CB} = \frac{9}{3} = \underline{}3$

The scale factor is $\underline{}3$.

$5 \times \underline{}3 = \underline{}15$

The length of side XZ is $\underline{}15$ units.

DISCUSS Ron asks what a scale diagram would look like if he used a scale factor of 1.
Possible response: The diagram would be the same site and dimensions as the original.

PRACTICE

Figure B is a dilation of figure A. Find the scale factor.

1

A 11
B 44

The scale factor is $\underline{}4$.

Figure B is a dilation of figure A using the given scale factor. Find the missing length.

2 Scale factor = $\frac{5}{2}$

12 A ? B

The length is $\underline{}30$ units.

125

• Model Application

DO **A** Explain how to find the scale factor for a dilation. Show students that they can use the names of the triangles to find corresponding side lengths. For example, $\overline{AB}$ in △ABC corresponds to $\overline{XY}$ in △XYZ because in the names of these two triangles, those are the first two letters.

• Support Discussion MP6 Have partners discuss briefly. Remind students that a scale factor greater than 1 enlarges a figure.

> *Prompt: What happens when you multiply a number by 1?*
> *Sentence Starter: If a scale factor of 1 were used, the scale diagram would …*

Practice and Assess

• Ask students to complete practice items 1 and 2 on page 125 independently or in pairs. Monitor ongoing work.

Observation	Action
Students fail to find missing side lengths because they do not set up the correct proportions.	For problem 1, have students rewrite the scale factor as $\frac{4}{1}$, highlighting 4 in yellow and 1 in green. Emphasize that the 4 describes the scale factor used to create figure B, so have students highlight the side labeled "44" in yellow. Have students highlight the 11-unit side in figure A in green. Explain that if the proportions are correct, the highlighted colors in each ratio will match.

SPOTLIGHT ON MATHEMATICAL LANGUAGE

MP6 Support students in using mathematical language as they work:

■ *How do you know this figure is a **dilation** of the original figure?*

■ *How can you find the **scale factor**?*

■ *Use the **scale drawing** to find the actual lengths of the room.*

Reducing a Figure Using Dilations

		OBJECTIVES	CONCEPTS AND SKILLS	VOCABULARY
FOUNDATIONAL UNDERSTANDING	**PLUG IN** **Enlarging a Figure Using Dilations**	• Find the scale factor of a dilation (enlargement). • Use a scale drawing to find actual lengths or measurements.	Understand dilation as the enlargement of a figure. **CCSS:** 7.G.1	• **dilation** • **scale factor** • **scale drawing**
	▶ POWER UP **Reducing a Figure Using Dilations** Student Edition pp. 126–127	• Find the scale factor of a dilation (reduction). • Use a scale drawing to find actual lengths or measurements.	Understand dilation as the reduction of a figure. **CCSS:** 7.G.1	
ON-LEVEL TARGET	**READY TO GO** **Dilations on a Coordinate Grid**	• Find the coordinates of a figure after a dilation. • Find the scale factor of a dilation on a coordinate grid.	Describe the effect of dilations on two-dimensional figures using coordinates. **CCSS:** 8.G.3	

MATERIALS
- Math Tool: Grid Paper, pp. A5, A6 (Student Edition pp. 217, 219)
- Inch ruler (*suggested*)

ENGLISH LANGUAGE LEARNERS

MP6 Whenever possible, encourage students to make connections between new words they learn in math class and words in their home languages. For example, students may notice that verb *to reduce* in English looks like *reducir* in Spanish or *reduzieren* in German or *réduire* in French. Making such connections can help students comprehend new terms more easily.

Build Background

- Talk to students about reasons to use dilations to reduce figures. For example, mapmakers must take actual measurements of places or things and reduce them using a scale factor in order to draw a map.

- MP4 Have students discuss additional examples of real situations in which they might reduce the size of a figure or object, without changing its shape.

Introduce and Model

- **Introduce Concepts** Guide students through the information about using dilations to reduce the size of figures. If students previously had the misconception that dilations always enlarge figures, emphasize that a reduction of a figure is also an example of a dilation.

- **Support Discussion** MP1 MP5 Have partners discuss briefly before group discussion. As needed, have students make up a length for Mark's drawing, such as 10 centimeters, to help them determine the answer.

> *Prompt: If you multiply a length by $\frac{1}{2}$ and then multiply it again by 2, what is the result? Why?*
>
> *Sentence Starter: The figure is now …*

- **Model Application**

  DO **A** Guide students through how to find the scale factor of a dilation that is a reduction. Emphasize that a scale factor can be represented as a decimal, 0.25, instead of a fraction, $\frac{1}{4}$.

  DO **B** Provide **Math Tool: Grid Paper** and a ruler to each student. Monitor that students correctly find the scale length, in inches, of each wall. Model how to create the scale drawing, if needed.

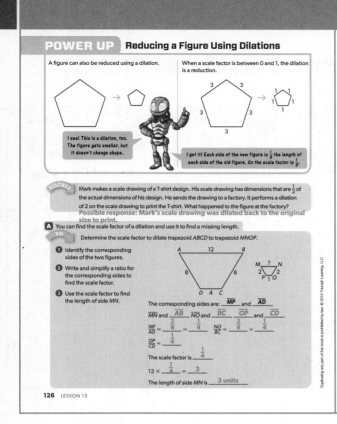

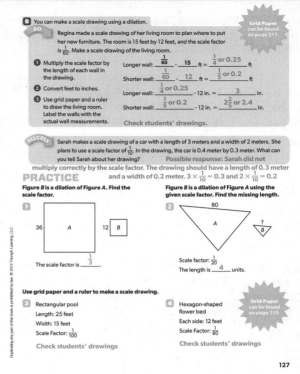

POWER UP Reducing a Figure Using Dilations

A figure can also be reduced using a dilation.

When a scale factor is between 0 and 1, the dilation is a reduction.

I see! This is a dilation, too. The figure gets smaller, but it doesn't change shape.

I get it! Each side of the new figure is $\frac{1}{3}$ the length of each side of the old figure. So the scale factor is $\frac{1}{3}$.

DISCUSS Mark makes a scale drawing of a T-shirt design. His scale drawing has dimensions that are $\frac{1}{2}$ of the actual dimensions of his design. He sends the drawing to a factory. It performs a dilation of 2 on the scale drawing to print the T-shirt. What happened to the figure at the factory? **Possible response: Mark's scale drawing was dilated back to the original size to print.**

A You can find the scale factor of a dilation and use it to find a missing length.

DO Determine the scale factor to dilate trapezoid *ABCD* to trapezoid *MNOP*.

❶ Identify the corresponding sides of the two figures.

❷ Write and simplify a ratio for the corresponding sides to find the scale factor.

❸ Use the scale factor to find the length of side *MN*.

The corresponding sides are: $\overline{MP}$ and $\overline{AD}$, $\overline{MN}$ and $\overline{AB}$, $\overline{NO}$ and $\overline{BC}$, $\overline{OP}$ and $\overline{CD}$.

$\frac{MP}{AD} = \frac{2}{8} = \frac{1}{4}$ $\frac{NO}{BC} = \frac{2}{8} = \frac{1}{4}$

$\frac{OP}{CD} = \frac{1}{4}$

The scale factor is $\frac{1}{4}$.

$12 \times \frac{1}{4} = 3$

The length of side *MN* is **3 units**.

B You can make a scale drawing using a dilation.

DO Regina made a scale drawing of her living room to plan where to put her new furniture. The room is 15 feet by 12 feet, and the scale factor is $\frac{1}{60}$. Make a scale drawing of the living room.

Grid Paper can be found on page 217.

❶ Multiply the scale factor by the length of each wall in the drawing.

Longer wall: $\frac{1}{60} \cdot 15$ ft = $\frac{1}{4}$ or 0.25 ft

Shorter wall: $\frac{1}{60} \cdot 12$ ft = $\frac{1}{5}$ or 0.2 ft

❷ Convert feet to inches.

Longer wall: $\frac{1}{4}$ or 0.25 · 12 in. = 3 in.

Shorter wall: $\frac{1}{5}$ or 0.2 · 12 in. = $2\frac{2}{5}$ or 2.4 in.

❸ Use grid paper and a ruler to draw the living room. Label the walls with the actual wall measurements. **Check students' drawings.**

DISCUSS Sarah makes a scale drawing of a car with a length of 3 meters and a width of 2 meters. She plans to use a scale factor of $\frac{1}{10}$. In the drawing, the car is 0.4 meter by 0.3 meter. What can you tell Sarah about her drawing? **Possible response: Sarah did not multiply correctly by the scale factor. The drawing should have a length of 0.3 meter and a width of 0.2 meter.** $3 \times \frac{1}{10} = 0.3$ and $2 \times \frac{1}{10} = 0.2$

PRACTICE

Figure *B* is a dilation of Figure *A*. Find the scale factor.

❶ 36   *A*   12   *B*

The scale factor is $\frac{1}{3}$.

Figure *B* is a dilation of Figure *A* using the given scale factor. Find the missing length.

❷ 80   *A*   ?   *B*

Scale factor: $\frac{1}{20}$
The length is 4 units.

Use grid paper and a ruler to make a scale drawing.

❸ Rectangular pool
Length: 25 feet
Width: 15 feet
Scale Factor: $\frac{1}{100}$

Check students' drawings

❹ Hexagon-shaped flower bed
Each side: 12 feet
Scale Factor: $\frac{1}{80}$

Grid Paper can be found on page 219.

Check students' drawings

126 LESSON 13

127

- **Support Discussion** MP3 Have partners discuss briefly before group discussion. As needed, remind students the scale factor is multiplied by the actual length to find the scale length.

> *Prompt:* Could you use a proportion to show that Sarah made an error?
>
> *Sentence Starter:* I know that Sarah made a mistake because …

Practice and Assess

- Ask students to complete practice items 1–4 on page 127 independently or in pairs. Monitor ongoing work.

- Observe whether students accurately identify scale factors, find missing lengths and create scale drawings. Use the chart below as needed.

Observation	Action
Students accurately find missing lengths, but struggle when asked to use a ruler to make a scale drawing.	Students may struggle when starting problems 3 and 4. Provide scaffolding. For example, write: Scale length: $25 \times \frac{1}{100} = $ _____ ft Scale width: $15 \times $ _____ = _____ ft If students are confused by how to draw a side that is 0.25 ft or 0.15 ft, ask: *how many inches are in 1 foot?* Help students reason that since there are 12 inches in 1 foot, students can multiply the decimal values by 12 to find the length and width in inches.

SPOTLIGHT ON MATHEMATICAL PRACTICES

MP3 Critiquing Others' Work

- Help students think about Sarah's work critically by asking probing questions: *Is one of the lengths correct?* (Yes, 0.3 meters is the scale width, but Sarah found it to be the scale length.) *How could you use a proportion to show that she made a mistake?*

Dilations on a Coordinate Grid

		OBJECTIVES	CONCEPTS AND SKILLS	VOCABULARY
FOUNDATIONAL UNDERSTANDING	**PLUG IN** Enlarging a Figure Using Dilations	• Find the scale factor of a dilation (enlargement). • Use a scale drawing to find actual lengths or measurements.	Understand dilation as the enlargement of a figure. **CCSS:** 7.G.1	• **dilation** • **scale factor** • **scale drawing**
	POWER UP Reducing a Figure Using Dilations	• Find the scale factor of a dilation (reduction). • Use a scale drawing to find actual lengths or measurements.	Understand dilation as the reduction of a figure. **CCSS:** 7.G.1	
ON-LEVEL TARGET	**► READY TO GO** Dilations on a Coordinate Grid Student Edition pp. 128–133	• Find the coordinates of a figure after a dilation. • Find the scale factor of a dilation on a coordinate grid.	Describe the effect of dilations on two-dimensional figures using coordinates. **CCSS:** 8.G.3	

MATERIALS

- Lesson 13 Quiz, Assessment Manual pp. 28–29
- Lesson 13 Quiz Answer Key, Assessment Manual
- Math Tool: Coordinate Grid, p. A15 (Student Edition p. 237)
- Index cards (*suggested*)
- Pencils (*suggested*)

ENGLISH LANGUAGE LEARNERS

MP4 ELL students may understand content better when mathematical language is used in conjunction with an English explanation. For example, as you explain how the coordinates of the vertices of △*ABC* were multiplied by 3 to get the vertices of △*XYZ*, show it on the board, like this:

$A(2, 1) \rightarrow (2 \times 3, 1 \times 3) \rightarrow X(6, 3)$

Do this for the other vertices as well, so ELL students see as well as hear how the coordinates are obtained.

Build Background

- Talk to students about reasons to use coordinates to show dilations. For example, suppose you want to create a logo for the school store. You draw your logo on a coordinate plane. If you want to make your logo larger, how could you do that? Explain that you could use a dilation to enlarge your logo and draw the image on the same coordinate plane.

- **MP4** Have students discuss additional examples of real situations in which coordinates could be used to draw figures and their dilations.

- Tell students they will dilate figures on the coordinate plane by multiplying coordinates by a scale factor.

Introduce and Model

- **Introduce Concepts** Guide students through the information about how the coordinates of the vertices of a figure may be multiplied by a scale factor to dilate it. Explain that the dilation may be an enlargement or a reduction.

- **Support Discussion MP3** Have partners discuss briefly before group discussion. As needed, suggest students look back at triangles *ABC* and *XYZ* to help them.

> **Prompt:** *Can you show, on a grid, how the value of the scale factor affects the size of a figure, if at all? The shape, if at all?*
>
> **Sentence Starter:** *If the scale factor is greater than …*

READY TO GO — Dilations on a Coordinate Grid

You can show a dilation of a figure on a coordinate plane.

The vertices of the dilated figure are found by multiplying the coordinates of the vertices of the original figure by a scale factor.

I see! The red triangle is smaller than the blue one, but they are the same shape.

I get it! When the coordinates of a vertex in the red triangle are multiplied by the scale factor 3, I get the coordinates of the corresponding vertex in the blue triangle.

DISCUSS When a figure is dilated on the coordinate plane, how does the value of the scale factor change its shape and size?
Possible response: Regardless of the scale factor, the shape stays the same. If the scale factor is between 0 and 1, the dilated figure is smaller. If the scale factor is greater than 1, the dilated figure is larger.

LESSON LINK

PLUG IN	POWER UP	GO!
You can enlarge a figure by multiplying its side lengths by a scale factor greater than 1.	You can reduce a figure by multiplying its side lengths by a scale factor between 0 and 1.	I get it! I can dilate figures on the coordinate plane by multiplying each of the coordinates by the scale factor.
$2 \triangle \rightarrow 3 \triangle$	$8 \square \rightarrow 6 \square$	
Scale factor = 1.5	Scale factor = $\frac{3}{4}$	
$2 \times 1.5 = 3$	$8 \times \frac{3}{4} = 6$	

WORK TOGETHER

You can use coordinate grids to determine if the blue triangle is an enlargement of the red triangle.

It's also true that the red triangle is a dilation of the blue triangle with a scale factor of $\frac{1}{2}$!

- List the coordinates of each figure.
- Find a constant scale factor between corresponding vertices.
- If the scale factor is consistent, the blue triangle is a dilation of the red triangle.
- The scale factor is 2.
- The blue triangle is an enlargement of the red triangle.

Red triangle: $(-2, -2)$, $(1, -1)$, $(0, 2)$
Blue triangle: $(-4, -4)$, $(2, -2)$, $(0, 4)$

Compare the coordinates of the vertices of the blue triangle with the coordinates of the vertices of the red triangle. Each coordinate of the blue triangle is two times the coordinate of the red triangle.

A You can calculate the coordinates of a reduced figure.

DO Dilate triangle *LMN* by a scale factor of $\frac{1}{2}$ to create triangle *OPQ*. Use the origin as the center of dilation.

I see! I name the vertices in the order given in the problem to match the vertices of the original figure.

1. List the coordinates of the vertices of the original figure.
2. Multiply each coordinate of the original figure by the scale factor to find the coordinates of the dilated figure.
3. Plot and connect the vertices of the dilated figure.

$L = \underline{(1, -2)}$, $M = \underline{(5, 8)}$, $N = \underline{(-1, 6)}$

$O = \underline{\left(\frac{1}{2}, -1\right)}$, $P = \underline{\left(2\frac{1}{2}, 4\right)}$, $Q = \underline{\left(-\frac{1}{2}, 3\right)}$

DISCUSS Gerald asks if figures on a coordinate grid with different numbers of sides can ever be dilations of each other. How would you respond?
Possible response: No. For figures to be dilations, they need to be the same shape. Figures with different numbers of sides cannot have the same shape.

LESSON LINK

Connect to Foundational Understanding Skills learned in the **Plug In** and **Power Up** are referenced in the **Lesson Link**. Explain that just as you can multiply side lengths by a scale factor to enlarge or reduce a figure, you can multiply the coordinates of a figure's vertices to dilate it on the coordinate plane.

- **Work Together** Explain that students will use coordinate grids to determine if a triangle is the result of a dilation. Begin by showing students how to identify the coordinates of the vertices of both triangles. Then show how the coordinates of the blue triangle's vertices are each 2 times those of the red triangle's vertices.

DO **A** Monitor students as they calculate the coordinates of the reduced figure. Be sure that students connect and label the vertices after plotting them.

- **Support Discussion** **MP3** Have partners discuss briefly before group discussion. As needed, provide **Math Tool: Coordinate Grid** and encourage students to sketch figures to help them answer Gerald's question.

> *Prompt:* What do you know about the size and shape of a figure and its dilation?
> *Sentence Starter:* I would tell Gerald that …

COMMON ERRORS

Some students may make careless errors if they confuse the order in which coordinates should be written, writing the *y*-coordinate first and the *x*-coordinate second, for example. To help students remember that ordered pairs are written in the form (x, y), tell students to remember this: "*x* comes before *y* when coordinates are written, just as *x* comes before *y* in the alphabet."

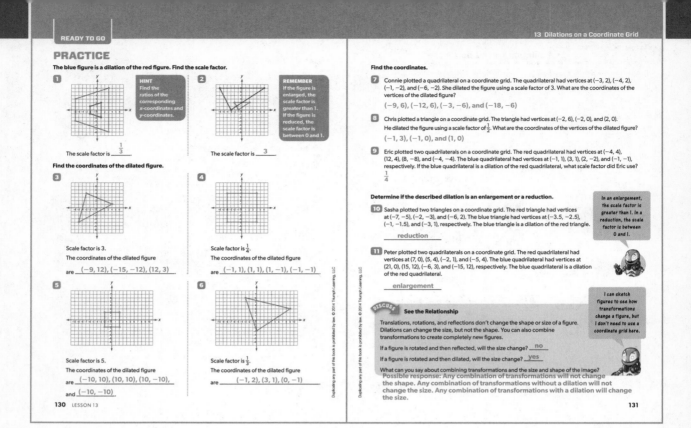

PRACTICE

The blue figure is a dilation of the red figure. Find the scale factor.

1 HINT Find the ratios of the corresponding x-coordinates and y-coordinates.

The scale factor is $\frac{1}{3}$

2 REMEMBER If the figure is enlarged, the scale factor is greater than 1. If the figure is reduced, the scale factor is between 0 and 1.

The scale factor is 3

Find the coordinates of the dilated figure.

3 Scale factor is 3.
The coordinates of the dilated figure are $(-9, 12), (-15, -12), (12, 3)$

4 Scale factor is $\frac{1}{4}$.
The coordinates of the dilated figure are $(-1, 1), (1, 1), (1, -1), (-1, -1)$

5 Scale factor is 5.
The coordinates of the dilated figure are $(-10, 10), (10, 10), (10, -10),$ and $(-10, -10)$

6 Scale factor is $\frac{1}{3}$.
The coordinates of the dilated figure are $(-1, 2), (3, 1), (0, -1)$

Find the coordinates.

7 Connie plotted a quadrilateral on a coordinate grid. The quadrilateral had vertices at $(-3, 2), (-4, 2), (-1, -2),$ and $(-6, -2)$. She dilated the figure using a scale factor of 3. What are the coordinates of the dilated figure?
$(-9, 6), (-12, 6), (-3, -6),$ and $(-18, -6)$

8 Chris plotted a triangle on a coordinate grid. The triangle had vertices at $(-2, 6), (-2, 0),$ and $(2, 0)$. He dilated the figure using a scale factor of $\frac{1}{2}$. What are the coordinates of the vertices of the dilated figure?
$(-1, 3), (-1, 0),$ and $(1, 0)$

9 Eric plotted two quadrilaterals on a coordinate grid. The red quadrilateral had vertices at $(-4, 4),$ $(12, 4), (8, -8),$ and $(-4, -4)$. The blue quadrilateral had vertices at $(-1, 1), (3, 1), (2, -2),$ and $(-1, -1)$, respectively. If the blue quadrilateral is a dilation of the red quadrilateral, what scale factor did Eric use?
$\frac{1}{4}$

Determine if the described dilation is an enlargement or a reduction.

10 Sasha plotted two triangles on a coordinate grid. The red triangle had vertices at $(-7, -5), (-2, -3),$ and $(-6, 2)$. The blue triangle had vertices at $(-3.5, -2.5),$ $(-1, -1.5),$ and $(-3, 1)$, respectively. The blue triangle is a dilation of the red triangle.
reduction

In an enlargement, the scale factor is greater than 1. In a reduction, the scale factor is between 0 and 1.

11 Peter plotted two quadrilaterals on a coordinate grid. The red quadrilateral had vertices at $(7, 0), (5, 4), (-2, 1),$ and $(-5, 4)$. The blue quadrilateral had vertices at $(21, 0), (15, 12), (-6, 3),$ and $(-15, 12)$, respectively. The blue quadrilateral is a dilation of the red quadrilateral.
enlargement

I can sketch figures to see how transformations change a figure, but I don't need to use a coordinate grid here.

DISCUSS See the Relationship

Translations, rotations, and reflections don't change the shape or size of a figure. Dilations can change the size, but not the shape. You can also combine transformations to create completely new figures.

If a figure is rotated and then reflected, will the size change? no
If a figure is rotated and then dilated, will the size change? yes
What can you say about combining transformations and the size and shape of the image?
Possible response: Any combination of transformations will not change the shape. Any combination of transformations without a dilation will not change the size. Any combination of transformations with a dilation will change the size.

ADDITIONAL PRACTICE

Provide students with additional practice. Find the coordinates of a dilated image, using △ABC with vertices $A(-6, -12)$, $B(0, 18)$, and $(6, -6)$:

| scale factor of 2 | scale factor of 3 |
| scale factor of $\frac{1}{3}$ | scale factor of $\frac{1}{2}$ |

Support Independent Practice

1–2 Remind students to read the **HINT** and **REMEMBER**. If needed, ask: *How do you compare coordinates to find the scale factor? How can you use the size of the blue figure to determine if the scale factor should be less than or greater than 1?*

3–6 *By what factor do you multiply each coordinate to solve this problem?*

7–9 *What are you asked to find?*

10–11 *Do you need to find the scale factor to determine the answer?*

- **Support Discussion** MP3 MP6 Have partners discuss briefly before group discussion. Provide students with **Math Tool: Coordinate Grid** to help them.

> *Prompt: If you combine any transformation with a dilation, will the size change?*
> *Sentence Starter: If I combine two transformations, then …*

Problem Solving

- **Model the Four-Step Method** MP1 MP6 Guide students through the four-step method using think-aloud strategies. Point out the dilation clue word *enlarge*.

   Think Aloud *The side lengths of a photo are 8 inches and 5 inches. A frame has side lengths of 48 inches and 30 inches The photo needs to be enlarged so it is the same size as the frame.*

- **Support Problem-Solving Practice** Have students use the Checklist as they complete each step.

READY TO GO

PROBLEM SOLVING

PICTURE PERFECT

READ
Beth prints out a photo of her dog, Belle. The photo is 8 inches by 5 inches. She would like to enlarge it so that it fits in a frame that is 48 inches by 30 inches. How can she enlarge the photo so that it fits the frame exactly?

PLAN
• What is the problem asking you to find?

the _____scale factor_____ for a dilation

• How can you find the scale factor of the picture frame?
Write a ratio of the corresponding sides of the photo and frame.

• Do you expect a scale factor greater than 1 or lesser than 1?

SOLVE
Because the frame is larger than the picture, the scale factor will be greater than 1.

Write and simplify the ratios of the corresponding sides of the photo and frame.

Length: $\frac{\text{frame}}{\text{photo}} = \frac{48}{8} = 6$

Width: $\frac{\text{frame}}{\text{photo}} = \frac{30}{5} = 6$

> I can work backwards to check my work. Instead of multiplying to find the dimensions of the enlargement, I can divide to find the dimensions of the original photo.

CHECK
Are the ratios equal? ___yes___

What is the scale factor? ___6___

Is the scale factor greater than or less than 1? ___greater than___

Does this scale factor represent an enlargement or a reduction? ___enlargement___

Divide the dimensions of the frame by the scale factor. What dimensions result?
the dimensions of the photo, 8 inches by 5 inches

The photo can fit the frame by ___dilation___ by a scale factor of ___6___.

PRACTICE

> The units of measurement do not matter as long as they are the same for all measurements.

Use the problem-solving steps to help you.

1 Images on computer screens can be measured in units called pixels. A computer programmer reduces an image from 500 by 400 pixels to 450 pixels by 360 pixels. What scale factor did she use?

The scale factor is 0.9.

CHECKLIST
☐ READ
☐ PLAN
☐ SOLVE
☐ CHECK

2 Tess designs a small skateboard by reducing the size of a standard skateboard. A standard skateboard and her new skateboard are sketched on the coordinate plane. The factory that will produce the new skateboards needs the scale factor to be between $\frac{1}{2}$ and $\frac{3}{4}$. Will her design work? Explain.

Yes. The scale factor is $\frac{2}{3}$, which is between $\frac{1}{2}$ and $\frac{3}{4}$.

CHECKLIST
☐ READ
☐ PLAN
☐ SOLVE
☐ CHECK

3 A scale drawing shows the length and width of a car as 4 inches by 2 inches. If a scale factor of 30 was used to create the scale drawing, what is the actual length and width, in feet, of the car?

The length is 10 feet and the width is 5 feet.

CHECKLIST
☐ READ
☐ PLAN
☐ SOLVE
☐ CHECK

> **Prompt:** What do you need to find to solve this problem? a scale factor? actual measurements?
> **Prompt:** What ratio or proportion will help you?

• **Explore Student Thinking** MP3 Invite students to explain how they found the scale factors. Have partners compare their work on a problem and describe their results.

Assess

• Use the table below to observe whether students accurately solve problems involving dilations, and to address any difficulties.

• When all students are ready, assign the Lesson 13 Quiz.

	Observation	Action
1	Frequent errors in determining scale factors and identifying coordinates after dilations; general confusion about how to dilate figures on the coordinate plane.	Have students write these hints on an index card: Ratio: $\dfrac{\text{dilated image}}{\text{original figure}} = \dfrac{\Box}{\Box}$ Original figure → Dilated image $(x, y) \rightarrow (x \times \text{scale factor}, y \times \text{scale factor})$
2	Makes occasional errors when determining scale factors or coordinates after dilations; some understanding of how to dilate figures on the coordinate plane.	Provide additional practice problems for finding the coordinates of dilated images. Have students draw the original figure and its dilation on a coordinate grid and use the scale factor to check that each answer is reasonable.
3	Accurately finds scale factors and determines the coordinates of the vertices of figures after dilations.	Assign the Lesson 13 Quiz.

PLUG IN Congruent Figures

		OBJECTIVES	CONCEPTS AND SKILLS	VOCABULARY
FOUNDATIONAL UNDERSTANDING	**▶ PLUG IN** Congruent Figures Student Edition pp. 134–135	• Determine if two figures are congruent. • Use a series of rigid motions to show two figures are congruent.	Understand the congruency of figures as a series of transformations. **CCSS:** 8.G.2	
	POWER UP Similar Figures	• Use congruency to decide if two figures are similar. • Use proportions to decide if two figures are similar.	Understand similar figures. **CCSS:** 8.G.4	• **similar**
ON-LEVEL TARGET	**READY TO GO** Similarity	• Describe a series of transformations that show if two figures are similar.	Describe the effect of dilations on two-dimensional figures using coordinates. **CCSS:** 8.G.4	

MATERIALS
- Math Tool: Grids, p. A17 (Student Edition p. 241)
- Rulers (suggested)
- Tracing paper (suggested)
- Scissors (suggested)

ENGLISH LANGUAGE LEARNERS

MP6 Review the meaning of *congruent figures*. Ask students to draw two congruent right triangles. Have students cut out one triangle and use it to demonstrate a flip, a slide, and a turn of the triangle on grid paper. Have them identify each rigid motion and explain how they know the figures are congruent.

Build Background

- Talk to students about reasons for determining congruent figures in real life. For example, when manufacturing the wheels of a car, it is important that all four wheels are exactly the same size, or congruent.
- MP4 Have students discuss additional examples of real situations that involve congruent figures.
- Tell students they will use rotations, reflections, and translations to show whether two figures are congruent.

Introduce and Model

- **Introduce Concepts and Vocabulary** Guide students through the information about congruent figures. As needed, review the terms *congruent, rigid motion, rotation, reflection, translation,* and *dilation* as a class. MP4 Have students use tracing paper to trace △ABC and show a partner how it was manipulated to create the rotation and a reflection.
- **Support Discussion** MP4 MP7 Have partners discuss briefly before group discussion. As needed, have students use grid paper to draw a triangle and its translation. Remind them to check corresponding angles and sides.

> *Prompt: What do you notice about the corresponding angles and sides of the triangles?*
> *Sentence Starter: To check for congruency, I can …*

LESSON 14 Similarity

PLUG IN Congruent Figures

In congruent figures, corresponding angles and corresponding sides have the same measures.

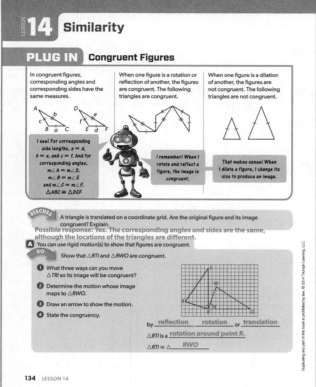

I see! For corresponding side lengths, a = d, b = e, and c = f. And for corresponding angles, m∠A = m∠D, m∠B = m∠E and m∠C = m∠F. △ABC ≅ △DEF

When one figure is a rotation or reflection of another, the figures are congruent. The following triangles are congruent.

I remember! When I rotate and reflect a figure, the image is congruent.

When one figure is a dilation of another, the figures are not congruent. The following triangles are not congruent.

That makes sense! When I dilate a figure, I change its size to produce an image.

DISCUSS A triangle is translated on a coordinate grid. Are the original figure and its image congruent? Explain.
Possible response: Yes. The corresponding angles and sides are the same, although the locations of the triangles are different.

A You can use rigid motion(s) to show that figures are congruent.

DO Show that △RTI and △RWO are congruent.

① What three ways can you move △TRI so its image will be congruent?

② Determine the motion whose image maps to △RWO.

③ Draw an arrow to show the motion.

④ State the congruency.

by ~~reflection~~ ~~rotation~~ or ~~translation~~

△RTI is a rotation around point R.

△RTI ≅ △ RWO

134 LESSON 14

B You can use a series of rigid motions to show that figures are congruent.

DO Show that trapezoid ABCD is congruent to trapezoid LMNO.

I see! In a congruence statement, I have to list the vertices of the figures in order of their correspondence.

① Use a reflection.

② Use a vertical translation.

③ Use a horizontal translation.

④ State the congruency.

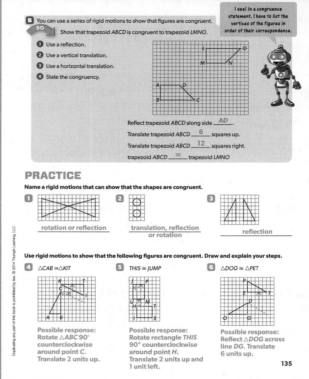

Reflect trapezoid ABCD along side ___AD___

Translate trapezoid ABCD ___6___ squares up.

Translate trapezoid ABCD ___12___ squares right.

trapezoid ABCD ___≅___ trapezoid LMNO

PRACTICE

Name a rigid motions that can show that the shapes are congruent.

① ___rotation or reflection___

② ___translation, reflection or rotation___

③ ___reflection___

Use rigid motions to show that the following figures are congruent. Draw and explain your steps.

④ △CAB ≅ △KIT

Possible response: Rotate △ABC 90° counterclockwise around point C. Translate 2 units up.

⑤ THIS ≅ JUMP

Possible response: Rotate rectangle THIS 90° counterclockwise around point H. Translate 2 units up and 1 unit left.

⑥ △DOG ≅ △PET

Possible response: Reflect △DOG across line DG. Translate 6 units up.

135

• Model Application

DO ▶ A Guide students through the steps for showing that two triangles are congruent. Monitor that students identify the rigid motion and the congruency correctly.

DO ▶ B Explain that two figures can still be congruent even if more than one translation was applied to the figure. Ask: *Why would you first use a motion so the orientations of the figures match?*

Practice and Assess

• Ask students to complete practice items 1–6 on page 135 independently or in pairs. Monitor ongoing work.

• Observe whether students can use rigid motions correctly to show that two figures are congruent. Check for correct descriptions. Use the chart below as needed to address any difficulties.

Observation	Action
Students struggle to decide on the series of rigid motions needed to show that two figures are congruent.	Provide tracing paper and ask students to trace the original figure. Have them use the tracing to try reflecting, rotating, and translating the figure to match the final image. Have them record the series of rigid motions required.

SPOTLIGHT ON MATHEMATICAL LANGUAGE

MP6 Support students in using mathematical language as they work:

• *What rigid motions did you use to show that the figures are congruent?*

• *Show the horizontal translation. Show the vertical translation.*

COMMON ERRORS

Students may make errors in labeling the corresponding vertices on an image of the original figure. Have students label the vertices of the original figure on tracing paper, overlay the tracing over the image, and use the tracing for reference when labeling the corresponding vertices of the image.

Similar Figures

		OBJECTIVES	CONCEPTS AND SKILLS	VOCABULARY
FOUNDATIONAL UNDERSTANDING	**PLUG IN** **Congruent Figures**	• Determine if two figures are congruent. • Use a series of rigid motions to show two figures are congruent.	Understand the congruency of figures as a series of transformations. **CCSS:** 8.G.2	
	▶ **POWER UP** **Similar Figures** Student Edition pp. 136–137	• Use congruency to decide if two figures are similar. • Use proportions to decide if two figures are similar.	Understand similar figures. **CCSS:** 8.G.4	• **similar**
ON-LEVEL TARGET	**READY TO GO** **Similarity**	• Describe a series of transformations that show if two figures are similar.	Describe the effect of dilations on two-dimensional figures using coordinates. **CCSS:** 8.G.4	

MATERIALS

- Math Tool: Coordinate Grid, p. A15 (Student Edition p. 237)
- Models of triangles, rectangles, quadrilaterals (*suggested*)
- Rulers (*suggested*)
- Tracing paper (*suggested*)
- Pencils (*suggested*)

ENGLISH LANGUAGE LEARNERS

MP5 Reinforce the concept of *similar figures*. Provide students with models of two similar rectangles. Have them measure sides and angles and explain how they know the rectangles are similar.

Build Background

- Talk to students about reasons for determining similarity in figures. Similar figures are involved in creating enlargements and reductions. Suppose you want to make an enlargement of a poster. How could you tell if the images are similar? Explain that you could use proportions to compare the side lengths.

- **MP4** Have students discuss additional examples of real situations involving similar figures.

- Tell students they will determine if two figures are similar using congruency and proportions.

Introduce and Model

- **Introduce Concepts and Vocabulary** Guide students through similar figures and reinforce the difference between similar and congruent figures. Show how a figure created by dilation is not congruent but similar to the original figure. Use **Words to Know** to clarify understanding of *similar*. **MP6** Have students explain to a partner how they know the triangles are similar.

- **Support Discussion** **MP4** Have students discuss briefly before group discussion. Ask them to sketch a diagram to help visualize the situation.

> *Prompt: What does it mean for two figures to be similar? congruent?*
>
> *Sentence Starter: Two similar figures that are congruent have ...*

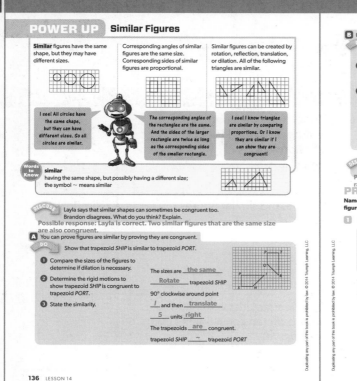

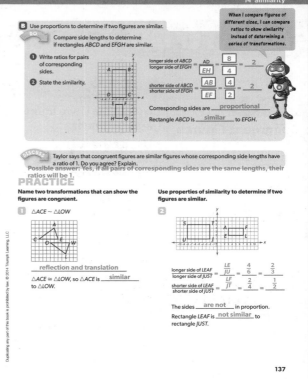

• Model Application

DO ▶ **A** Guide students through proving similarity in two figures by proving they are congruent. Discuss how to determine if a dilation is involved and how to choose a series of motions to check for similar figures.

DO ▶ **B** Coach students to set up and solve proportions for each pair of corresponding sides. Ask: *What does it mean if the ratios of pairs of corresponding sides are equivalent?*

• **Support Discussion** **MP3** Have partners discuss briefly before group discussion. Direct students to model using two congruent figures.

> *Prompt: What are the conditions for similar figures?*
> *Sentence Starter: In congruent figures, the ratio of each pair of corresponding sides is …*

Practice and Assess

• Ask students to complete practice items 1 and 2 on page 137 independently or in pairs. Monitor ongoing work.

• Observe whether students use properties of similarity correctly and select series of motions appropriately. Use the chart below to address any difficulties.

Observation	Action
Students may have difficulty deciding on a series of motions to check for similarity.	Encourage students to manipulate a model or a tracing of the figure and try different rigid motions. Coach them to use a motion that orients the figures in the same way (e.g., rotation, reflection) before continuing with different motions.

SPOTLIGHT ON
MATHEMATICAL PRACTICES

MP3 Constructing Viable Arguments

Help students build their argument by asking probing questions: *For any two congruent figures, what do you know about the value of the ratios representing all pairs of corresponding sides? Are the ratios of congruent figures equivalent? What are the conditions for similar figures?*

		OBJECTIVES	CONCEPTS AND SKILLS	VOCABULARY
FOUNDATIONAL UNDERSTANDING	**PLUG IN** **Congruent Figures**	• Determine if two figures are congruent. • Use a series of rigid motions to show two figures are congruent.	Understand the congruency of figures as a series of transformations. **CCSS:** 8.G.2	
	POWER UP **Similar Figures**	• Use congruency to decide if two figures are similar. • Use proportions to decide if two figures are similar.	Understand similar figures. **CCSS:** 8.G.4	• **similar**
ON-LEVEL TARGET	**▶ READY TO GO** **Similarity** Student Edition pp. 138–143	• Describe a series of transformations that show if two figures are similar.	Describe the effect of dilations on two-dimensional figures using coordinates. **CCSS:** 8.G.4	

MATERIALS

- Lesson 14 Quiz, Assessment Manual pp. 30–31
- Lesson 14 Quiz Answer Key, Assessment Manual
- Math Tool: Grid Paper, pp. A9, A11 (Student Edition pp. 225, 229)
- Photograph and an enlargement (suggested)
- Rulers (suggested)
- Tracing paper (suggested)
- Scissors (suggested)
- Pencils (suggested)

ENGLISH LANGUAGE LEARNERS

MP5 **MP6** Use a photograph and its enlargement to reinforce the concept of *scale factor*. Have students measure the length and width of both photos and use proportions to determine the scale factor. Ask: *What is the meaning of a scale factor greater than 1? Between 0 and 1? Equal to 1?*

Build Background

- Talk about reasons for using transformations to show similarity between figures. A Web site designer wants to create a logo using different sizes of a graphic with proportional dimensions. How can you assure that the graphics are similar? Explain that describing the rigid motions and dilation between the graphics is one way to ensure the figures are similar.

- **MP4** Have students discuss additional examples of real situations that involve describing similarity between figures.

- Tell students they will describe motions that show if figures are similar.

Introduce and Model

- **Introduce Concepts and Vocabulary** Guide students through the transformations. For the dilation, coach students to use equations such as $2x = 4$ to compare side lengths. **MP5** Have students compare the coordinates of the original and the dilation for each vertex and discuss their findings with a partner.

- **Support Discussion** **MP4** **MP6** Have students discuss briefly before group discussion. Have them sketch a diagram to visualize the situation.

> *Prompt: How do the ratios of corresponding sides in a scale drawing and a dilation compare?*
> *Sentence Starter: The corresponding side lengths change by …*

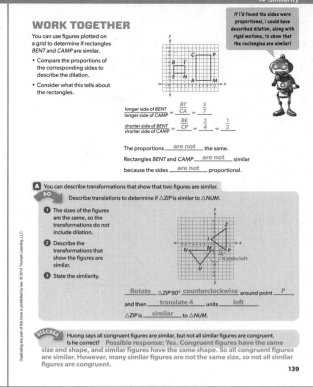

READY TO GO Similarity

You can use transformations that show the similarity of two figures.

Compare side lengths to define the dilation.

Reflect the image over the *y*-axis, and translate the reflection until one vertex aligns with △FIN.

The side lengths of △FIN are half the length of the side lengths of △BAY.

I see that the orientations of the figures are different.

I see! The vertex coordinates of the image are each one half times the vertex coordinates of the original figure!

I see! If I can describe a series of rigid motions and a dilation between figures, I know the two triangles are similar.

DISCUSS On a scale drawing, the scale factor is the ratio of the lengths on the drawing to the actual lengths. How is a scale factor related to dilation of a figure used to prove similarity? Possible response: A scale factor can describe the dilation. It is equal to the ratio of corresponding sides. In a scale drawing, it is equal to the ratio of actual lengths to drawing lengths.

LESSON LINK

PLUG IN	POWER UP	GO!
You can use transformations to show that figures are congruent.	You can use proportions to show that figures are similar.	I get it! I can use what I've learned to show that figures are similar. I can describe rigid motions and dilations that show whether figures are similar.

138 LESSON 14

WORK TOGETHER

You can use figures plotted on a grid to determine if rectangles *BENT* and *CAMP* are similar.

- Compare the proportions of the corresponding sides to describe the dilation.
- Consider what this tells about the rectangles.

If I'd found the sides were proportional, I could have described dilation, along with rigid motions, to show that the rectangles are similar!

$$\frac{\text{longer side of } BENT}{\text{longer side of } CAMP} = \frac{BT}{CA} = \frac{3}{7}$$

$$\frac{\text{shorter side of } BENT}{\text{shorter side of } CAMP} = \frac{BE}{CP} = \frac{2}{4} = \frac{1}{2}$$

The proportions ___are not___ the same.

Rectangles *BENT* and *CAMP* ___are not___ similar

because the sides ___are not___ proportional.

A You can describe transformations that show that two figures are similar.

DO Describe translations to determine if △ZIP is similar to △NUM.

❶ The sizes of the figures are the same, so the transformations do not include dilation.

❷ Describe the transformations that show the figures are similar.

❸ State the similarity.

Rotate ___△ZIP 90°___ ___counterclockwise___ around point ___P___

and then ___translate 4___ units ___left___

△ZIP is ___similar___ to △NUM.

DISCUSS Huong says all congruent figures are similar, but not all similar figures are congruent. Is he correct? Possible response: Yes. Congruent figures have the same size and shape, and similar figures have the same shape. So all congruent figures are similar. However, many similar figures are not the same size, so not all similar figures are congruent.

139

LESSON LINK

Connect to Foundational Understanding Skills learned in the **Plug In** and **Power Up** are referenced in the **Lesson Link**. Explain that transformations and proportions can be used to show the similarity of figures.

- **Work Together** Explain that students will use a dilation to show if two rectangles are similar. Ask: *Why did you start with a dilation? How else might you start? Which method is more efficient?*

DO **A** Monitor students as they decide on the sequence. Ask: *How do you know a dilation is not needed? Why did you start with a rotation instead of a translation?* You may wish to have students map △NUM to △ZIP and compare the results.

- **Support Discussion** **MP2** **MP3** Have students discuss briefly before group discussion. As needed, students can draw diagrams to visualize congruent figures and similar figures that are/are not congruent.

> *Prompt: Do all similar figures have the same size? Explain.*
> *Sentence Starter: Congruent figures have... Similar figures have ...*

SPOTLIGHT ON MATHEMATICAL LANGUAGE

MP6 Support students in using mathematical language as they work:

- *What **ratio** represents the corresponding sides?*
- *Are the corresponding sides **proportional**?*
- *Which **transformations** show that the figures are similar?*
- *The **scale factor** relates the corresponding sides.*

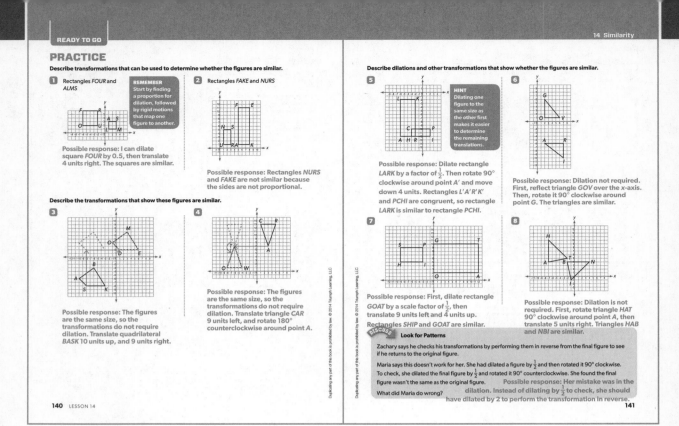

ADDITIONAL PRACTICE

Provide students with additional practice to model and solve:

△*BOG* has coordinates *B*(1, 3), *O*(1, 1), and *G*(3, 1). △*FED* has coordinates *F*(3, 9), *E*(3, 3), and *D*(9, 3). Define the dilation from △*BOG* to △*FED*.

COMMON ERRORS

Students set up proportions comparing corresponding side lengths incorrectly. If the figures are not positioned so that the corresponding sides are in the same place, encourage students to redraw the figures so that they are in the same location. Tell them to use words and numbers to represent corresponding sides.

Support Independent Practice

1–2 Remind students to read the **REMEMBER**. If needed, coach students to make a list of the order of transformations. Ask: *How can you check that your ratios are set up correctly?*

3–4 Coach students by asking: *What is your strategy to start? Is a dilation required? If not, what rigid motion will you start with? Why?*

5–8 Remind students to read the **HINT**. *What strategies can you use to help determine if figures are similar?*

- **Support Discussion** MP1 MP7 Have partners discuss briefly before group discussion. As needed, have students model the situation using real numbers.

> *Prompt:* What factor relates the corresponding sides from the final to the original figure?
> *Sentence Starter:* To do the transformations in reverse, first I need to …

Problem Solving

- **Model the Four-Step Method** MP4 MP6 Guide students through the four-step method using think-aloud strategies. Point out the clue word *similar*.

  Think Aloud *I need to check that the triangles are similar by describing the transformations. I see that the triangles are different sizes. So, I need to use a dilation and then decide on any rigid motions.*

- **Support Problem-Solving Practice** Have students use the Checklist as they complete each step.

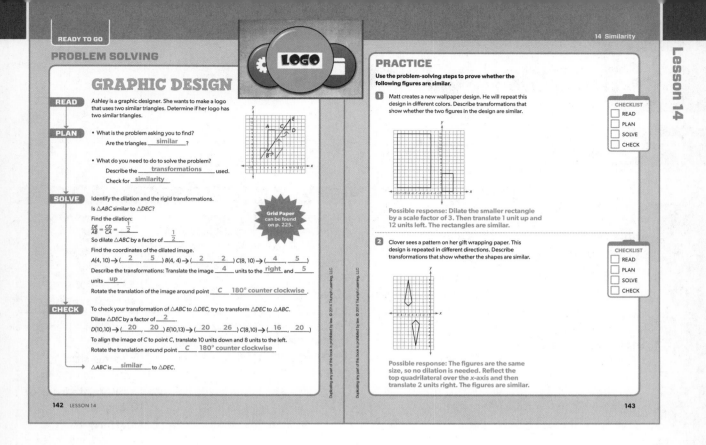

READY TO GO

PROBLEM SOLVING

GRAPHIC DESIGN

READ Ashley is a graphic designer. She wants to make a logo that uses two similar triangles. Determine if her logo has two similar triangles.

PLAN
- What is the problem asking you to find?
  Are the triangles ___similar___ ?

- What do you need to do to solve the problem?
  Describe the ___transformations___ used.
  Check for ___similarity___ .

SOLVE Identify the dilation and the rigid transformations.
Is △ABC similar to △DEC?

Find the dilation:
$\frac{DE}{AB} = \frac{CD}{CA} = \frac{1}{2}$

So dilate △ABC by a factor of ___$\frac{1}{2}$___ .

Find the coordinates of the dilated image.
A(4, 10) → (__2__ , __5__) B(4, 4) → (__2__ , __2__) C(8, 10) → (__4__ , __5__)

Describe the transformations: Translate the image ___4___ units to the ___right___ and ___5___ units ___up___ .

Rotate the translation of the image around point ___C___ 180° counter clockwise .

CHECK To check your transformation of △ABC to △DEC, try to transform △DEC to △ABC.
Dilate △DEC by a factor of ___2___ .
D(10,10) → (__20__ , __20__) E(10,13) → (__20__ , __26__) C(8,10) → (__16__ , __20__)

To align the image of C to point C, translate 10 units down and 8 units to the left.
Rotate the translation around point ___C___ 180° counter clockwise .

△ABC is ___similar___ to △DEC.

Grid Paper can be found on p. 225.

PRACTICE

Use the problem-solving steps to prove whether the following figures are similar.

1 Matt creates a new wallpaper design. He will repeat this design in different colors. Describe transformations that show whether the two figures in the design are similar.

CHECKLIST
- [ ] READ
- [ ] PLAN
- [ ] SOLVE
- [ ] CHECK

Possible response: Dilate the smaller rectangle by a scale factor of 3. Then translate 1 unit up and 12 units left. The rectangles are similar.

2 Clover sees a pattern on her gift wrapping paper. This design is repeated in different directions. Describe transformations that show whether the shapes are similar.

CHECKLIST
- [ ] READ
- [ ] PLAN
- [ ] SOLVE
- [ ] CHECK

Possible response: The figures are the same size, so no dilation is needed. Reflect the top quadrilateral over the x-axis and then translate 2 units right. The figures are similar.

Prompt: *What strategies will help describe the transformations?*

Prompt: *What other sequence can you use to check your answer?*

- **Explore Student Thinking** **MP3** Invite students to explain the strategy they used for the order of transformations for a problem and why. Have partners compare their work and discuss their results.

Assess

- Use the table below to observe whether students accurately describe rigid motions and dilations when testing for similarity, and to address any difficulties as needed before the quiz.

- When all students are ready, assign the Lesson 14 Quiz.

SPOTLIGHT ON MATHEMATICAL PRACTICES

MP7 Look for Patterns

Help students think about the pattern in doing each transformation in reverse. Ask probing questions: *What does a scale factor of $\frac{1}{2}$ indicate? What is the inverse of $\frac{1}{2}$? What scale factor indicates a dilation from the smaller figure to the larger figure?*

	Observation	Action
1	Errors in selecting and describing transformations are frequent or irregular; confusion about rigid motions and dilations, and testing for similarity.	For a dilation, have students dilate one figure to the same size as the other one. Next, have them trace and cut out these two figures and superimpose them correctly on the grid. Have students manipulate the figures to decide on the remaining sequence of motions.
2	Makes occasional errors in selecting and describing transformations; some understanding of testing for similarity.	Provide additional practice problems for selecting and describing transformations, including how to find the scale factor for dilations.
3	Selects and describes transformations accurately when testing for similarity.	Assign the Lesson 14 Quiz.

LESSON **15** # Angles in Triangles

PLUG IN Angle Pairs

		OBJECTIVES	CONCEPTS AND SKILLS	VOCABULARY
FOUNDATIONAL UNDERSTANDING	▶ PLUG IN **Angle Pairs** Student Edition pp. 144–145	• Define complementary, supplementary, adjacent, and vertical angles. • Solve for the size of unknown angles.	Use facts about supplementary, complementary, vertical, and adjacent angles in a multi-step problem to solve for an unknown angle. **CCSS:** 7.G.5	• **complementary angles** • **supplementary angles** • **adjacent angles** • **vertical angles**
FOUNDATIONAL UNDERSTANDING	POWER UP **Angles Formed by a Transversal**	• Define and identify the different angles on a transversal. • Solve for the size of unknown angles on a transversal.	Establish and use facts about the angles created when parallel lines are cut by a transversal. **CCSS:** 8.G.5	• **corresponding angles** • **same-side interior angles** • **alternate interior angles** • **alternate exterior angles**
ON-LEVEL TARGET	READY TO GO **Angles in Triangles**	• Define and identify the interior angles and exterior angles of a triangle. • Identify the angle sum of any triangle. • Solve for the measure of unknown angles related to a triangle.	Establish and use facts about the angle sum and exterior angle of triangles, and the angle-angle criterion for similarity of triangles. **CCSS:** 8.G.5	• **interior angle** • **exterior angle**

MATERIALS
- Poster paper *(suggested)*
- Markers *(suggested)*

ENGLISH LANGUAGE LEARNERS

MP4 ELL students would find it helpful to make a poster of the different types of angles. Have them draw and label sample complementary and supplementary angles. At the bottom, have them draw and label two vertical lines and two *vertical angles*. Discuss the difference between these two uses of the term *vertical*.

Build Background

- Have students look for examples of each type of angle in real life. Examples: complementary angles, the angles between the flap and the side of an envelope; supplementary angles, the angle where two streets meet; adjacent angles, the angle that a branch meets the trunks of its tree as seen from the top and the bottom; vertical angles, opposite angles at an intersection.

Introduce and Model

- **Introduce Concepts and Vocabulary** Guide students through a discussion of the different types of angles shown.
- **Support Discussion** MP7 Have partners discuss briefly. Refer students to the Avatar speech bubbles and the various diagrams.

Prompt: *What types of angles are always adjacent?*
Sentence Starter: *Lines that form vertical angles also form…*

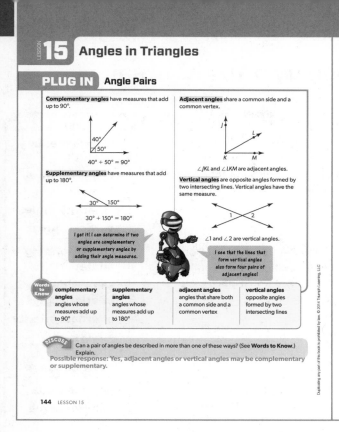

LESSON 15 Angles in Triangles

PLUG IN Angle Pairs

Complementary angles have measures that add up to 90°.

40°
50°

40° + 50° = 90°

Supplementary angles have measures that add up to 180°.

30° 150°

30° + 150° = 180°

I get it! I can determine if two angles are complementary or supplementary angles by adding their angle measures.

Adjacent angles share a common side and a common vertex.

J
L
K   M

∠JKL and ∠LKM are adjacent angles.

Vertical angles are opposite angles formed by two intersecting lines. Vertical angles have the same measure.

1   2

∠1 and ∠2 are vertical angles.

I see that the lines that form vertical angles also form four pairs of adjacent angles!

Words to Know

complementary angles	supplementary angles	adjacent angles	vertical angles
angles whose measures add up to 90°	angles whose measures add up to 180°	angles that share both a common side and a common vertex	opposite angles formed by two intersecting lines

DISCUSS Can a pair of angles be described in more than one of these ways? (See **Words to Know**.) Explain.
Possible response: Yes, adjacent angles or vertical angles may be complementary or supplementary.

144 LESSON 15

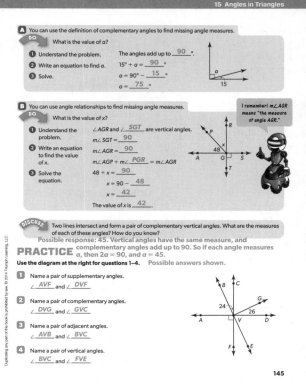

A You can use the definition of complementary angles to find missing angle measures.

DO What is the value of *a*?

❶ Understand the problem. The angles add up to __90__°.

❷ Write an equation to find *a*. 15° + *a* = __90__°

❸ Solve. *a* = 90° − __15__°
a = __75__°

a
15

B You can use angle relationships to find missing angle measures.

I remember! m∠AGR means "the measure of angle AGR."

DO What is the value of *x*?

❶ Understand the problem. ∠AGR and ∠__SGT__ are vertical angles.
m∠SGT = __90__

❷ Write an equation to find the value of *x*. m∠AGR = __90__
m∠AGP + m∠__PGR__ = m∠AGR

❸ Solve the equation. 48 + *x* = __90__
x = 90 − __48__
x = __42__

The value of *x* is __42__.

P   R
48 x
A   G   S
T

DISCUSS Two lines intersect and form a pair of complementary vertical angles. What are the measures of each of these angles? How do you know?
Possible response: 45. Vertical angles have the same measure, and complementary angles add up to 90. So if each angle measures *a*, then 2*a* = 90, and *a* = 45.

PRACTICE Use the diagram at the right for questions 1–4. Possible answers shown.

❶ Name a pair of supplementary angles.
∠__AVF__ and ∠__DVF__

❷ Name a pair of complementary angles.
∠__DVG__ and ∠__GVC__

❸ Name a pair of adjacent angles.
∠__AVB__ and ∠__BVC__

❹ Name a pair of vertical angles.
∠__BVC__ and ∠__FVE__

B   C
G
24   26
A   V   D
F   E

145

■ Model Application

DO **A** Guide students through using the definition of complementary angles to solve for the size of an unknown angle. Have them discuss the different forms of the necessary equation: 90 − *x* = *unknown angle* or *x* + *unknown angle* = 90.

DO **B** Have students identify and mark the vertical and adjacent angles shown in the diagram. *How can you use your knowledge of vertical and complementary angles to answer this question?*

■ **Support Discussion** **MP1** Suggest that students draw a pair of vertical angles. *For the vertical angles to be complementary, at what angle do the lines have to cross?*

> *Prompt: How can you make a pair of complementary angles on each vertical 90° angle? Are these angles also vertical?*
>
> *Sentence Starter: I can do this by drawing lines that meet at…*

Practice and Assess

■ Ask students to complete practice items 1–4 on page 145 independently or in pairs. Monitor ongoing work.

Observation	Action
Students confuse complementary and supplementary angles.	Have students refer to the poster diagrams made earlier in the lesson or develop their own original mnemonics to help them remember the difference.

COMMON ERRORS

Students may be able to show an angle but not use the correct letters to name it. Have students mark each angle, then highlight the arms. Review naming an angle by using three letters with the letter of the vertex in the middle. Discuss that ∠AVF could also be written ∠FVA.

SPOTLIGHT ON MATHEMATICAL PRACTICES

MP1 In diagrams such as the one in the Practice set, students may have difficulty finding the needed information. Model the use of think-alouds.

■ *What angles are adjacent to ∠3?*
■ *What do I know about ∠AVF?*
■ *What do I know about ∠BVC?*
■ *What do these two angles and ∠3 add to?*
■ *What equation shows this?*

Angles Formed by a Transversal

		OBJECTIVES	CONCEPTS AND SKILLS	VOCABULARY
FOUNDATIONAL UNDERSTANDING	**PLUG IN** **Angle Pairs**	• Define complementary, supplementary, adjacent, and vertical angles. • Solve for the size of unknown angles.	Use facts about supplementary, complementary, vertical, and adjacent angles in a multi-step problem to solve for an unknown angle. **CCSS:** 7.G.5	• **complementary angles** • **supplementary angles** • **adjacent angles** • **vertical angles**
	▶ POWER UP **Angles Formed by a Transversal** Student Edition pp. 146–147	• Define and identify the different angles on a transversal. • Solve for the size of unknown angles on a transversal.	Establish and use facts about the angles created when parallel lines are cut by a transversal. **CCSS:** 8.G.5	• **corresponding angles** • **same-side interior angles** • **alternate interior angles** • **alternate exterior angles**
ON-LEVEL TARGET	**READY TO GO** **Angles in Triangles**	• Define and identify the interior angles and exterior angles of a triangle. • Identify the angle sum of any triangle. • Solve for the measure of unknown angles related to a triangle.	Establish and use facts about the angle sum and exterior angle of triangles, and the angle-angle criterion for similarity of triangles. **CCSS:** 8.G.5	• **interior angle** • **exterior angle**

MATERIALS

• Large picture of railway bridge or other structure made from girder spans *(suggested)*
• Large picture of Golden Gate Bridge *(suggested)*
• Poster paper *(suggested)*
• Markers *(suggested)*
• Tracing paper *(suggested)*

Build Background

• Talk to students about where they might see corresponding angles, same-side interior angles, alternate interior angles, and alternate exterior angles. These are common on many railway bridges and on the Golden Gate bridge, where parallel lines of girders are crossed by a transversal. Display large pictures of structures such as these. Have students identify and highlight the various types of angles.

Introduce and Model

• **Introduce Concepts and Vocabulary** Guide students through the similarity and difference between corresponding angles, same-side interior angles, alternate interior angles, and alternate exterior angles using the diagrams in the introduction and Words to Know.

• **Support Discussion** MP7 Have partners discuss briefly before group discussion.

> *Prompt: Identify any complementary (or supplementary or adjacent or vertical) angles in these diagrams.*
>
> *Sentence Starter: I see some of the types of angles in the Power Up, such as…*

POWER UP — Angles Formed by a Transversal

Special angle pairs are formed when parallel lines are intersected by a transversal (a line that intersects two or more lines). In the diagrams below, line j and line m are parallel. Line k is a transversal.

Corresponding angles are on the same side of a transversal and on the same side of the parallel lines. Corresponding angles have the same measure.

$\angle 1$ and $\angle 5$, $\angle 2$ and $\angle 6$, $\angle 4$ and $\angle 8$, $\angle 3$ and $\angle 7$ are corresponding angle pairs.

Same-side interior angles are between the parallel lines and on the same side of the transversal. Same-side interior angles are supplementary.

$\angle 3$ and $\angle 6$ and $\angle 4$ and $\angle 5$ are same-side interior angle pairs.

Alternate interior angles are inside the parallel lines and on the opposite sides of the transversal. Alternate interior angles have the same measure.

$\angle 3$ and $\angle 5$ and $\angle 4$ and $\angle 6$ are alternate-interior angle pairs.

Alternate exterior angles are outside the parallel lines and on the opposite sides of the transversal. Alternate exterior angles have the same measure.

$\angle 1$ and $\angle 7$ and $\angle 2$ and $\angle 8$ are alternate exterior angle pairs.

Wow! I can use these definitions to find the measures of angles formed by parallel lines and a transversal!

Words to Know

corresponding angles	same-side interior angles	alternate interior angles	alternate exterior angles
angles that are in the same position when a transversal intersects two parallel lines	angles that are between two parallel lines and on the same side of the transversal	angles that are between two parallel lines and on opposite sides of the transversal	angles that are outside two parallel lines and on opposite sides of the transversal

DISCUSS What other special angle pairs do you see in the diagrams above?
Possible response: $\angle 1$ and $\angle 3$, $\angle 2$ and $\angle 4$, $\angle 5$ and $\angle 7$, and $\angle 6$ and $\angle 8$ are pairs of vertical angles.

146 LESSON 15

A You can use what you know about angles formed by a transversal to find congruent angles.

DO Line a is parallel to line b. Line t is a transversal. Identify all of the angles that are congruent to $\angle 1$. Then identify all of the angles congruent to $\angle 2$.

1 Identify the angle pairs that have the same measure.

Which types of angles have the same measure?
corresponding, vertical, alternate interior

2 List all of the angles that have the same measure as $\angle 1$.
$m\angle 1 = m\angle\underline{4} = m\angle\underline{5} = m\angle\underline{8}$

3 List all of the angles that have the same measure as $\angle 2$.
$m\angle 2 = m\angle\underline{3} = m\angle\underline{6} = m\angle\underline{7}$

I get it! $m\angle 1$ means "the measure of angle 1."

DISCUSS Kiera says if she knows just one angle measure in a diagram with a pair of parallel lines and a transversal, she can find all of the other angle measures. Explain why Kiera is correct.
Possible response: Every other angle is either congruent, or supplementary, to the angle measure she knows.

PRACTICE

Use the diagram to answer questions 1–6. Line r is parallel to line s. Line t is a transversal.

1 $\angle 8$ and $\angle\underline{6}$ are corresponding angles.
2 $\angle 3$ and $\angle\underline{2}$ are same-side interior angles.
3 $\angle 5$ and $\angle\underline{4}$ are alternate exterior angles.
4 $\angle 6$ and $\angle\underline{3}$ are alternate interior angles.
5 Which angles have the same measure as $\angle 7$?
$m\angle 7 = m\angle\underline{2} = m\angle\underline{4} = m\angle\underline{5}$
6 Which angles are supplementary to $\angle 6$?
$\angle\underline{2}, \angle\underline{4}, \angle\underline{5}, \angle\underline{7}$

147

• Model Application

DO A Guide students through identifying all of the angle pairs and all congruent angles. Discuss how they know.

• **Support Discussion** **MP3** Have partners discuss briefly before group discussion. Suggest that they consider the types of angles from the Plug In as well as the ones here.

Prompt: If I know the measure of this angle (point to any angle on a transversal), how can I determine the measure of this angle? (point to the related supplementary angle).

Sentence Starter: When a transversal crosses a set of parallel lines, the angles on the transversal are either …

Practice and Assess

• Ask students to complete practice items 1–6 on page 147 independently or in pairs. Monitor ongoing work.

Observation	Action
Students have difficulty identifying the 3 angles needed for item 5.	Ask: • What angle is vertical to this angle? • Where is the corresponding angle? • What angle is vertical to that angle? • How are all of the angles you pointed to related? (They're all the same size.)

SPOTLIGHT ON MATHEMATICAL LANGUAGE

MP3 Support students in making sense of the relationships between and among various angles:
• What is the meaning of **congruent**?
• How can congruent angles help you find the size of an unknown angle?

FOCUS ON FLUENCY

MP6 Have students produce large posters of a transversal crossing a pair of parallel lines. On one set of posters, have them label how the various angles are related. On another set of posters, have them label supplementary angles. Display the posters where students can refer to them during class.

		OBJECTIVES	CONCEPTS AND SKILLS	VOCABULARY
FOUNDATIONAL UNDERSTANDING	**PLUG IN** **Angle Pairs**	• Define complementary, supplementary, adjacent, and vertical angles. • Solve for the size of unknown angles.	Use facts about supplementary, complementary, vertical, and adjacent angles in a multi-step problem to solve for an unknown angle. **CCSS:** 7.G.5	• **complementary angles** • **supplementary angles** • **adjacent angles** • **vertical angles**
	POWER UP **Angles Formed by a Transversal**	• Define and identify the different angles on a transversal. • Solve for the size of unknown angles on a transversal.	Establish and use facts about the angles created when parallel lines are cut by a transversal. **CCSS:** 8.G.5	• **corresponding angles** • **same-side interior angles** • **alternate interior angles** • **alternate exterior angles**
ON-LEVEL TARGET	**▶ READY TO GO** **Angles in Triangles** Student Edition pp. 148–153	• Define and identify the interior angles and exterior angles of a triangle. • Identify the angle sum of any triangle. • Solve for the measure of unknown angles related to a triangle.	Establish and use facts about the angle sum and exterior angle of triangles, and the angle-angle criterion for similarity of triangles. **CCSS:** 8.G.5	• **interior angle** • **exterior angle**

MATERIALS
- Lesson 15 Quiz, Assessment Manual pp. 32–33
- Lesson 15 Quiz Answer Key, Assessment Manual
- Rulers (*suggested*)
- Protractors (*suggested*)

FOCUS ON FLUENCY

MP6 Review with students how to use a protractor with questions such as: *How do you place the protractor on each angle? Which protractor scale do you use? Why is it important to predict each angle size before measuring? How do you read the degree measure?*

Build Background

- Talk to students about the use of knowledge about angles in a triangle. This knowledge was used in building various structures, such as the Egyptian pyramids.

- **MP7** Display pictures of various geodesic domes, such as the model of Spaceship Earth at the Epcot Center and Missouri's Climatron. Discuss how the architects, engineers, and construction workers on these structures needed knowledge about angles in triangles.

Introduce and Model

- **Introduce Concepts and Vocabulary** Guide students through the information about interior angles and exterior angles of triangles. Use **Words to Know** to clarify their understanding of vocabulary. **MP4** Have students sketch triangles and identify the exterior and interior angles.

- **Support Discussion** **MP2** Have partners discuss briefly before group discussion. If needed, have students extend each side of the triangle and identify each exterior angle.

> **Prompt:** How might you show all exterior angles for this triangle?
>
> **Sentence Starter:** Each interior angle has …

READY TO GO · Angles in Triangles

Every triangle has three **interior angles**. The measures of the angles of a triangle add up to 180°.

interior angle

Any side of a triangle can be extended, forming an **exterior angle** outside the triangle.

exterior angle

exterior angle

If two interior angles of two triangles are congruent, then the triangles are similar.

$m\angle Q = m\angle K = 90$

$m\angle R = m\angle L = 45$

$\triangle PQR$ is similar to $\triangle JKL$.

I see! "Interior" means inside. Interior angles are inside the triangle.

This makes sense. "Exterior" means outside, and exterior angles are outside of the triangle.

I get it! Because two of the angles are congruent, the third one must also be congruent.

Words to Know

interior angle an angle inside a polygon that is formed by two sides of a polygon

exterior angle an angle outside of a polygon formed by extending one side of the polygon

DISCUSS How many exterior angles does a triangle have? How are they related to the interior angles? Explain.
Possible response: 6. There are two exterior angles for each interior angle. Each pair of exterior angles is congruent, and each exterior angle is supplementary to the related interior angle.

LESSON LINK

PLUG IN
You can use the relationships of angle pairs to find their measures.

POWER UP
Other special angle pairs are formed when a transversal intersects parallel lines.

GO!
I get it! I can use what I know about angle relationships to determine how the interior and exterior angles of triangles are related.

148 LESSON 15

WORK TOGETHER

Determine the relationship of the exterior angle measures of a triangle.

• Find the sum of the exterior angle measures.

• Write a general statement about the measures of the exterior angles of a triangle.

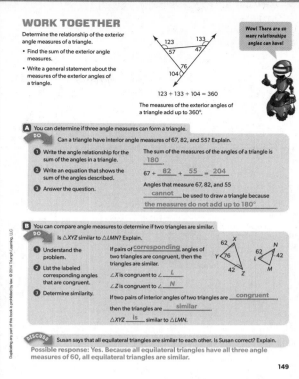

Wow! There are so many relationships angles can have!

$123 + 133 + 104 = 360$

The measures of the exterior angles of a triangle add up to 360°.

A You can determine if three angle measures can form a triangle.

DO Can a triangle have interior angle measures of 67, 82, and 55? Explain.

❶ Write the angle relationship for the sum of the angles in a triangle.
The sum of the measures of the angles of a triangle is 180

❷ Write an equation that shows the sum of the angles described.
$67 + 82 + 55 = 204$

❸ Answer the question.
Angles that measure 67, 82, and 55 cannot be used to draw a triangle because the measures do not add up to 180°

B You can compare angle measures to determine if two triangles are similar.

DO Is $\triangle XYZ$ similar to $\triangle LMN$? Explain.

❶ Understand the problem.

❷ List the labeled corresponding angles that are congruent.

❸ Determine similarity.

If pairs of corresponding angles of two triangles are congruent, then the triangles are similar.

$\angle X$ is congruent to $\angle$ L

$\angle Z$ is congruent to $\angle$ N

If two pairs of interior angles of two triangles are congruent, then the triangles are similar.

$\triangle XYZ$ is similar to $\triangle LMN$.

DISCUSS Susan says that all equilateral triangles are similar to each other. Is Susan correct? Explain.
Possible response: Yes. Because all equilateral triangles have all three angle measures of 60, all equilateral triangles are similar.

149

LESSON LINK

Connect to Foundational Understanding Skills learned in the **Plug In** and **Power Up** are referenced in the **Lesson Link**. Review the different relationships between angles from the Plug In and Power Up. Display a diagram of a triangle. Say: You can use what you know about angle relationships to learn how the internal and external angles of triangles are related.

• **Work Together** Explain that students will draw a triangle and measure each interior angle. They will then extend each side and measure the exterior angles. Have students predict what they might find. Expect a comment such as that an exterior angle and its related interior angle add to 180°. Challenge students to do the activity and see.

DO A Ask: *What was the sum of the interior angles in the triangles we made? Can we use this to predict whether the angles here make a triangle?* Monitor students as they work through the steps. Ask them what angle measures might work and how they know.

DO B Monitor student work as they complete each line in the calculation. Ask: *What is the measure of ∠M? How do you know?*

• **Support Discussion** **MP8** Have partners discuss briefly before group discussion. If needed, refresh student memories about the definition of an equilateral triangle.

> *Prompt:* If equilateral triangles have equal angles, what is the measure of each angle? How do you know?
> *Sentence Starter:* Because equilateral triangles have three equal angles, each angle must …

SPOTLIGHT ON MATHEMATICAL PRACTICES

MP5 Use Tools Strategically

Once students have measured each interior angle, ask them to predict what the related exterior angle will be. Pointing to the straight line that forms the extension of one triangle side, ask: *What is the measure of this angle? What type of angles do the internal and external angles make? How can you use this information to predict the measure of the external angle?*

SPOTLIGHT ON MATHEMATICAL PRACTICES

MP7 Look for Patterns

Discuss: *If the interior angles of a triangle are 62° and 42°, what will the third angle measure be? Will this always be true?*

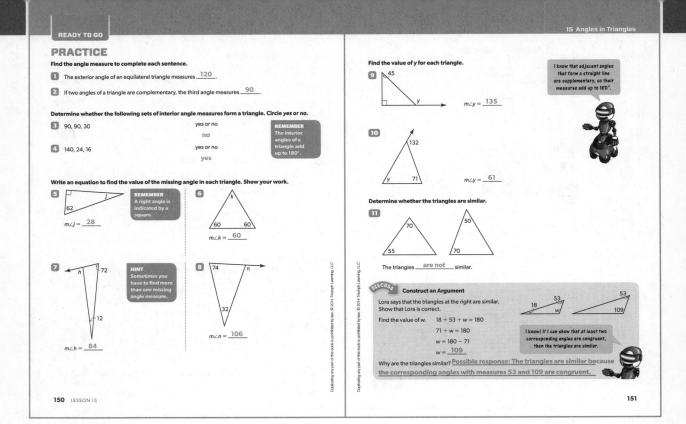

READY TO GO
PRACTICE

Find the angle measure to complete each sentence.

1. The exterior angle of an equilateral triangle measures __120__.

2. If two angles of a triangle are complementary, the third angle measures __90__.

Determine whether the following sets of interior angle measures form a triangle. Circle yes or no.

3. 90, 90, 30   yes or no
   no

> **REMEMBER**
> The interior angles of a triangle add up to 180°.

4. 140, 24, 16   yes or no
   yes

Write an equation to find the value of the missing angle in each triangle. Show your work.

5. 62   m∠j = __28__

> **REMEMBER**
> A right angle is indicated by a square.

6. k   60   60   m∠k = __60__

7. h 72 12   m∠h = __84__

> **HINT**
> Sometimes you have to find more than one missing angle measure.

8. 74   n   32   m∠n = __106__

Find the value of y for each triangle.

9. 45   y   m∠y = __135__

> I know that adjacent angles that form a straight line are supplementary, so their measures add up to 180°.

10. 132   y   71   m∠y = __61__

Determine whether the triangles are similar.

11. 70 55   50 70

The triangles __are not__ similar.

DISCUSS Construct an Argument

Lora says that the triangles at the right are similar. Show that Lora is correct.

Find the value of w.   18 + 53 + w = 180
                         71 + w = 180
                         w = 180 − 71
                         w = __109__

18 53   53 109

> I know! If I can show that at least two corresponding angles are congruent, then the triangles are similar.

Why are the triangles similar? Possible response: The triangles are similar because the corresponding angles with measures 53 and 109 are congruent.

ADDITIONAL PRACTICE

Provide students with additional practice to model and solve:

- A right triangle has a second angle measuring 60°. What is the size of the smallest angle?

- Can you make a triangle from two interior angles that measure 45° and one that measures 95°? How do you know?

SPOTLIGHT ON MATHEMATICAL LANGUAGE

MP2 Support students in transferring learning about similarity to the work on angles of triangles:

- *What makes two triangles* **similar**?

- *How can you use what we have learned about the angle measures of triangles to prove whether these two triangles are similar?*

Support Independent Practice

1–4 If needed for item 1, ask: *What is the size of the interior angles of an equilateral triangle?* If needed for item 2, ask: *What are complementary angles? So, if two angles of a triangle are complementary, what must the third angle be?*

5–8 If needed for items 7 and 8, ask: *What is the size of the unlabeled interior angle of this triangle? How do you find out? If this angle is x degrees, what is the measure of the related exterior angle?*

9–11 If needed for item 11, ask: *What do you know about the angles of similar triangles? What is the third measure of this triangle? Now you have the measure of three angles of this triangle. Are the two triangles similar?*

Support Discussion **MP7** **MP4** Have partners discuss briefly before group discussion. As needed, suggest that students check the conclusion by determining the measure of the third angle in the other triangle.

> *Prompt: If two angles of two different triangles are the same size, why will the third angle always be the same size?*
> *Sentence Starter: Triangles are similar when …*

Problem Solving

- **Model the Four-Step Method** **MP1** **MP5** Guide students through the four-step method using think-aloud strategies.

  Think Aloud *The triangle has one 90° angle and an external angle of 105°. I need to find the size of the interior angle for that exterior angle. Then I can use the two interior measures to find the size of the third interior angle.*

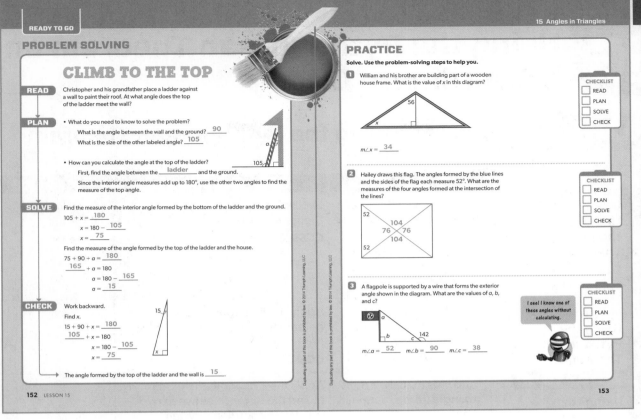

READY TO GO

PROBLEM SOLVING

CLIMB TO THE TOP

READ Christopher and his grandfather place a ladder against a wall to paint their roof. At what angle does the top of the ladder meet the wall?

PLAN
- What do you need to know to solve the problem?

  What is the angle between the wall and the ground? __90__

  What is the size of the other labeled angle? __105__

- How can you calculate the angle at the top of the ladder?

  First, find the angle between the __ladder__ and the ground.

  Since the interior angle measures add up to 180°, use the other two angles to find the measure of the top angle.

SOLVE Find the measure of the interior angle formed by the bottom of the ladder and the ground.

$105 + x =$ __180__

$x = 180 -$ __105__

$x =$ __75__

Find the measure of the angle formed by the top of the ladder and the house.

$75 + 90 + a =$ __180__

$165 + a = 180$

$a = 180 -$ __165__

$a =$ __15__

CHECK Work backward.

Find x.

$15 + 90 + x =$ __180__

__105__ $+ x = 180$

$x = 180 -$ __105__

$x =$ __75__

The angle formed by the top of the ladder and the wall is __15__.

152 LESSON 15

PRACTICE

Solve. Use the problem-solving steps to help you.

1 William and his brother are building part of a wooden house frame. What is the value of x in this diagram?

$m\angle x =$ __34__

CHECKLIST
☐ READ
☐ PLAN
☐ SOLVE
☐ CHECK

2 Hailey draws this flag. The angles formed by the blue lines and the sides of the flag each measure 52°. What are the measures of the four angles formed at the intersection of the lines?

52 52
104
76 76
104
52 52

CHECKLIST
☐ READ
☐ PLAN
☐ SOLVE
☐ CHECK

3 A flagpole is supported by a wire that forms the exterior angle shown in the diagram. What are the values of a, b, and c?

I see! I know one of these angles without calculating.

$m\angle a =$ __52__ $m\angle b =$ __90__ $m\angle c =$ __38__

CHECKLIST
☐ READ
☐ PLAN
☐ SOLVE
☐ CHECK

153

- **Support Problem-Solving Practice** Have students use the Checklist as they complete each step.

  Prompt: Which angle sizes do you already know in this problem?
  Prompt: What angle measure(s) do you need to find?

- **Explore Student Thinking** **MP2** Invite students to explain how they used various relationships between angle measures to solve these problems. Ask students to name the relationships they used.

Assess

- Use the table below to observe whether students correctly use the relationships between angles in a triangle, and to address any difficulties.

- When all students are ready, assign the Lesson 15 Quiz.

COMMON ERRORS

In item 1, students focus on all the different triangles in the truss and don't see that they are being asked to use the known measure of two angles to find the measure of a third. Ask students to highlight the triangle with the angle measure they are trying to find.

	Observation	Action
1	Errors in calculating angle measures are frequent; general confusion about what angle relationship(s) to use when finding the measure of unknown angles.	Have students highlight each triangle they are working with. Ask them to label the size of each known angle and add the size of each of the other angles as they find it. As they work on each problem, have students list the angle relationships they use.
2	Makes occasional errors in choosing appropriate angle relationships and in calculating angle measures; some understanding of angle relationships.	Provide additional practice problems that require choosing and using the problem angle relationships and calculating angle measures. Encourage students to label each angle measure as they find it.
3	Makes appropriate choice(s) of angle relationships and precise calculations when solving problems related to angle relationships.	Assign the Lesson 15 Quiz.

Using the Pythagorean Theorem on a Coordinate Grid

PLUG IN   Understanding the Pythagorean Theorem

<table>
<tr><th></th><th>OBJECTIVES</th><th>CONCEPTS AND SKILLS</th><th>VOCABULARY</th></tr>
<tr>
<td rowspan="2">FOUNDATIONAL UNDERSTANDING

▶ PLUG IN
Understanding the Pythagorean Theorem
Student Edition
pp. 154–155</td>
<td>• identify the Pythagorean theorem and its converse
• use the theorem to determine whether or not a triangle is a right triangle</td>
<td>Explain a proof of the Pythagorean theorem and its converse.
CCSS: 8.G.6</td>
<td>• Pythagorean theorem
• hypotenuse
• legs</td>
</tr>
<tr>
<td>POWER UP
Using the Pythagorean Theorem</td>
<td>• use the Pythagorean theorem to find the length of the unknown side of a right triangle</td>
<td>Apply the Pythagorean theorem to determine unknown side lengths in right triangles.
CCSS: 8.G.7</td>
<td></td>
</tr>
<tr>
<td>ON-LEVEL TARGET

READY TO GO
Using the Pythagorean Theorem on a Coordinate Grid</td>
<td>• add legs to make a right triangle from a diagonal line
• use the Pythagorean theorem to calculate the length of the diagonal</td>
<td>Apply the Pythagorean theorem to find the distance between two points in a coordinate system.
CCSS: 8.G.8</td>
<td></td>
</tr>
</table>

MATERIALS
• Math Tool: Pythagorean Theorem Proof, p. A7 (Student Edition p. 221)
• Measuring tape *(suggested)*

ENGLISH LANGUAGE LEARNERS

MP2 ELL students may need some practice learning how to pronounce *Pythagorean theorem* and *hypotenuse*.

MP4 Reinforce the mathematical use of the word *leg*. Touch the leg on your body. It's the same word used differently. Have students draw a right triangle, label the legs, and discuss how these legs form the 90° angle.

Build Background

• Discuss with students when the Pythagorean theorem is used in real life. For example, many carpenters refer to a 3-4-5 triangle when checking whether something they have built is square or at a 90° angle. They measure 3 units from one leg of the corner and make a mark, and then measure 4 units from the second leg of the corner and make a mark. The distance between the marks should be the hypotenuse of a right triangle or 5 units. Use a diagram to explain this theory. Brainstorm when carpenters might use such a test (e.g., building walls, fencelines, doors, windows).

• **MP5** Have students use the 3-4-5 triangle test to see whether the corner of their classroom, a doorframe, or a piece of furniture is a right angle. Encourage them to find an item that is a right angle and one that is not, even though it appears so.

Introduce and Model

• **Introduce Concepts and Vocabulary** Provide each student with a copy of **Math Tool: Pythagorean Theorem Proof**. **MP4** Have students label the legs and the hypotenuse of the right triangle on the tool. Guide students through a discussion of what the diagram shows: $a^2 + b^2 = c^2$ or $3^2 + 4^2 = 5^2$.

• **Support Discussion** **MP3** Discuss what angle a right triangle must have and how they can use this information in building an argument to support their point of view.

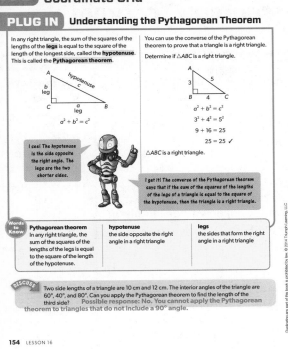
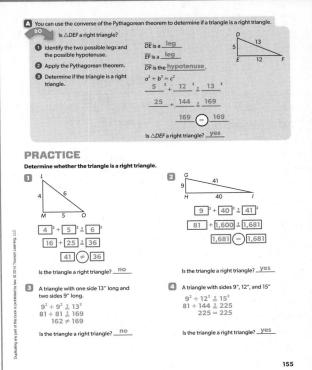

> **Prompt:** What types of triangles does the Pythagorean theorem refer to?
>
> **Sentence Starter:** The angles in the triangle are 60°, 40°, and 80°, I think …

• Model Application

DO ▶ Ⓐ Guide students through identifying the possible hypotenuse and legs of the triangle. Have them fill the appropriate numbers into the equation and solve it. Ask: *How does this answer show that the triangle has one 90° angle?*

Practice and Assess

- Ask students to complete practice items 1–4 on page 155 independently or in pairs. Monitor ongoing work.

- For all items, observe whether students fill in the correct measurements. You may wish to have them highlight the possible hypotenuse on each triangle. After they have completed the set, ask: *How are the answers to the last two statements in each question related?*

Observation	Action
Students confuse which numbers to fill into the *c*-box.	Review that the hypotenuse is the longest side of a right triangle. If this is a right triangle, the longest side is the *c*-side. Ask students to highlight the longest side of each triangle and place that measurement in the *c*-box.

COMMON ERRORS

Some students may correctly feel that they cannot identify the *c*-side of a triangle until they know whether the triangle is a right triangle. Praise the logic of this thinking. Point out that, for the purposes of this exercise, the boxes refer to what would be the *a*, *b*, and *c* sides if the triangle were a right triangle. Have students later put an X through the sides that were marked as a possible hypotenuse but are not.

Using the Pythagorean Theorem

		OBJECTIVES	CONCEPTS AND SKILLS	VOCABULARY
FOUNDATIONAL UNDERSTANDING	**PLUG IN** **Understanding the Pythagorean Theorem**	• Identify the Pythagorean theorem and its converse. • Use the theorem to determine whether or not a triangle is a right triangle.	Explain a proof of the Pythagorean theorem and its converse. **CCSS:** 8.G.6	• **Pythagorean theorem** • **hypotenuse** • **legs**
	▶ POWER UP **Using the Pythagorean Theorem** Student Edition pp. 156–157	• Use the Pythagorean theorem to find the length of the unknown side of a right triangle.	Apply the Pythagorean theorem to determine unknown side lengths in right triangles. **CCSS:** 8.G.7	
ON-LEVEL TARGET	**READY TO GO** **Using the Pythagorean Theorem on a Coordinate Grid**	• Add legs to make a right triangle from a diagonal line. • Use the Pythagorean theorem to calculate the length of the diagonal.	Apply the Pythagorean theorem to find the distance between two points in a coordinate system. **CCSS:** 8.G.8	

MATERIALS
• Math Tool: Grid Paper, p. A11 (Student Edition p. 229)
• Math Tool: Pythagorean Theorem Proof, p. A7 (Student Edition, p. 221)
• Scientific calculator *(suggested)*

Build Background

● Discuss with students the use of the Pythagorean theorem to determine the length of the leg of a right triangle when it cannot easily be measured. For example, a carpenter may know the length of a ladder and how far out from the wall it has to sit, but not know how far up the wall the ladder will reach. This formula will help him make that calculation.

● **MP5** Have students discuss additional situations when people use this skill.

Introduce and Model

● **Introduce Concepts** Guide students through the calculations shown in the introduction. Make sure that they understand where each number comes from in the calculation.

● **Support Discussion** **MP1** **MP4** **MP7** Have partners discuss briefly before group discussion. Suggest that they draw this diagram on grid paper and highlight the right triangle before starting the discussion.

> *Prompt:* What do you know about the legs of this right triangle and how do you know?
>
> *Sentence Starter:* I know that the two legs are the same size, so another way of writing the converse would be …

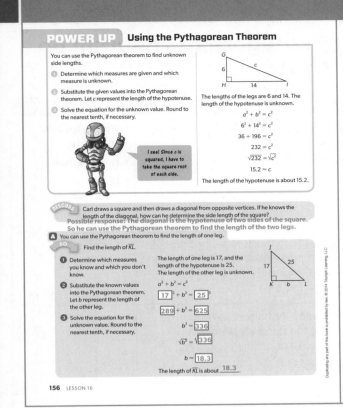

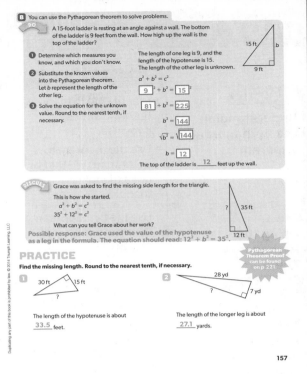

Model Application

DO **A** Guide students through the steps of filling in and solving the equation. Ask: *Does it matter whether the unknown leg is* a *or* b*?* If students aren't sure, review the distributive property.

DO **B** Review the steps needed to solve this problem. Ask: *How is this question different from* A?

- **Support Discussion** **MP3** Have partners discuss briefly before group discussion. Suggest that they highlight the hypotenuse and consider how they would solve this question before looking at Grace's start.

> *Prompt:* Which length forms the hypotenuse of this triangle?
> *Sentence Starter:* I would tell Grace that the labeled side lengths show...

Practice and Assess

- Ask students to complete practice items 1 and 2 on page 157 independently or in pairs. Monitor ongoing work.

Observation	Action
Students use the hypotenuse as a leg in items 1 or 2.	Students may need to be walked through the first solution of this type. ■ Have students circle the hypotenuse. ■ Ask: *What sides are shown?* ■ Ask: *How do you fit them into the formula?* ■ Have them write the equation.

MP6 **Attend to Precision**

Review how to solve equations when

- the variable is with another value
$$7^2 + b^2 = 28^2$$

- the variable is on the right
$$40^2 + 22^2 = c^2$$

COMMON ERRORS

MP5 Students record unreasonable answers for square root calculations. Have students estimate an answer to each square root calculation before making the calculation. For example, the answer to $b = \sqrt{1,175}$ in item 1 is going to be higher than both 30 (longer leg) and 15 (shorter leg). Have students check this estimate against what the calculator says. Discuss what to do if the answer is too high or too low.

		OBJECTIVES	CONCEPTS AND SKILLS	VOCABULARY
FOUNDATIONAL UNDERSTANDING	**PLUG IN** **Understanding the Pythagorean Theorem**	• Identify the Pythagorean theorem and its converse. • Use the theorem to determine whether or not a triangle is a right triangle.	Explain a proof of the Pythagorean theorem and its converse. **CCSS:** 8.G.6	• **Pythagorean theorem** • **hypotenuse** • **legs**
	POWER UP **Using the Pythagorean Theorem**	• Use the Pythagorean theorem to find the length of the unknown side of a right triangle.	Apply the Pythagorean theorem to determine unknown side lengths in right triangles. **CCSS:** 8.G.7	
ON-LEVEL TARGET	**▸ READY TO GO** **Using the Pythagorean Theorem on a Coordinate Grid** Student Edition pp. 158–163	• Add legs to make a right triangle from a diagonal line. • Use the Pythagorean theorem to calculate the length of the diagonal.	Apply the Pythagorean theorem to find the distance between two points in a coordinate system. **CCSS:** 8.G.8	

MATERIALS

- Lesson 16 Quiz, Assessment Manual pp. 34–35
- Lesson 16 Quiz Answer Key, Assessment Manual
- Math Tool: Grid Paper, p. A11 (Student Edition p. 229)
- Math Tool: Coordinate Grid, p. A15 (Student Edition, p. 237)
- Rulers *(suggested)*
- Measuring tapes *(suggested)*

SPOTLIGHT ON MATHEMATICAL PRACTICES

MP6 Focus on Precision

Review how to round the decimals on a calculator display to tenths:

- Work only with the numeral in the hundredths place.
- If it is below 5, leave the tenths digit as is.
- If it is 5 or above, round the tenths digit up one.

Build Background

- Explain that this lesson will discuss finding the lengths of diagonal lines on a coordinate grid. Discuss when this might be used in real life. For example, a surveyor may need to know the distance across a lake. If she knows the length and width of the lake, she can determine that distance.

- **MP5** Have students identify other times when this skill might be used. For example, it can be used to find the length of shortcuts on a map or other grid. Pilots use it to determine the distance between inaccessible places.

Introduce and Model

- **Introduce Concepts** Guide students through the information about drawing the legs for a diagonal line on a coordinate grid, thus creating a right triangle. **MP4** Provide students with rulers and **Math Tool: Coordinate Grid**. Have them sketch a diagonal line on the grid, then draw a related triangle to see for themselves how this works. Have them calculate the length of the line using the Pythagorean theorem, then measure the actual line to check.

- **Support Discussion** Have partners discuss briefly before group discussion. **MP4** If students did not use the activity with **Math Tool: Coordinate Grid** mentioned above, then provide copies of the grid and encourage them to experiment with the skill using a diagonal with endpoints in different quadrants.

READY TO GO — Using the Pythagorean Theorem on a Coordinate Grid

You can use the Pythagorean theorem to solve problems on the coordinate grid.

What is the length of $\overline{AB}$?

> I can draw a right triangle and then use the Pythagorean theorem.

Add legs to make a right triangle. Determine the lengths of each leg.

> I can find the lengths of $\overline{AC}$ and $\overline{CB}$ by counting the units.

Use the length of the legs to find the length of the hypotenuse.

Length of $\overline{AC}$ = 4 units
Length of $\overline{CB}$ = 9 units
$a^2 + b^2 = c^2$
$4^2 + 9^2 = c^2$
$16 + 81 = c^2$
$97 = c^2$
$c = \sqrt{97}$
$c = 9.848\ldots$

AB is about 9.8 units.

> I can round the length to the nearest tenth, when necessary.

DISCUSS Will this method work for segments whose endpoints are in different quadrants? Explain.
Possible response: Yes. Legs of a right triangle can be drawn for any segment on a coordinate grid. Even if the legs cross quadrants, their lengths can still be counted and the Pythagorean theorem can still be applied.

LESSON LINK

PLUG IN	POWER UP	GO!
You can use the Pythagorean theorem to prove that a triangle is a right triangle.	You can use the Pythagorean theorem to find the length of an unknown side.	I get it! I can apply the Pythagorean theorem in other problem situations, like finding the lengths of segments on coordinate grids!

PLUG IN:
$a^2 + b^2 = c^2$
$3^2 + 4^2 = 5^2$
$9 + 16 = 25$
$25 = 25$
This is a right triangle.

POWER UP:
$a^2 + b^2 = c^2$
$5^2 + 12^2 = c^2$
$25 + 144 = c^2$
$169 = c^2$
$13 = c$

158 LESSON 16

WORK TOGETHER

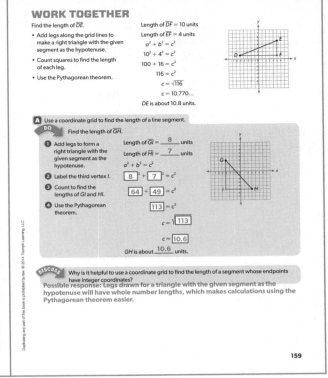

Find the length of $\overline{DE}$.

- Add legs along the grid lines to make a right triangle with the given segment as the hypotenuse.
- Count squares to find the length of each leg.
- Use the Pythagorean theorem.

Length of $\overline{DF}$ = 10 units
Length of $\overline{EF}$ = 4 units
$a^2 + b^2 = c^2$
$10^2 + 4^2 = c^2$
$100 + 16 = c^2$
$116 = c^2$
$c = \sqrt{116}$
$c = 10.770\ldots$

DE is about 10.8 units.

A Use a coordinate grid to find the length of a line segment.

DO Find the length of $\overline{GH}$.

1. Add legs to form a right triangle with the given segment as the hypotenuse.
   Length of $\overline{GI}$ = __8__ units
   Length of $\overline{HI}$ = __7__ units
   $a^2 + b^2 = c^2$
2. Label the third vertex I.
   $\boxed{8}^2 + \boxed{7}^2 = c^2$
3. Count to find the lengths of GI and HI.
   $\boxed{64} + \boxed{49} = c^2$
4. Use the Pythagorean theorem.
   $\boxed{113} = c^2$
   $c = \boxed{\sqrt{113}}$
   $c \approx \boxed{10.6}$

GH is about __10.6__ units.

DISCUSS Why is it helpful to use a coordinate grid to find the length of a segment whose endpoints have integer coordinates?
Possible response: Legs drawn for a triangle with the given segment as the hypotenuse will have whole number lengths, which makes calculations using the Pythagorean theorem easier.

159

> **Prompt:** Draw a diagonal with endpoints in two different quadrants, and then construct a right triangle with the diagonal as the hypotenuse. How can you determine the lengths of the two legs?
>
> **Sentence Starter:** I think that I can work with a diagonal with endpoints anywhere on the coordinate grid as long as…

LESSON LINK

Connect to Foundational Understanding Skills learned in the **Plug In** and **Power Up** are referenced in the **Lesson Link**. Review the different ways to use the Pythagorean theorem outlined in the Plug In and Power Up. Discuss how the Ready to Go repeats and extends these uses.

- **Work Together** Explain that students will draw a right triangle by adding legs to the endpoints of a diagonal line on a grid. Discuss how to draw each leg and how to find the length of each leg.

DO **A** Monitor students as they work through the steps. Make sure that they understand the purpose of each calculation.

- **Support Discussion** **MP2** **MP3** Have partners discuss briefly before group discussion. If students cannot think of a reason, write this question on the board: How long is a diagonal line that starts at (2, 2) and ends at (−5, −19)?

> **Prompt:** How can you find the length of a diagonal line if you just have the coordinates of that line?
>
> **Sentence Starter:** When I place a line segment on a coordinate grid, I can …

SPOTLIGHT ON MATHEMATICAL PRACTICES

MP5 Use Tools Strategically

Have students use benchmarks to estimate the answer to square root calculations. For example, $\sqrt{113}$ will be between 10 ($\sqrt{100}$) and 11 ($\sqrt{121}$).

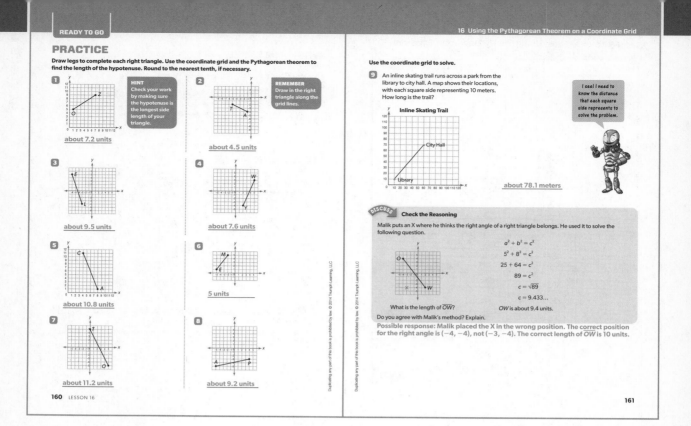

PRACTICE

Draw legs to complete each right triangle. Use the coordinate grid and the Pythagorean theorem to find the length of the hypotenuse. Round to the nearest tenth, if necessary.

1

HINT
Check your work by making sure the hypotenuse is the longest side length of your triangle.

about 7.2 units

2

REMEMBER
Draw in the right triangle along the grid lines.

about 4.5 units

3

about 9.5 units

4

about 7.6 units

5

about 10.8 units

6

5 units

7

about 11.2 units

8

about 9.2 units

Use the coordinate grid to solve.

9 An inline skating trail runs across a park from the library to city hall. A map shows their locations, with each square side representing 10 meters. How long is the trail?

Inline Skating Trail

City Hall

Library

about 78.1 meters

I see I need to know the distance that each square side represents to solve the problem.

DISCUSS Check the Reasoning

Malik puts an X where he thinks the right angle of a right triangle belongs. He used it to solve the following question.

$$a^2 + b^2 = c^2$$
$$5^2 + 8^2 = c^2$$
$$25 + 64 = c^2$$
$$89 = c^2$$
$$c = \sqrt{89}$$
$$c = 9.433...$$

What is the length of $\overline{OW}$? OW is about 9.4 units.

Do you agree with Malik's method? Explain.

Possible response: Malik placed the X in the wrong position. The correct position for the right angle is $(-4, -4)$, not $(-3, -4)$. The correct length of $\overline{OW}$ is 10 units.

ADDITIONAL PRACTICE

Provide students with additional practice to model and solve. Students will need the **Math Tool: Coordinate Grid** to do these questions:

Draw a line from (10, 1) to (1, 10). How long is the line?

Draw a line from $(-7, 2)$ to $(-1, -15)$. How long is the line?

Support Independent Practice

1–8 Remind students to read both the **HINT** and the **REMEMBER**. Monitor that students draw the right triangle correctly and fill the correct numbers into the formula.

9 Monitor student work. For item 9, ask: *What does each number on this grid represent? How can you reflect that in your answer?*

Support Discussion **MP5** **MP6** Have partners discuss briefly before group discussion. As needed, suggest that students use the coordinate grid on the left of this Discuss to draw the way they think the right triangle should appear.

> **Prompt:** How is your right triangle different from Malik's?
> **Sentence Starter:** Instead of drawing the right triangle, Malik put an X where he thought the vertex should go; however,...

Problem Solving

• **Model the Four-Step Method** **MP1** **MP7** **MP8** Guide students through the four-step method using think-aloud strategies. Discuss what they already know about the dive and what they can find out using a right triangle on a coordinate grid.

Think Aloud *The dive started at (0, 22). It ended at (10, 0). I need to draw a right triangle using these end points. The scale of the dive is 2; I need to count by 2s. So the legs of the triangle are 10 feet and 22 feet. I need to use these measurements as a and b in the formula.*

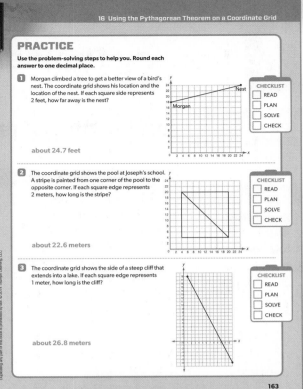

READY TO GO

PROBLEM SOLVING

DIVING

READ The winner of a diving contest made the dive represented here. What was the length of his dive, in feet? Show the distance to one decimal place.

Champion Dive

PLAN
- What is the problem asking you to find?
  You need to find the __length__ of the dive.

- What do you need to solve the problem?
  What does each square side represent? __2 ft__
  From what height was the dive made? __22 ft__
  How far from the end of the pool did the diver land? __10 ft__

- What method can you use?
  The coordinate grid shows a slanted line. You can use the Pythagorean theorem.

Each square's side in the grid represents 2 feet. I need to count by 2s.

SOLVE $a^2 + b^2 = c^2$

$\underline{22}^2 + \underline{10}^2 = c^2$

$\underline{484} + \underline{100} = c^2$

$\underline{584} = c^2$

$c = \sqrt{584}$

$c \approx \underline{24.166}$

The dive was about __24.2__ feet.

Champion Dive

CHECK Check using the Pythagorean theorem.

$a^2 + b^2 = c^2$

$22^2 + 10^2 \stackrel{?}{=} 24.2^2$

$\underline{484} + \underline{100} \stackrel{?}{=} 585.64$

$\underline{584} \approx \underline{585.64}$ ✓

The dive was about __24.2__ feet.

I had to round my answer, so 24.2 was an approximation. And 584 ≈ 585.64. My answer checks!

162 LESSON 16

PRACTICE

Use the problem-solving steps to help you. Round each answer to one decimal place.

1 Morgan climbed a tree to get a better view of a bird's nest. The coordinate grid shows his location and the location of the nest. If each square side represents 2 feet, how far away is the nest?

Nest
Morgan

CHECKLIST
- [ ] READ
- [ ] PLAN
- [ ] SOLVE
- [ ] CHECK

about 24.7 feet

2 The coordinate grid shows the pool at Joseph's school. A stripe is painted from one corner of the pool to the opposite corner. If each square edge represents 2 meters, how long is the stripe?

CHECKLIST
- [ ] READ
- [ ] PLAN
- [ ] SOLVE
- [ ] CHECK

about 22.6 meters

3 The coordinate grid shows the side of a steep cliff that extends into a lake. If each square edge represents 1 meter, how long is the cliff?

CHECKLIST
- [ ] READ
- [ ] PLAN
- [ ] SOLVE
- [ ] CHECK

about 26.8 meters

163

- **Support Problem-Solving Practice** Have students use the Checklist as they complete each step.

> **Prompt:** What lengths are provided in this problem?
> **Prompt:** How are the lengths shown on the grid?

- **Explore Student Thinking** MP2 Invite students to explain how they know that the answer to each question is reasonable.

COMMON ERRORS
Students may have run out of benchmarks for these square root calculations and fail to check whether their answers are reasonable. Suggest that they make benchmarks using the squares of tens: 400, 900, 1,600, 2,500, 3,600. Discuss how benchmarks such as these can help them to check the reasonableness of the answers to these questions, and what to do if the calculation seems too high or too low.

Assess

- Use the table below to address any difficulties.

1	**Observation**	**Action**
	Errors in identifying the length of legs, writing the numbers into the formula, and/or calculating the length of the hypotenuse are frequent.	■ Have students draw each right triangle and label each leg as either a or b and with its length. ■ Have students write the formula as $a^2 + b^2 = c^2$ and then fill in the appropriate numbers from the labeled triangle.
2	**Observation**	**Action**
	Makes occasional errors in transcription or calculation using the Pythagorean theorem; some understanding of how to use the Pythagorean theorem.	Provide additional practice problems that include scenarios with a diagonal line on a coordinate grid. Encourage students to continue to draw each triangle, to write down the formula, and to record each step as they complete their calculations.
3	**Observation**	**Action**
	Uses correct lengths and makes precise calculations when solving problems related to the Pythagorean theorem.	Assign the Lesson 16 Quiz.

Solving Problems with Volume

PLUG IN Evaluating Algebraic Expressions

<table>
<tr><th></th><th></th><th>OBJECTIVES</th><th>CONCEPTS AND SKILLS</th><th>VOCABULARY</th></tr>
<tr>
<td rowspan="2">FOUNDATIONAL UNDERSTANDING</td>
<td>▶ **PLUG IN**
Evaluating Algebraic Expressions
Student Edition pp. 164–165</td>
<td>• Use substitution and the order of operations to evaluate a variable expression.
• Evaluate an algebraic expression containing parentheses for given values.
• Evaluate an algebraic expression containing exponents for given values.</td>
<td>Evaluate algebraic expressions for given values.
CCSS: 6.EE.2.c</td>
<td>• **algebraic expression**
• **substitution**
• **arithmetic expression**
• **order of operations**</td>
</tr>
<tr>
<td>**POWER UP**
Volume Formulas</td>
<td>• Use a formula to determine the volume of a cylinder, a cone, and a sphere.</td>
<td>Use formulas to find volume.
CCSS: 8.G.9</td>
<td>• **volume**
• **cubic units**</td>
</tr>
<tr>
<td>ON-LEVEL TARGET</td>
<td>**READY TO GO**
Solving Problems with Volume</td>
<td>• Use multiple formulas to find the volume of a solid.</td>
<td>Use formulas to solve volume problems.
CCSS: 8.G.9</td>
<td></td>
</tr>
</table>

Build Background

- Talk to students about when they will solve algebraic expressions in real life. For example, if four of the same sandwiches cost $16, how much does each sandwich cost?

- **MP4** Have students discuss additional examples of when they might mentally use an algebraic expression to find the answer to a problem.

Introduce and Model

- **Introduce Concepts and Vocabulary** Guide students through using substitution to evaluate an algebraic expression. Make sure students use the correct sign. Also, ensure that students follow the order of operations when evaluating an expression. Use **Words to Know** to clarify their understanding of vocabulary. **MP6** Have students demonstrate their understanding of *algebraic expression* and *arithmetic expression*.

- **Support Discussion** **MP3** Have partners discuss briefly before group discussion. Review with students how to add variable expressions.

> *Prompt: Will Dennis get a different answer if he simplifies first?*
> *Sentence Starter: Simplifying an expression first before evaluating it will …*

ENGLISH LANGUAGE LEARNERS

MP4 Help ELL students differentiate between algebraic expressions and arithmetic expressions by breaking down the terms by their root words. Explain that algebraic expressions contain variables that you study in algebra. Explain that arithmetic expressions contain numbers that you need to perform arithmetic on.

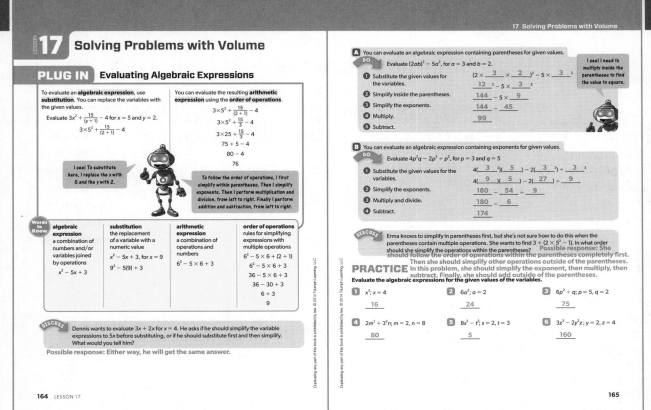

Model Application

DO ▶ A Guide students as they evaluate expressions with parentheses. Remind students to always simplify inside the parentheses first, before doing any other calculations.

DO ▶ B Guide students as they evaluate expressions containing exponents. Remind students that an exponent tells you how many times you multiply the base by itself.

Support Discussion MP7 Have partners discuss briefly before group discussion.

> **Prompt:** *Focus on the expression within the parentheses. What should Erma do first?*
>
> **Sentence Starter:** *To follow the order of operations, the first rule to apply within the parentheses is …*

Practice and Assess

- Ask students to complete practice items 1–6 on page 165 independently or in pairs. Monitor ongoing work.

Observation	Action
Students have difficulty following the order of operations when evaluating an algebraic expression.	Some students find the mnemonic *Please Excuse My Dear Aunt Sally* (Parentheses, Exponents, Multiply/Divide, Add/Subtract) helpful when trying to remember the order of operations.

SPOTLIGHT ON MATHEMATICAL PRACTICES

MP2 Reason Abstractly Help students think about Dennis's reasoning by asking students to look at each term in the expression and evaluate it individually. Then have them compare this sum with 5(4).

SPOTLIGHT ON MATHEMATICAL LANGUAGE

MP6 Support students in using mathematical language as they work:

- *According to the **order of operations**, which operation should you do first?*
- *When you **substitute** the value of the variable into the expression, how many terms are you left with?*

Volume Formulas

		OBJECTIVES	CONCEPTS AND SKILLS	VOCABULARY
FOUNDATIONAL UNDERSTANDING	**PLUG IN** **Evaluating Algebraic Expressions**	• Use substitution and the order of operations to evaluate a variable expression. • Evaluate an algebraic expression containing parentheses for given values. • Evaluate an algebraic expression containing exponents for given values.	Evaluate algebraic expressions for given values. **CCSS:** 6.EE.2.c	• **algebraic expression** • **substitution** • **arithmetic expression** • **order of operations**
	▶ POWER UP **Volume Formulas** Student Edition pp. 166–167	• Use a formula to determine the volume of a cylinder, a cone, and a sphere.	Use formulas to find volume. **CCSS:** 8.G.9	• **volume** • **cubic units**
ON-LEVEL TARGET	**READY TO GO** **Solving Problems with Volume**	• Use multiple formulas to find the volume of a solid.	Use formulas to solve volume problems. **CCSS:** 8.G.9	

MATERIALS

- Math Tool: Volume Formulas, p. A8 (Student Edition p. 223)
- Small empty box *(suggested)*
- Unit cubes *(suggested)*

Build Background

- Discuss with students different real world situations in which the volume of an object is needed. For example, Richard needs to fill his circular pool with water. If the pool is 4 feet deep and 12 feet across, how much water will he need to fill the pool? Explain that substituting the dimensions of the pool into the formula for the volume of a cylinder is the way to find the answer.

- **MP4** Have students discuss additional examples of real situations where the volume of an object is needed.

Introduce and Model

- **Introduce Concepts and Vocabulary** Guide students through the information about finding volume. Emphasize that the volume of an object will always be expressed in cubic units. Use **Words to Know** to clarify their understanding of vocabulary. **MP3** Have students demonstrate to a partner their understanding of *volume*.

- **Support Discussion** **MP3** Have partners discuss briefly before group discussion. As needed, discuss the similarities and differences between a cone and a cylinder.

> *Prompt: What difference do you notice between the formulas for the volume of a cone and the volume of a cylinder?*
> *Sentence Starter: If a cone and a cylinder have the same radius and height, the cone will be …*

ENGLISH LANGUAGE LEARNERS

MP4 ELL students may or may not be familiar with volume. Show students a glass full of water and say: *The amount of water in this glass is measured in cubic units. The number of cubic units is the volume of the glass.*

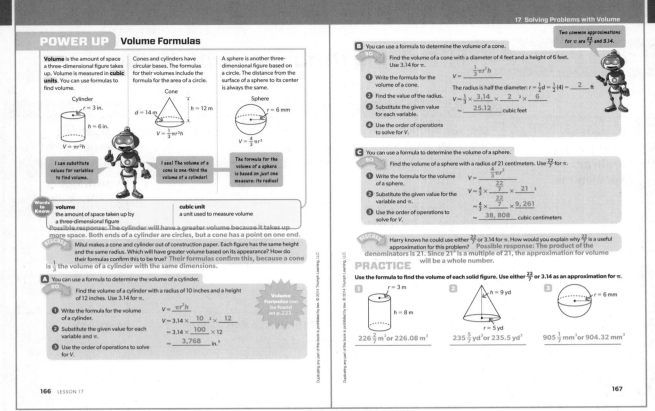

Model Application

DO ▶ A Monitor that students do not transpose the values for the height and radius in the formula for the volume of a cylinder.

DO ▶ B Guide students through using the formula for finding the volume of a cone. Monitor that students are using the correct formula.

DO ▶ C Guide students through using the formula for finding the volume of a sphere. Monitor that students use $\frac{22}{7}$ for the value of π.

Support Discussion **MP7** Have partners discuss briefly before group discussion. As needed, review multiplying and simplifying fractions.

> *Prompt: Are there any situations where it is easier to multiply a fraction by a fraction?*
>
> *Sentence Starter: $\frac{22}{7}$ is a useful approximation because …*

Practice and Assess

- Ask students to complete practice items 1–3 on page 167 independently or in pairs. Monitor ongoing work.

Observation	Action
Students correctly perform the volume calculations, but forget to write their answer in cubic units.	Provide unit cubes to model volume. Place a box on a desk. Tell students that 1 cube will equal 1 cubic unit. *Count as many cubes as are needed to fill this box. What would you identify as the units for this volume?*

		OBJECTIVES	CONCEPTS AND SKILLS	VOCABULARY
FOUNDATIONAL UNDERSTANDING	**PLUG IN** Evaluating Algebraic Expressions	• Use substitution and the order of operations to evaluate a variable expression. • Evaluate an algebraic expression containing parentheses for given values. • Evaluate an algebraic expression containing exponents for given values.	Evaluate algebraic expressions for given values. **CCSS:** 6.EE.2.c	• **algebraic expression** • **substitution** • **arithmetic expression** • **order of operations**
	POWER UP Volume Formulas	• Use a formula to determine the volume of a cylinder, a cone, and a sphere.	Use formulas to find volume **CCSS:** 8.G.9	• **volume** • **cubic units**
ON-LEVEL TARGET	**► READY TO GO** Solving Problems with Volume Student Edition pp. 168–173	• Use multiple formulas to find the volume of a solid.	Use formulas to solve volume problems **CCSS:** 8.G.9	

MATERIALS

- Lesson 17 Quiz, Assessment Manual pp. 36–37
- Lesson 17 Quiz Answer Key, Assessment Manual
- Math Tool: Two-Dimensional Shapes, p. A18 (Student Edition p. 243)
- Math Tool: Volume Formulas, pp. A8, A10 (Student Edition pp. 223, 227)
- 3-D Rectangular prism (suggested)

ENGLISH LANGUAGE LEARNERS

MP6 ELL students may confuse solid figures with plane figures. Distribute **Math Tool: Two-Dimensional Shapes** and **Math Tool: Volume Formulas** to review the characteristics of each type of figure.

Build Background

- Talk to students about reasons to work with volume in real life. For example, you buy a rectangular fish tank that is 24 inches long, 10 inches deep, and 8 inches wide. How much water will you need to fill the tank? Explain that students should use a formula to find the volume of this prism.
- **MP4** Have students discuss additional examples of real situation that involve finding the volume of figures.
- Tell students they will use formulas to solve volume problems.

Introduce and Model

- **Introduce Concepts** Guide students through the information about using formulas to find the volume of solid figures. Remind students that volume is always measured in cubic units.
- **Support Discussion** **MP4** Have students discuss briefly before group discussion. If students are struggling, have them draw a picture of the figure in the problem.

> **Prompt:** Suppose a cube has side lengths of 5 cm. How would you find the volume of the cube?
> **Sentence Starter:** The volume of a cube …

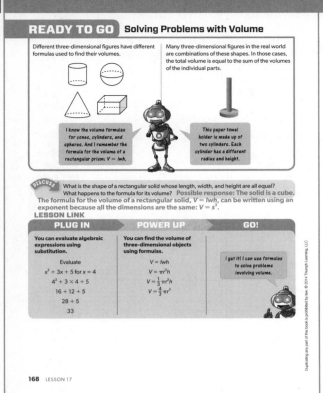

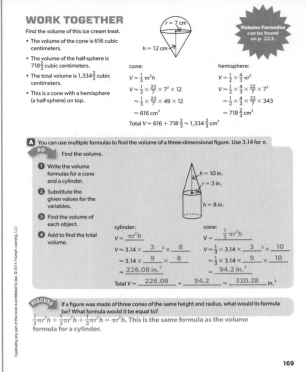

LESSON LINK

Connect to Foundational Understanding Skills learned in the **Plug In** and **Power Up** are referenced in the **Lesson Link**. Explain that a formula is also an algebraic expression, which can be evaluated for different values using substitution.

- **Work Together** Explain that students will find the total volume of a composite object that is made up of a cone and a half-sphere. Begin by working together with students to identify which formulas should be used to find the total volume. If necessary, draw the two shapes as separate figures on the board and shade in the parts for which the volume is to be found.

DO ▶ **A** Monitor students as they find the volume of a composite figure. If necessary, remind students that they will have to use two formulas and then find the sum in order to find the total volume of the composite figure.

- **Support Discussion** **MP** Have partners discuss briefly before group discussion. As needed, suggest that students write an algebraic expression to represent the situation.

> *Prompt: What is the formula for the volume of a cone? How can you find the total volume of three identical cones?*
> *Sentence Starter: The volume of three identical cones …*

COMMON ERRORS

MP2 Students may mistake the ice cream cone for a cone, rather than a composite figure made up of a cone and a half-sphere. Have students explain the steps they use to make an ice cream cone at home, by taking a spherical scoop of ice cream and placing it into an empty cone.

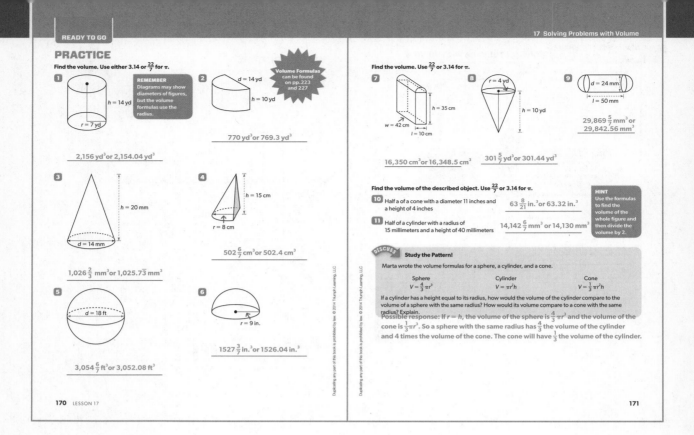

ADDITIONAL PRACTICE

Provide students with additional practice to model and solve:

A cubic prism has side length 8 cm. What is its volume?

What is the volume of a sphere that has radius 5 mm?

SPOTLIGHT ON MATHEMATICAL LANGUAGE

MP6 Support students in using mathematical language as they work:

- *How can you evaluate an **algebraic expression** for a value?*
- *What does the **volume** of a figure tell you?*

Support Independent Practice

1–6 Remind students to read the **REMEMBER**. If needed, ask: *How are the diameter and the radius of a figure related?*

7–9 *What composite figures do you see? What formulas will you use?*

10–11 Remind students to read the **HINT**. *What does it mean if the figure is cut in half?*

- **Support Discussion** **MP7** Have partners compare the formulas and discuss before sharing. As needed, review comparing fractions.

> **Prompt:** *How would the formula for the volume of a cylinder be written if the height is equal to the radius?*
> **Sentence Starter:** *If r = h, then the exponent for r in the formula is …*

Problem Solving

- **Model the Four-Step Method** **MP6** Guide students through the four-step method using think-aloud strategies. Remind students to write their answers in cubic feet.

  Think Aloud Since you are finding the volume of the whole barn, you will need to calculate two volumes.

- **Support Problem-Solving Practice** Have students use the Checklist as they complete each step.

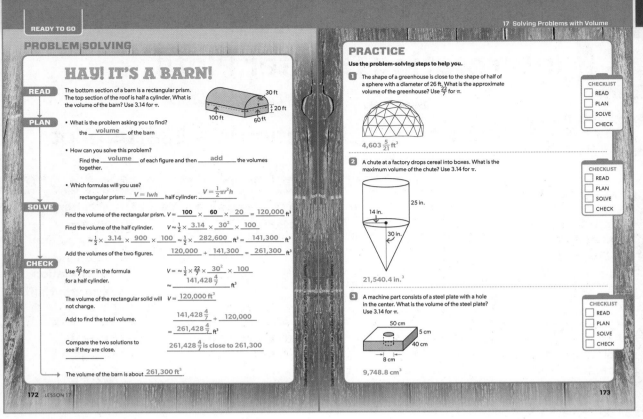

READY TO GO

PROBLEM SOLVING

HAY! IT'S A BARN!

READ The bottom section of a barn is a rectangular prism. The top section of the roof is half a cylinder. What is the volume of the barn? Use 3.14 for π.

30 ft
20 ft
100 ft
60 ft

PLAN
• What is the problem asking you to find?
  the ___volume___ of the barn

• How can you solve this problem?
  Find the ___volume___ of each figure and then ___add___ the volumes together.

• Which formulas will you use?
  rectangular prism: $V = lwh$ half cylinder: $V = \frac{1}{2}\pi r^2 h$

SOLVE Find the volume of the rectangular prism. $V = $ ___100___ × ___60___ × ___20___ = ___120,000___ ft³

Find the volume of the half cylinder. $V \approx \frac{1}{2} \times$ ___3.14___ × ___30²___ × ___100___

$\approx \frac{1}{2} \times$ ___3.14___ × ___900___ × ___100___ $\approx \frac{1}{2} \times$ ___282,600___ ft³ = ___141,300___ ft³

Add the volumes of the two figures. ___120,000___ + ___141,300___ = ___261,300___ ft³

CHECK Use $\frac{22}{7}$ for π in the formula for a half cylinder.

$V = \approx \frac{1}{2} \times \frac{22}{7} \times$ ___30²___ × ___100___
$\approx$ ___141,428 $\frac{4}{7}$___ ft³

The volume of the rectangular solid will not change. $V = $ ___120,000___ ft³

Add to find the total volume.
___141,428 $\frac{4}{7}$___ + ___120,000___
= ___261,428 $\frac{4}{7}$___ ft³

Compare the two solutions to see if they are close. 261,428 $\frac{4}{7}$ is close to 261,300.

The volume of the barn is about ___261,300 ft³___

172 LESSON 17

PRACTICE

Use the problem-solving steps to help you.

1 The shape of a greenhouse is close to the shape of half of a sphere with a diameter of 26 ft. What is the approximate volume of the greenhouse? Use $\frac{22}{7}$ for π.

4,603 $\frac{5}{21}$ ft³

CHECKLIST
☐ READ
☐ PLAN
☐ SOLVE
☐ CHECK

2 A chute at a factory drops cereal into boxes. What is the maximum volume of the chute? Use 3.14 for π.

25 in.
14 in.
30 in.

21,540.4 in.³

CHECKLIST
☐ READ
☐ PLAN
☐ SOLVE
☐ CHECK

3 A machine part consists of a steel plate with a hole in the center. What is the volume of the steel plate? Use 3.14 for π.

50 cm
5 cm
40 cm
8 cm

9,748.8 cm³

CHECKLIST
☐ READ
☐ PLAN
☐ SOLVE
☐ CHECK

173

Prompt: *Are there any dimensions of the two figures that are the same?*

Prompt: *Would you find each volume first and then add the volumes or add the formulas and then find the total volume?*

Prompt: *How does using a different approximation of π help you check your answer for mistakes?*

• **Explore Student Thinking** **MP1** Invite students to discuss how they solved the problem in groups. Have groups present any alternative methods aloud to the class.

ENGLISH LANGUAGE LEARNERS

MP4 ELL students may have difficulty with the term "rectangular solid." Have students identify the root word "rectangle" and ask them to give a definition and draw an example. Then show a three-dimensional rectangular solid to the students and relate the two drawings.

Assess

• Use the table below to address any difficulties.

	Observation	Action
1	Errors in evaluating formulas are frequent; general confusion about volume.	Have students write and solve their own volume problems, using simple three-dimensional figures rather than composite figures.
2	Makes occasional computational errors when using volume formulas.	Provide additional practice problems for evaluating volume formulas. Remind students to follow the order of operations for each step in their computation. Have students work in groups to help minimize computational errors.
3	Chooses the correct formula to use, and evaluates volumes accurately.	Assign the Lesson 17 Quiz.

Interpreting Scatter Plots

PLUG IN Identifying Association in a Scatter Plot

		OBJECTIVES	CONCEPTS AND SKILLS	VOCABULARY
FOUNDATIONAL UNDERSTANDING	▶ PLUG IN **Identifying Association in a Scatter Plot** Student Edition pp. 174–175	• Determine a pattern of association between two quantities represented in a scatter plot. • Describe a pattern of association between two quantities represented in a scatter plot.	Identify correlation in a scatter plot. **CCSS:** 8.SP.1	• **scatter plot** • **linear association** • **nonlinear association** • **no association**
	POWER UP **Constructing Scatter Plots**	• Plot points to show ordered pairs of data. • Construct a scatter plot to show the data in a table.	Construct scatter plots. **CCSS:** 8.SP.1	• ***x*-axis** • **scale** • ***y*-axis**
ON-LEVEL TARGET	**READY TO GO** **Interpreting Scatter Plots**	• Interpret a scatter plot. • Construct a scatter plot to see if pairs of data are related.	Interpret scatter plots. **CCSS:** 8.SP.1	• **outliers**

MATERIALS
• Math Tool: Coordinate Grids, p. A12 (Student Edition, p. 231)

ENGLISH LANGUAGE LEARNERS
MP6 ELL students may need additional support to understand how the term *association* is used in terms of scatter plots. In business, an association is group of people who join together for a common purpose. In mathematics, *association* refers to the way the data points tend to relate to each other.

Build Background
■ Talk to students about uses for scatter plots in real life. For example, if the relationship between air temperature and elevation above sea level were graphed on a scatter plot, the data would show a linear correlation. Explain that knowing how two different factors relate to each other can be useful in decision-making.

■ **MP2** Have students discuss additional examples of relationships between two real situations that could be represented in scatter plots.

Introduce and Model
■ **Introduce Concepts and Vocabulary** Guide students through the information on scatter plots. Use **Words to Know** to clarify their understanding of vocabulary. **MP4** Have student describe the difference between data that has a *linear association* and data that has a *nonlinear association*.

■ **Support Discussion** **MP3** Have students discuss briefly before group discussion. As needed, direct students to **Words to Know** as they formulate their reasoning.

> *Prompt:* Could the association be described as positive, negative, or curved? Explain.
> *Sentence Starter:* A horizontal line means…

LESSON 18 Interpreting Scatter Plots

PLUG IN Identifying Association in a Scatter Plot

You can look at how the data points are clustered in this **scatter plot** to determine if there is a relationship between outside temperature and ice cream sales.

Outside Temperature and Ice Cream Sales

Ice Cream Cones Sold vs *Outside Temperature (in °F)*

In this scatter plot, the x-coordinate in each ordered pair represents the temperature and the y-coordinate represents ice cream sales.

Decide if the data points cluster in a straight line or a curve, or if they look randomly scattered. Then you can identify the **association** between the sets of data.

- **Linear association:** The data resembles a straight line. You can also describe a linear association as positive or negative, depending on the slope of the line.
- **Nonlinear association:** The data resembles a curve.
- **No association:** The data is randomly scattered.

I see! The data in this scatter plot shows a positive linear association because the points cluster together like a line with a positive slope.

Words to Know

scatter plot	association	linear association	nonlinear association
a graph of ordered pairs that shows the relationship between two sets of data	the relationship between data points on a scatter plot	a relationship shown on a scatter plot in which data points resemble a straight line	a relationship shown on a scatter plot in which data points resemble a curve

DISCUSS Maja sees a scatter plot in which each point lies along a horizontal line. She says the line that the points would cluster around has zero slope, so the scatter plot shows no association. Is she correct? Explain why or why not.
Possible response: no; The association is linear, regardless of the slope.

174 LESSON 18

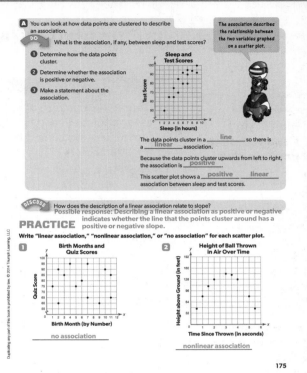

A You can look at how data points are clustered to describe an association.

DO What is the association, if any, between sleep and test scores?

1. Determine how the data points cluster.
2. Determine whether the association is positive or negative.
3. Make a statement about the association.

The association describes the relationship between the two variables graphed on a scatter plot.

Sleep and Test Scores

Test Score vs *Sleep (in hours)*

The data points cluster in a ___line___ so there is a ___linear___ association.

Because the data points cluster upwards from left to right, the association is ___positive___.

This scatter plot shows a ___positive___ ___linear___ association between sleep and test scores.

DISCUSS How does the description of a linear association relate to slope?
Possible response: Describing a linear association as positive or negative indicates whether the line that the points cluster around has a positive or negative slope.

PRACTICE
Write "linear association," "nonlinear association," or "no association" for each scatter plot.

1 **Birth Months and Quiz Scores**

Quiz Score vs *Birth Month (by Number)*

no association

2 **Height of Ball Thrown in Air Over Time**

Height above Ground (in feet) vs *Time Since Thrown (in seconds)*

nonlinear association

175

▪ Model Application

DO ▶ A Guide students as they evaluate the data points on the graph. *What conclusion can you make about sleep and test scores based on the scatter plot?*

▪ Support Discussion MP3 Have students discuss briefly before group discussion.

> *Prompt: How are the x- and y-values of a line with a positive slope related to each other?*
> *Sentence Starter: As the x-values increase, the y-values …*

Practice and Assess

- Ask students to complete practice items 1 and 2 on page 175 independently or in pairs. Monitor ongoing work.
- Use the table below to address any difficulties.

Observation	Action
Students have difficulty identifying the association between the data points on the scatter plots.	Suggest students place their fingers on the first point on the x-axis, and then trace the progression of the data along the x-axis. Students will be able to feel that there is no pattern to the data in Problem 1, so there is no association. Repeat with the other data on the remaining graph.

SPOTLIGHT ON MATHEMATICAL PRACTICES

MP4 Model with Mathematics

Not all types of data are appropriate for every type of graph. The purpose of a scatter plot is to show how one variable affects another. *Are the number of hours of sleep a person gets each night related to the amount of time he or she spends using technology?* Work together as a class to gather and graph the data in a scatter plot. *Is there an association between the two variables? If so, what is it?*

Constructing Scatter Plots

		OBJECTIVES	CONCEPTS AND SKILLS	VOCABULARY
FOUNDATIONAL UNDERSTANDING	**PLUG IN** **Identifying Association in a Scatter Plot**	• Determine a pattern of association between two quantities represented in a scatter plot. • Describe a pattern of association between two quantities represented in a scatter plot.	Identify correlation in a scatter plot. **CCSS:** 8.SP.1	• **scatter plot** • **linear association** • **nonlinear association** • **no association**
	▶ POWER UP **Constructing Scatter Plots** Student Edition pp. 176–177	• Plot points to show ordered pairs of data. • Construct a scatter plot to show the data in a table.	Construct scatter plots. **CCSS:** 8.SP.1	• **x-axis** • **scale** • **y-axis**
ON-LEVEL TARGET	**READY TO GO** **Interpreting Scatter Plots**	• Interpret a scatter plot. • Construct a scatter plot to see if pairs of data are related.	Interpret scatter plots. **CCSS:** 8.SP.1	• **outliers**

MATERIALS
• Graph paper (suggested)

ENGLISH LANGUAGE LEARNERS

MP6 ELL students may need additional support to understand the mathematical meaning of *scale*. Ask students to brainstorm different meanings of the word such as scales on fish or scales to weigh things. In mathematics, one of the meanings of scale is a range of numbers set at fixed intervals. The interval of a scale is dependent on the relationship between the values in a data set.

Build Background

■ Talk to students about scatter plots in real life. For example, a scatter plot can be used to demonstrate the relationship between the duration of an eruption of Old Faithful and the length of time between eruptions. Researchers may choose to display their findings in a scatter plot because it is a visually easy way to see the relationship between two variables.

■ **MP4** Have students discuss additional examples of real situations in which scatter plots might be used to display data.

■ Tell students they will use given data to construct scatter plots.

Introduce and Model

■ **Introduce Concepts and Vocabulary** Guide students through the information about creating a scatter plot. Emphasize that the scale should represent the data values as closely as possible. Use **Words to Know** to clarify their understanding of vocabulary. **MP5** Have students explain to a partner how to use the data to determine a *scale* for the *x-axis* and the *y-axis*.

■ **Support Discussion** **MP5** Have partners discuss briefly before group discussion. As needed, have students use graph paper to model the scale on a coordinate grid.

> *Prompt: How would changing the scale of the x-axis impact the look of the scatter plot?*
> *Sentence Starter: A smaller scale on the x-axis would…*

POWER UP Constructing Scatter Plots

You can construct a scatter plot using data in a table.

Children's Ages and Heights

Age (in years)	1	2	3	3	4	4	5	7	8	9
Height (in inches)	25	30	35	40	35	40	40	45	45	50

Children's Ages and Heights

① **Title the scatter plot.** Use the title of the table.

② **Label and number the x-axis.** Use the label from the top row of the table. The values for data in that row range from 1 to 9. A good **scale** to use is 0 to 10, with intervals of 1.

③ **Label and number the y-axis.** Use the label from the bottom row of the table. The values for that variable range from 25 to 50. A good scale to use is 0 to 50, with intervals of 5.

④ **Plot a point for each ordered pair.** Plot points at (1, 25), (2, 30), (3, 35), (3, 40), and so on.

I get it! I have to choose a scale that lets me fit all the data points I have on the scatter plot.

Words to Know

x-axis	scale	y-axis
the horizontal number line on an x-y coordinate graph	numbers that change at regular intervals along an axis of a graph	the vertical number line on an x-y coordinate graph

DISCUSS Devon is planning a scatter plot for the data points (1, 5), (5, 45), (9, 28). He decides to make the scale for each axis 0 to 50. Would you agree or disagree with his choice? Explain.
Possible response: Disagree. The scale of each axis should be based on the values for each variable, not both variables. So a more reasonable scale would be 0 to 10 for the x-axis and 0 to 50 for the y-axis.

176 LESSON 18

Ⓐ You can construct a scatter plot to show the data in a table.
Construct a scatter plot to show these data.

Choosing the right scale for each axis lets me see all of the data clearly.

DVD Sales and Release Dates

Weeks Since Release	0	1	1	2	3	3	4	4	5
Number Sold	18	16	14	12	13	10	12	8	9

① Label the x-axis using the name of the variable in the first row. Choose a scale.

② Label the y-axis using the name of the variable in the second row. Choose a scale.

③ Plot each ordered pair in the table as a point.

For the x-axis, use a scale of ___0___ to ___5___, with intervals of $\frac{1}{2}$.

For the y-axis, use a scale of 0 to ___20___, with intervals of 2.

DVD Sales and Release Dates

PRACTICE

Construct a scatter plot to show the data in the table. Include a title, scales, and axis labels.

① **Rainfall and Umbrella Sales**

Rainfall (in inches)	0	1	1	2	2	3	4	4
Number Sold	1	2	3	3	5	6	8	9

Rainfall and Umbrella Sales

② **Temperature and Scarf Sales**

Temperature (in °F)	20	30	40	50	50	60	80
Number Sold	18	16	12	10	7	4	2

Temperature and Scarf Sales

177

• Model Application

DO Ⓐ Remind students that the usefulness of a scatter plot is dependent on how clearly the information is presented. Labels should accurately describe the meaning of the variable. *Which variable should be represented on the x-axis? The y-axis?*

Practice and Assess

- Ask students to complete practice items 1 and 2 on page 177 independently or in pairs. Monitor ongoing work.
- Use the table below to address any difficulties.

Observation	Action
Students have difficulty assigning a scale for the axes.	Remind students to first identify the greatest and least values of x and y in the data table. Tell them the scale must encompass these two values. Then have students summarize the relationship between the data values.

SPOTLIGHT ON MATHEMATICAL PRACTICES

MP7 Make Use of Structure

Traditionally, the x-values represent the independent variable. Its value is not affected by a change in the y-values. The y-values represent the dependent variable. A change in x results in a change in y. For example, the amount of snowfall (x) causes an increase in the number of skiers (y). Conversely, the number of skiers has no effect on the amount of snowfall received. Guide students as they determine the independent and dependent variables in the data tables.

		OBJECTIVES	CONCEPTS AND SKILLS	VOCABULARY
FOUNDATIONAL UNDERSTANDING	**PLUG IN** **Identifying Association in a Scatter Plot**	• Determine a pattern of association between two quantities represented in a scatter plot. • Describe a pattern of association between two quantities represented in a scatter plot.	Identify correlation in a scatter plot. **CCSS:** 8.SP.1	• **scatter plot** • **linear association** • **nonlinear association** • **no association**
	POWER UP **Constructing Scatter Plots**	• Plot points to show ordered pairs of data. • Construct a scatter plot to show the data in a table.	Construct scatter plots. **CCSS:** 8.SP.1	• **x-axis** • **scale** • **y-axis**
ON-LEVEL TARGET	▶ **READY TO GO** **Interpreting Scatter Plots** Student Edition pp. 178–183	• Interpret a scatter plot. • Construct a scatter plot to see if pairs of data are related.	Interpret scatter plots. **CCSS:** 8.SP.1	• **outliers**

MATERIALS
- Lesson 18 Quiz, Assessment Manual pp. 38–39
- Lesson 18 Quiz Answer Key, Assessment Manual
- Graph paper (suggested)

ENGLISH LANGUAGE LEARNERS

MP3 ELL students may need additional support to understand the impact of an outlier on a data set. For example, in the Ticket Prices and Sales scatter plot, the outlier represents an unusual relationship between ticket prices and ticket sales. Perhaps the concert held especially high appeal for some reason. That is not true in general, so taking the outlier into consideration when evaluating the data presents a falsely high association between the two variables.

Build Background

- Talk to students about why scatter plots are used in real-life decision making. For example, a restaurant wants to know the best time to stop serving breakfast. A scatter plot can show the relationship between the time of day and whether more people order breakfast or lunch. By studying the association between the data points, the restaurant can satisfy the greatest number of customers.

- **MP4** Have students discuss additional examples of real situations that involve using scatter plots to identify an association between different kinds of data.

Introduce and Model

- **Introduce Concepts and Vocabulary** Guide students through the information about identifying associations between data displayed in a scatter plot. Use **Words to Know** to clarify their understanding of vocabulary. **MP6** Have students explain the impact of an *outlier* on a data set.

- **Support Discussion** **MP2** Have partners briefly discuss before group discussion. If students have difficulty understanding the impact of an outlier, suggest they find the average of the quiz grades with and without the outlier: 90, 84, 95, 86, 92, 62.

> **Prompt:** *If the outlier were considered when interpreting the data, what impact would it have on the relationship between ticket prices and the number of tickets sold?*
>
> **Sentence Starter:** *The outlier makes it appear as if higher ticket prices result in…*

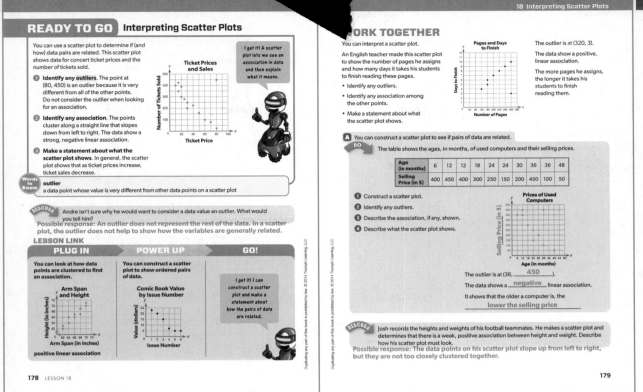

READY TO GO Interpreting Scatter Plots

You can use a scatter plot to determine if (and how) data pairs are related. This scatter plot shows data for concert ticket prices and the number of tickets sold.

I get it! A scatter plot lets me see an association in data and then explain what it means.

❶ **Identify any outliers.** The point at (80, 450) is an outlier because it is very different from all of the other points. Do not consider the outlier when looking for an association.

❷ **Identify any association.** The points cluster along a straight line that slopes down from left to right. The data show a strong, negative linear association.

❸ **Make a statement about what the scatter plot shows.** In general, the scatter plot shows that as ticket prices increase, ticket sales decrease.

Words to Know **outlier**
a data point whose value is very different from other data points on a scatter plot

DISCUSS Andre isn't sure why he would want to consider a data value an outlier. What would you tell him?
Possible response: An outlier does not represent the rest of the data. In a scatter plot, the outlier does not help to show how the variables are generally related.

LESSON LINK

PLUG IN	POWER UP	GO!
You can look at how data points are clustered to find an association.	You can construct a scatter plot to show ordered pairs of data.	*I get it! I can construct a scatter plot and make a statement about how the pairs of data are related.*

Arm Span and Height

positive linear association

Comic Book Value by Issue Number

178 LESSON 18

WORK TOGETHER

You can interpret a scatter plot.

An English teacher made this scatter plot to show the number of pages he assigns and how many days it takes his students to finish reading these pages.

• Identify any outliers.
• Identify any association among the other points.
• Make a statement about what the scatter plot shows.

Pages and Days to Finish

The outlier is at (320, 3).

The data show a positive, linear association.

The more pages he assigns, the longer it takes his students to finish reading them.

Ⓐ You can construct a scatter plot to see if pairs of data are related.

DO The table shows the ages, in months, of used computers and their selling prices.

Age (in months)	6	12	12	18	24	24	30	36	36	48
Selling Price (in $)	400	450	400	300	250	150	200	450	100	50

❶ Construct a scatter plot.
❷ Identify any outliers.
❸ Describe the association, if any, shown.
❹ Describe what the scatter plot shows.

Prices of Used Computers

The outlier is at (36, ___450___).

The data shows a ___negative___ linear association.

It shows that the older a computer is, the ___lower the selling price___

DISCUSS Josh records the heights and weights of his football teammates. He makes a scatter plot and determines that there is a weak, positive association between height and weight. Describe how his scatter plot must look.
Possible response: The data points on his scatter plot slope up from left to right, but they are not too closely clustered together.

179

LESSON LINK

Connect to Foundational Understanding Skills learned in the **Plug In** and **Power Up** are referenced in the **Lesson Link**. Explain that an association represents the way variables interact with each other. It is easier to see associations by graphing data in a scatter plot. Associations can be used to make decisions based on the data.

• **Work Together** Explain that students will use data points on a scatter plot to identify any association between the variables. Point out that in a scatter plot, an *x*-value may be correlated to more than one *y*-value. *What does the outlier on the scatter plot represent?*

DO Ⓐ Guide students as they graph the data on a scatter plot. Ask student partners to discuss what age of used computer they would buy based on the scatter plot. *What characteristics of a computer might cause the relationship between age and price to be an outlier?*

• **Support Discussion** **MP1** Have partners discuss briefly before group discussion. As needed, suggest that students use graph paper to sketch a possible representation of the relationship between height and weight.

> *Prompt: What does a positive association mean? What does it mean if the positive association is weak?*
> *Sentence Starter: A positive association means …*

COMMON ERRORS

Students may reason that a negative association is negative, or bad. Explain that the term negative association refers to the relationship between the variables. If the *y*-values decrease as the *x*-values increase, or vice versa, the association will be negative. If both the *x*- and *y*-values either increase or decrease, the association will be positive. For example, as the age of a puppy increases, the occurrence of bad behavior decreases. This negative association is a positive result.

SPOTLIGHT ON MATHEMATICAL LANGUAGE

MP6 Support students in using mathematical language as they work.

• *Is it possible to have an* **outlier** *when the scatter plot shows no association between the points?*

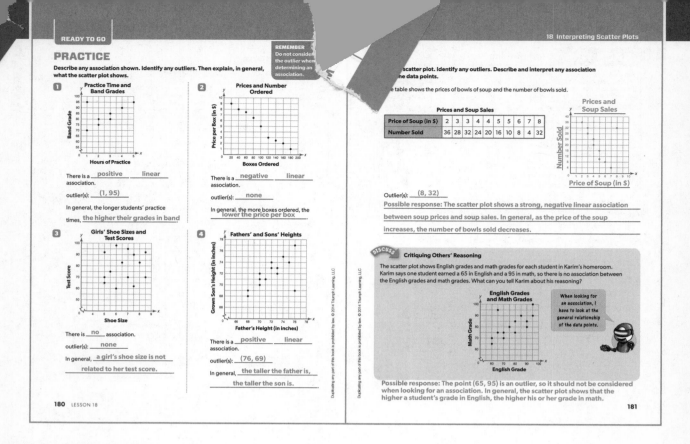

PRACTICE

Describe any association shown. Identify any outliers. Then explain, in general, what the scatter plot shows.

REMEMBER
Do not consider the outlier when determining an association.

1 Practice Time and Band Grades

There is a ___positive___ ___linear___ association.

outlier(s): ___(1, 95)___

In general, the longer students' practice times, the higher their grades in band.

2 Prices and Number Ordered

There is a ___negative___ ___linear___ association.

outlier(s): ___none___

In general, the more boxes ordered, the lower the price per box.

3 Girls' Shoe Sizes and Test Scores

There is ___no___ association.

outlier(s): ___none___

In general, a girl's shoe size is not related to her test score.

4 Fathers' and Sons' Heights

There is a ___positive___ ___linear___ association.

outlier(s): ___(76, 69)___

In general, the taller the father is, the taller the son is.

...scatter plot. Identify any outliers. Describe and interpret any association ...e data points.

...e table shows the prices of bowls of soup and the number of bowls sold.

Prices and Soup Sales

Price of Soup (in $)	2	3	3	4	4	5	5	6	7	8
Number Sold	36	28	32	24	20	16	10	8	4	32

Outlier(s): ___(8, 32)___

Possible response: The scatter plot shows a strong, negative linear association between soup prices and soup sales. In general, as the price of the soup increases, the number of bowls sold decreases.

DISCUSS Critiquing Others' Reasoning

The scatter plot shows English grades and math grades for each student in Karim's homeroom. Karim says one student earned a 65 in English and a 95 in math, so there is no association between the English grades and math grades. What can you tell Karim about his reasoning?

When looking for an association, I have to look at the general relationship of the data points.

Possible response: The point (65, 95) is an outlier, so it should not be considered when looking for an association. In general, the scatter plot shows that the higher a student's grade in English, the higher his or her grade in math.

180 LESSON 18

181

ADDITIONAL PRACTICE

Provide students with additional practice to model and solve:

Create a scatter plot of the data. Describe any association of the data.

High School Football Games and Attendance

Total Wins	Attendance
0	225
1	250
2	225
3	270
4	320
5	300
6	365
7	410

Support Independent Practice

1–4 Remind students to read the **REMEMBER**. If needed, ask: *How do the points cluster if there is a positive association? A negative association?*

5 *What will be the title of the scatter plot? Which is the dependent variable? Which is the independent variable? What will be the labels on the x- and y-axes? What would be a good scale for the x-axis? The y-axis?*

- **Support Discussion** MP3 Have partners discuss before group discussion. As needed, have students verbally summarize the meaning of the data points: A grade of 60 in English corresponds to a grade of 65 in math. A grade of 90 in English corresponds to a grade of 80 or 85 in math.

> *Prompt:* What summary statement could you make about how English grades relate to math grades?
> *Sentence Starter:* If a student has good grades in English, his or her math grades are…

Problem Solving

- **Model the Four-Step Method** MP1 MP4 Guide students through the four-step method using think-aloud strategies. Point out that both variables are independent.

  Think Aloud All of the data is in multiples of 10. I can use a broken scale from 40 to 160 in intervals of 20 for the drink data.

- **Support Problem-Solving Practice** Have students use the Checklist as they complete each step.

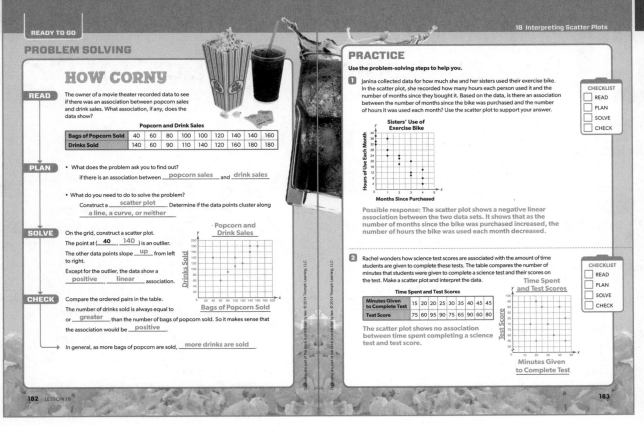

READY TO GO

PROBLEM SOLVING

HOW CORNY

READ The owner of a movie theater recorded data to see if there was an association between popcorn sales and drink sales. What association, if any, does the data show?

Popcorn and Drink Sales

Bags of Popcorn Sold	40	60	80	100	100	120	140	140	160
Drinks Sold	140	60	90	110	140	120	160	180	180

PLAN
• What does the problem ask you to find out?
if there is an association between ___popcorn sales___ and ___drink sales___

• What do you need to do to solve the problem?
Construct a ___scatter plot___. Determine if the data points cluster along ___a line, a curve, or neither___.

SOLVE On the grid, construct a scatter plot.
The point at (__40__, __140__) is an outlier.
The other data points slope __up__ from left to right.
Except for the outlier, the data show a __positive__ __linear__ association.

Popcorn and Drink Sales

CHECK Compare the ordered pairs in the table.
The number of drinks sold is always equal to or __greater__ than the number of bags of popcorn sold. So it makes sense that the association would be __positive__.

In general, as more bags of popcorn are sold, __more drinks are sold__.

182 LESSON 18

PRACTICE

Use the problem-solving steps to help you.

1 Janina collected data for how much she and her sisters used their exercise bike. In the scatter plot, she recorded how many hours each person used it and the number of months since they bought it. Based on the data, is there an association between the number of months since the bike was purchased and the number of hours it was used each month? Use the scatter plot to support your answer.

Sisters' Use of Exercise Bike

CHECKLIST
☐ READ
☐ PLAN
☐ SOLVE
☐ CHECK

Possible response: The scatter plot shows a negative linear association between the two data sets. It shows that as the number of months since the bike was purchased increased, the number of hours the bike was used each month decreased.

2 Rachel wonders how science test scores are associated with the amount of time students are given to complete these tests. The table compares the number of minutes that students were given to complete a science test and their scores on the test. Make a scatter plot and interpret the data.

Time Spent and Test Scores

Minutes Given to Complete Test	15	20	20	25	30	35	40	45	45
Test Score	75	60	95	90	75	65	90	60	80

Time Spent and Test Scores

CHECKLIST
☐ READ
☐ PLAN
☐ SOLVE
☐ CHECK

The scatter plot shows no association between time spent completing a science test and test score.

183

Prompt: *Why are there three data points for each month?*
Prompt: *What conclusion might the scatter plot suggest?*
Prompt: *Which variable will be placed on the x-axis? Which variable will be placed on the y-axis?*

• **Explore Student Thinking** MP4 Ask students to consider what information a scatter plot can and cannot show. *In Problem 1, does the scatter plot show which girl used the bike a certain number of hours each month? Is there a way to show that information in a scatter plot?*

Assess

• Use the table below to address any difficulties.

MP6 Attend to Precision

Students should be aware that graphs are often used to display data in a way most favorable to the desired interpretation. When interpreting graphs, students should pay close attention to the scale. An unusually close or broad scale can significantly change the appearance of the data.

	Observation	Action
1	Frequent errors in graphing data in a scatter plot and interpreting any association between the data points	Provide additional data for variables that have a strong association or no association. Guide students as they work to determine a title and labels for the graph, as well as appropriate scales. Have students verbally explain their thought processes as they plot and interpret the data points.
2	Occasional errors in graphing data in a scatter plot or interpreting any association between the data points	Provide opportunities for students to gather live data and work in small groups to display the data in a scatter plot. Allow time for students to display their work for the class.
3	Accurately graphs data in a scatter plot and interprets any association between the data points.	Assign Lesson 18 Quiz.

19 Solving Problems with Scatter Plots

PLUG IN   Identifying a Trend Line

		OBJECTIVES	CONCEPTS AND SKILLS	VOCABULARY
FOUNDATIONAL UNDERSTANDING	▶ **PLUG IN** **Identifying a Trend Line** Student Edition pp. 184–185	• Determine the association represented by a trend line. • Use the association represent by a trend line to predict data points.	Describe the association represented by a trend line on a scatter plot. **CCSS:** 8.SP.2	• **trend line** • **association**
	POWER UP **Drawing a Trend Line**	• Draw a trend line for a scatter plot.	Draw a trend line on a scatter plot. **CCSS:** 8.SP.2	• **outlier**
ON-LEVEL TARGET	**READY TO GO** **Solving Problems with Scatter Plots**	• Compare the fit of two trend lines. • Redraw a trend line for a better fit.	Discuss the closeness of the data points to the trend line. **CCSS:** 8.SP.2	

MATERIALS
• Math Tool: Grids, p. A17 (Student Edition, p. 241)

ENGLISH LANGUAGE LEARNERS

MP6 It may be helpful for ELL students to link the terms *trend line* and *trend*. Students may be familiar with the noun *trend* associated with a fashion trend or a sales trend, but may not be familiar with the verb *trend* meaning to change or develop in a general direction. Relate this definition to a trend line, which develops a line in the general direction of the data.

Build Background

■ Talk to students about reasons to describe the association represented by a trend line in real life. For example, when comparing city census data, population experts find and use a trend line to predict future populations or other information.

■ **MP4** Have students discuss additional examples of real situations that involve the association of a trend line to a scatter plot.

■ Tell students they will determine the association represented by a trend line and they will use this association to predict data points.

Introduce and Model

■ **Introduce Concepts and Vocabulary** Guide students through the information about trend lines. Relate that a trend line is also called the line of best fit, which may be easier for students to remember. Use **Words to Know** to clarify their understanding of vocabulary. **MP6** Have students demonstrate to a partner their understanding of *trend line* and *association*.

■ **Support Discussion** **MP7** Have partners discuss briefly before group discussion. As needed, direct students to **Words to Know** and have them draw an example of a nonlinear association.

> *Prompt: What does a trend line represent?*
> *Sentence Starter: The purpose of a trend line is to…*

LESSON 19 Solving Problems with Scatter Plots

PLUG IN Identifying a Trend Line

A **trend line** is a straight line that shows how data points cluster on a scatter plot. A trend line can show a positive linear **association**.

Battery Life and Charge
Minutes of Battery Life
Percent Charged

Or a trend line can show a negative linear association.

Lemonade and Watermelon Sold
Slices of Watermelon Sold
Cups of Lemonade Sold

A trend line is also called the line of best fit. The trend line shown has a positive slope because the trend in the data is that as x increases, y increases.

The trend in these data is that as x increases, y decreases. That means the trend line has a negative slope.

Words to Know
trend line
a straight line that best shows the linear relationship between data points on a scatter plot

association
the relationship between data points on a scatter plot

DISCUSS Would it be useful to draw a trend line for a scatter plot that shows a nonlinear association? Explain. Possible response: No, because many data points would not be represented.

A You can determine the association represented by a trend line.

DO Describe the association shown by the trend line.

❶ Look at the pattern of the data points.
❷ Check the sign of the slope of the trend line.
❸ Describe the association shown by the trend line.

Hair Length and Haircuts
Number of Haircuts Per Year
Hair Length (in inches)

The trend is that as x increases, y decreases

The slope is negative

The trend line shows a negative linear association.

184 LESSON 19

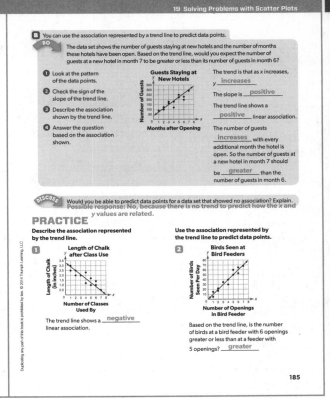

B You can use the association represented by a trend line to predict data points.

DO The data set shows the number of guests staying at new hotels and the number of months these hotels have been open. Based on the trend line, would you expect the number of guests at a new hotel in month 7 to be greater or less than its number of guests in month 6?

❶ Look at the pattern of the data points.
❷ Check the sign of the slope of the trend line.
❸ Describe the association shown by the trend line.
❹ Answer the question based on the association shown.

Guests Staying at New Hotels
Number of Guests
Months after Opening

The trend is that as x increases, y increases

The slope is positive

The trend line shows a positive linear association.

The number of guests increases with every additional month the hotel is open. So the number of guests at a new hotel in month 7 should be greater than the number of guests in month 6.

DISCUSS Would you be able to predict data points for a data set that showed no association? Explain. Possible response: No, because there is no trend to predict how the x and y values are related.

PRACTICE

Describe the association represented by the trend line.

1
Length of Chalk after Class Use
Length of Chalk (in inches)
Number of Classes Used By

The trend line shows a negative linear association.

Use the association represented by the trend line to predict data points.

2
Birds Seen at Bird Feeders
Number of Birds Seen Per Day
Number of Openings in Bird Feeder

Based on the trend line, is the number of birds at a bird feeder with 6 openings greater or less than at a feeder with 5 openings? greater

185

• Model Application

DO A Emphasize that the slope of the trend line will determine the type of association shown by the data points.

DO B Guide students as they use the trend line to predict data points. As needed, have students refer to the **Words to Know** to clarify the symbols or terms.

• **Support Discussion** **MP7** Have partners discuss briefly before group discussion. If needed, have students model a situation that shows data points with no association.

Prompt: How does a trend line represent data points?
Sentence Starter: A set of data that shows no association …

Practice and Assess

• Ask students to complete practice items 1 and 2 on page 185 independently or in pairs. Monitor ongoing work.

• Use the chart below as needed to address any difficulties.

Observation	Action
Students have difficulty extrapolating information from a scatter plot with a trend line.	Ask students to redraw the graphs without the plotted points, leaving only the line of best fit. This may help students read the information in the graph easier without being distracted by the points. Also, emphasize the importance of reading the labels on the axes to avoid confusion.

COMMON ERRORS

Students may see that the trend line describing lemonade and watermelon sold is negative. However, students may have trouble understanding the fact that as x increases, y decreases. Since the line has a negative slope, students may view this as "*as x decreases, y decreases.*" Reaffirm that in the first quadrant, the values on the x-axis increase as they get farther from the origin.

		OBJECTIVES	CONCEPTS AND SKILLS	VOCABULARY
FOUNDATIONAL UNDERSTANDING	**PLUG IN** Identifying a Trend Line	• Determine the association represented by a trend line. • Use the association represent by a trend line to predict data points.	Describe the association represented by a trend line on a scatter plot. **CCSS:** 8.SP.2	• **trend line** • **association**
	▶ POWER UP Drawing a Trend Line Student Edition pp. 186–187	• Draw a trend line for a scatter plot.	Draw a trend line on a scatter plot. **CCSS:** 8.SP.2	• **outlier**
ON-LEVEL TARGET	**READY TO GO** Solving Problems with Scatter Plots	• Compare the fit of two trend lines. • Redraw a trend line for a better fit.	Discuss the closeness of the data points to the trend line. **CCSS:** 8.SP.2	

MATERIALS
• Graph paper *(suggested)*

Build Background

■ Talk to students about reasons to draw a trend line in the real world. For example, city planners create a graph of the number of cars on a road during each month of the year. In order to predict whether there is a relationship between the month of the year and number of cars on the road, they would find a line of best fit for the data on the graph and then determine an equation of the line.

■ **MP4** Have students discuss additional examples of real situations that involve drawing a trend line for data.

■ Tell students they will be drawing a trend line to fit data points in a scatter plot.

Introduce and Model

■ **Introduce Concepts and Vocabulary** Guide students through the information about drawing a trend line. Emphasize that a trend line does not (and usually will not) fit every point in the scatter plot exactly. Use **Words to Know** to clarify their understanding of vocabulary. **MP6** Have students describe *outliers* to a partner.

■ **Support Discussion** **MP1** **MP5** Have partners discuss briefly before group discussion. Students can work together to draw trend lines for one particular graph in the lesson.

> *Prompt: How many trend lines could be used to describe the data?*
> *Sentence Starter: The lines should show the same trend, but …*

ENGLISH LANGUAGE LEARNERS

MP6 It may be helpful for ELL students to associate the word *outliers* with "lying out of the norm of the data." By associating outliers as lying out of the norm, it may be easier for some students to remember the term.

POWER UP Drawing a Trend Line

A trend line follows the general association between the data points.

Number of Sandwiches in an Office Vending Machine

Do not consider **outliers** when drawing a trend line.

Number of Sandwiches in an Office Vending Machine

@ outlier

Draw a trend line that has about the same number of points above it as below it.

Number of Sandwiches in an Office Vending Machine

6 points above line

6 points below line

Data points do not have to fall on the trend line.

A trend line rarely fits every point exactly. Instead, it represents the general trend of the entire data set.

Since the trend line should show the main trend of the data points, I won't consider outliers when I draw it.

I feel The trend line is a good fit if it passes through the middle of the data points.

Words to Know outlier a data point whose value is very different from other data points on a scatter plot

DISCUSS Could you draw more than one possible trend line for a scatter plot? Possible response: Yes. If there is no single line that fits all the data points perfectly, several trend lines could be drawn for which about the same number of points are above it as below it.
A You can draw a trend line for a scatter plot. These lines would show roughly the same trend.

DO Draw a trend line for this graph of the number of cookies eaten after meals based on the number of hours since the last meal.

❶ Identify outliers of the data set.

❷ Describe the association between the data points.

❸ Identify the sign of the slope of the trend line.

❹ Draw a line that best fits the data points.

Cookies Eaten after Meals

There is an outlier at (5 , 2). Do not consider this point when drawing the trend line.

The linear association is ___positive___

The slope will be ___positive___

DISCUSS Tamiko drew this trend line on the scatter plot. What can you tell her about her work?

Possible response: Tamiko's trend line is incorrect. There should be about the same number of points above and below the line, but there are many more points above her line than below it.

Butterflies Seen on Flowering Bushes

PRACTICE
Draw a trend line for each scatter plot.

❶ Temperature of Food in Freezer

❷ Snow Shovel Sales and Snowfall

❸ Dinosaur Body Length and Tooth Length

❹ Effects of Coffee Drinking on Sleep

186 LESSON 19

187

• Model Application

DO A Guide students through determining the association represented by a trend line. If needed, review how to find the slope of a linear graph.

• **Support Discussion** **MP4** Have partners discuss briefly before group discussion. If needed, review how a trend line is fit to data.

Prompt: What does a trend line tell you about a data set?

Sentence Starter: In order for a trend line to be accurate, …

SPOTLIGHT ON MATHEMATICAL LANGUAGE

MP2 Support students in using mathematical language as they work:

• What is an **outlier**?

• Does the **trend line** have about the same number of points below and above it?

Practice and Assess

• Ask students to complete practice items 1–4 on page 187 independently or in pairs. Monitor ongoing work.

• Use the table below to address any difficulties.

Observation	Action
Students do not accurately draw a trend line for the scatter plots.	Have students keep a tally of the number of data points that fall above and below their drawn trend lines. Emphasize that an equal number of points should fall above and below each trend line in order for it to accurately describe the data points. Remind students to ignore outliers when drawing the trend lines.

		OBJECTIVES	CONCEPTS AND SKILLS	VOCABULARY
FOUNDATIONAL UNDERSTANDING	**PLUG IN** **Identifying a Trend Line**	• Determine the association represented by a trend line. • Use the association represent by a trend line to predict data points.	Describe the association represented by a trend line on a scatter plot. **CCSS:** 8.SP.2	• **trend line** • **association**
	POWER UP **Drawing a Trend Line**	• Draw a trend line for a scatter plot.	Draw a trend line on a scatter plot. **CCSS:** 8.SP.2	• **outlier**
ON-LEVEL TARGET	**▶ READY TO GO** **Solving Problems with Scatter Plots** Student Edition pp. 188–193	• Compare the fit of two trend lines. • Redraw a trend line for a better fit.	Discuss the closeness of the data points to the trend line. **CCSS:** 8.SP.2	

MATERIALS

- Lesson 19 Quiz, Assessment Manual pp. 40–41
- Lesson 19 Quiz Answer Key, Assessment Manual
- Math Tool: Grids, p. A17 (Student Edition p. 241)
- Graphing calculators (*suggested*)

ENGLISH LANGUAGE LEARNERS

MP6 ELL students may have difficulty with the term *linear association*. Ask a volunteer to describe their understanding of the term, looking for them to use the words *line* and *relationship*.

Build Background

- Talk to students about reasons to determine the fit of a trend line to data. For example, when modeling population growth or decrease, after determining a trend line for a set of data points, land developers would want to check their trend line to see if it accurately describes all of the data points in order to make precise predictions on future trends.

- **MP4** Have students discuss additional examples of real situations that involve determining the fit of a trend line.

- Tell students they will be determining the fit of a trend line.

Introduce and Model

- **Introduce Concepts** Guide students through the information about judging the fit of a trend line. Emphasize that in order for a trend line to have a good fit, there needs to be about an equal number of data points below and above the line.

- **Support Discussion** **MP2** **MP3** Have partners discuss briefly before group discussion. If students are struggling, remind them that the outlier should not be counted as a point farthest above the line.

> *Prompt: How does an outlier affect the graph of data points?*
> *Sentence Starter: The line appears to be right in the middle of the data points…*

LESSON LINK

Connect to Foundational Understanding Skills learned in the **Plug In** and **Power Up** are referenced in the **Lesson Link**. Explain when you have a set of data points in a scatter plot, it is often helpful to find a trend line to describe the data, and then determine if that trend line fits the data well.

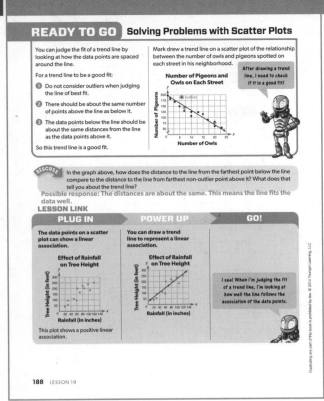

READY TO GO Solving Problems with Scatter Plots

You can judge the fit of a trend line by looking at how the data points are spaced around the line.

For a trend line to be a good fit:

① Do not consider outliers when judging the line of best fit.

② There should be about the same number of points above the line as below it.

③ The data points below the line should be about the same distances from the line as the data points above it.

So this trend line is a good fit.

Mark drew a trend line on a scatter plot of the relationship between the number of owls and pigeons spotted on each street in his neighborhood.

Number of Pigeons and Owls on Each Street

After drawing a trend line, I need to check if it is a good fit!

DISCUSS In the graph above, how does the distance to the line from the farthest point below the line compare to the distance to the line from farthest non-outlier point above it? What does that tell you about the trend line?
Possible response: The distances are about the same. This means the line fits the data well.

LESSON LINK

PLUG IN	POWER UP	GO!
The data points on a scatter plot can show a linear association.	You can draw a trend line to represent a linear association.	

Effect of Rainfall on Tree Height

This plot shows a positive linear association.

Effect of Rainfall on Tree Height

I see! When I'm judging the fit of a trend line, I'm looking at how well the line follows the association of the data points.

188 LESSON 19

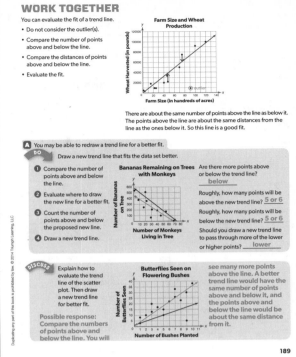

WORK TOGETHER

You can evaluate the fit of a trend line.

• Do not consider the outlier(s).

• Compare the number of points above and below the line.

• Compare the distances of points above and below the line.

• Evaluate the fit.

Farm Size and Wheat Production

There are about the same number of points above the line as below it. The points above the line are about the same distances from the line as the ones below it. So this line is a good fit.

A You may be able to redraw a trend line for a better fit.

DO Draw a new trend line that fits the data set better.

① Compare the number of points above and below the line.

② Evaluate where to draw the new line for a better fit.

③ Count the number of points above and below the proposed new line.

④ Draw a new trend line.

Bananas Remaining on Trees with Monkeys

Are there more points above or below the trend line? _below_

Roughly, how many points will be above the new trend line? _5 or 6_

Roughly, how many points will be below the new trend line? _5 or 6_

Should you draw a new trend line to pass through more of the lower or higher points? _lower_

DISCUSS Explain how to evaluate the trend line of the scatter plot. Then draw a new trend line for better fit.

Possible response: Compare the numbers of points above and below the line. You will

Butterflies Seen on Flowering Bushes

see many more points above the line. A better trend line would have the same number of points above and below it, and the points above and below the line would be about the same distance from it.

189

• **Work Together** Explain that students will evaluate the fit of a trend line. Begin by having students compare the number of points above and below the trend line. Then have them compare the distances from these points to the trend line. Remind students not to include any outliers.

DO **A** Monitor students as they determine that a trend line is not a good fit and that they must draw another trend line. Remind students that the new line should have about the same number of points above and below the line, and these points should be about the same distance from the line.

• **Support Discussion** **MP2** Have partners discuss briefly before group discussion. Students should follow the same line of questioning as with the previous problem. Suggest that students use a coordinate grid to create a new line.

> **Prompt:** What do you look for to determine if a trend line is a good fit for the data?
> **Sentence Starter:** There are more data points …

SPOTLIGHT ON MATHEMATICAL PRACTICES

MP3 **Critiquing Others' Reasoning**

Help students with explaining why a trend line is a good fit or not by asking the following questions:

■ *Are the data points evenly spaced above and below the trend line?*

■ *Are the data points below the line about the same distances from the line as the data points above it?*

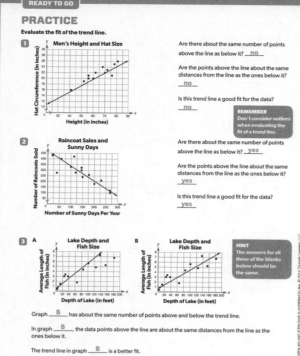

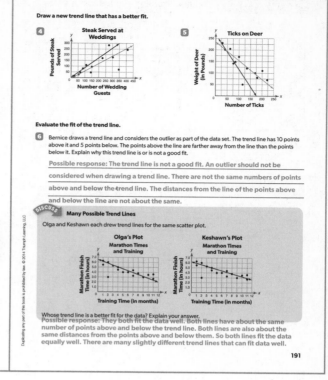

ADDITIONAL PRACTICE

Provide students with additional practice to model and solve:

Cammie draws a trend line that considers the outlier as part of the data set. The trend line has 3 points above it and 8 points below it. The points above and below the line are evenly spaced away from the line. Explain why this trend line is or is not a good fit.

COMMON ERRORS

Students may consider a trend line that includes an outlier to have a good fit. Remind students that in most cases, if a trend line includes an outlier it will likely not represent all of the points as closely as it should.

Support Independent Practice

1–3 Remind students to read the **HINT** and **REMEMBER**. If needed, ask: *How do you know if a trend line has a good fit or not?*

4–5 *What steps do you need to take to make sure your new line has the best fit possible for the data points?*

6 *What keywords should you look for in this problem?*

- **Support Discussion** MP4 Have partners write a solid explanation before group discussion. If needed, have partners make tables to evaluate the number of points above and below the lines and their distances from the line.

> **Prompt:** *Is it possible to have two trend lines to describe the same set of data?*
> **Sentence Starter:** *The lines seem to describe the data …*

Problem Solving

- **Model the Four-Step Method** MP4 Guide students through the four-step method using think-aloud strategies. Point out the outlier, if necessary.

  Think Aloud *If my trend line has good fit, I can use the graph to find the y-value for when the x-value equals 6. This will be the number of words I would expect a 6-page book to have.*

- **Support Problem-Solving Practice** Have students use the Checklist as they complete each step.

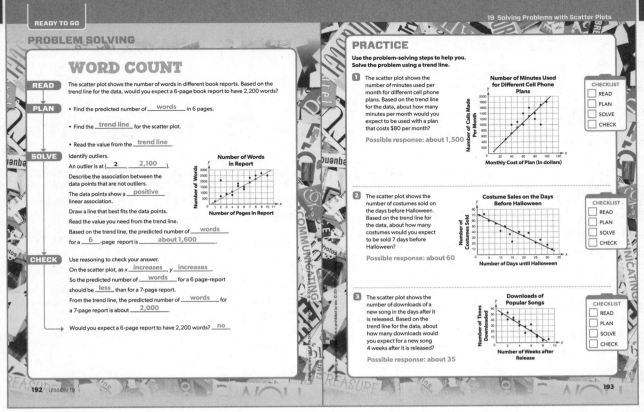

Prompt: *Are there any outliers in this data set?*
Prompt: *Does this show a positive or a negative association?*
Prompt: *How many points on the graph have an x-value of 4?*

- **Explore Student Thinking** MP3 Invite students to describe strategy they used to determine whether a line was a good fit for the data.

SPOTLIGHT ON MATHEMATICAL PRACTICES

MP5 Use Tools Strategically

Have students use the scatter plot application on their graphing calculators. Students can create two lists of data points and model the points on a graph. Then have students find the line of best fit for the data on the calculator.

Assess

- Use the table below to address to any difficulties.

	Observation	Action
1	Errors in creating a trend line for the data, which leads to inaccurate predictions.	Make extra copies of the Math Tool: Grids. Have students use a random number generator to generate two sets (*x*- and *y*-values) of 10–20 random numbers. Have students plot the two sets of numbers on the grid and find a trend line for the data.
2	Accurately creates a trend line with good fit for the data, but does not make accurate predictions based on the line.	Provide additional problems for making predictions. Finding a trend line with a good fit is a great start. Have students extend this by choosing points on their line that are close to the desired prediction and rule out any unnecessary points.
3	Creates a line of best fit for the data and makes accurate predictions based on the line.	Assign the Lesson 19 Quiz.

20 Solving Problems with Linear Models

PLUG IN Identifying the Slope and Intercept of a Line

		OBJECTIVES	CONCEPTS AND SKILLS	VOCABULARY
FOUNDATIONAL UNDERSTANDING	▶ **PLUG IN** **Identifying the Slope and Intercept of a Line** Student Edition pp. 194–195	• Find the slope of a linear model using two coordinates. • Find the *y*-intercept of a linear model using the slope and the coordinates of a point.	Identify the slope and *y*-intercept of a linear model. **CCSS:** 8.SP.3	• **linear model** • **slope** • *y*-intercept
	POWER UP **Writing Equations for Linear Models**	• Find the slope and *y*-intercept of a linear model using a graph. • Graph a linear model written in slope-intercept form.	Write the equation for a linear model. **CCSS:** 8.SP.3	
ON-LEVEL TARGET	**READY TO GO** **Solving Problems with Linear Models**	• Use the graph of a linear model to solve problems. • Use the equation of a linear model to solve problems.	Solve real-world problems using the equation of a linear model. **CCSS:** 8.SP.3	

MATERIALS

• Math Tool: Coordinate Grid, p. A15 (Student Edition, p. 237)
• Rulers *(suggested)*

Build Background

▪ Talk to students about reasons to use linear models in real life. For example, a coffee buyer spends a set amount each month on shipping expenses. What will be the cost of purchasing any amount of coffee? Explain that linear models can show the rate of change and project costs.

▪ **MP4** Have students discuss additional examples of real situations that involve linear change.

Introduce and Model

▪ **Introduce Concepts and Vocabulary** Guide students through the information about identifying the slope and *y*-intercept of a line. Use **Words to Know** to clarify their understanding of vocabulary. **MP6** Have students explain how the *slope* and *y-intercept* are represented in a *linear model*.

▪ **Support Discussion** **MP3** Have partners discuss briefly before group discussion.

ENGLISH LANGUAGE LEARNERS

MP7 ELL students may need additional support understanding slope. Using a ruler, have students model a line with a steep, positive slope. Then have students model a line with a steep, negative slope.

> **Prompt:** *In the equation, y = 3x + 3, the slope is 3. Describe this in terms of $\frac{rise}{run}$.*
>
> **Sentence Starter:** *A slope of 3 means …*

LESSON 20 Solving Problems with Linear Models

PLUG IN Identifying the Slope and Intercept of a Line

A **linear model** is a line that represents a data set. The equation of a line can be written in the form $y = mx + b$.

$y = 4x - 1$

You can read the **slope**, m, and the **y-intercept**, b, of a line from an equation in this form.

$y = 4x - 1$ slope = 4
y-intercept = −1

You can use the slope and y-intercept to write an equation for a line.

slope = 2, so $m = 2$
y-intercept = 1, so $b = 1$
$y = 2x + 1$

I can use this form of a linear equation to model certain data sets.

I see! A slope measures the rate of change, and the y-intercept tells me where the line crosses the y-axis.

I get it! I can substitute these values into the linear equation $y = mx + b$.

| **Words to Know** | **linear model** a line that represents a data set, whose equation can be written in the form $y = mx + b$ | **slope** a ratio of the change in y-coordinates (*rise*) of a graph to the change in corresponding x-coordinates (*run*); the symbol for slope is m | **y-intercept** the y-coordinate of the point at which a line crosses the y-axis |

DISCUSS Mabel says a linear model can have the equation $y = 3x + 3$. Owen says that the slope and y-intercept can't have the same value. Who is correct? Explain.
Possible answer: Mabel. In her equation, the slope is 3 and the y-intercept is 3. The values of slope and the y-intercept are unrelated in a linear model, so the value of one does not affect the value of the other.

A You can find the slope of a linear model using two coordinates.

DO Find the slope of a linear model that passes through the points (−2, 3) and (1, 6).

1. Identify the x and y-coordinates for each point.
The x-coordinates are −2 and $\boxed{1}$.
The y-coordinates are $\boxed{3}$ and 6.

2. Calculate $\frac{\text{change in } y}{\text{change in } x}$ to find the slope, m.
The slope is $\frac{\boxed{6} - \boxed{3}}{\boxed{1} - \boxed{-2}} = \frac{\boxed{3}}{\boxed{3}} = \boxed{1}$

The slope is $\boxed{1}$.

B You can find the y-intercept of a linear model using the slope and the coordinates of a point.

DO Find the y-intercept of a linear model whose slope is 3 and which contains the point (3, 4).

1. Write the equation of a line. $y = mx + b$
2. Replace the m with the value given for the slope. $\boxed{4} = (\boxed{3})(\boxed{3}) + b$
3. Replace x and y with the coordinates of the point. $\boxed{4} = \boxed{9} + b$
   $\boxed{-5} = b$
4. Solve for the y-intercept, b. The y-intercept is $\boxed{-5}$.

PRACTICE

Identify the slope and y-intercept of the following linear models.

1. $y = \frac{3}{2}x - 4$
   $m = \frac{3}{2}, b = -4$

2. $y = 7x + 5$
   $m = 7, b = 5$

Find the slope of the linear model that contains the following coordinate pairs.

3. (−1, 2), (4, 1)
   $m = -\frac{1}{5}$

4. (3, −1), (0, 2)
   $m = -1$

Find the y-intercept of each linear model.

5. Slope is 4 and it contains the point (1, 1).
   −3

6. Slope is −3 and it contains the point (0, 0).
   0

• Model Application

DO A Guide students through finding the slope of a line given the coordinates of two points on the line. Monitor that students use the difference in the y-coordinates in the numerator and the difference in the x-coordinates in the denominator.

DO B Guide student through finding the y-intercept of a line using the slope and the coordinates of one point on the line. Monitor that students use the slope-intercept form of an equation of a line and the meaning of the variables in the equation.

Practice and Assess

• Ask students to complete practice items 1–6 on page 195 independently or in pairs. Monitor ongoing work.

• Observe whether students apply the slope of the line and the coordinates of points on the line to the equation of a line written in slope-intercept form.

Observation	Action
Students have difficulty substituting known values into the equation of a line written in slope-intercept form.	Have students write a definition of each variable in the equation. The variables x and y represent the corresponding coordinates of a point on the line. The variable m represents the slope in the form $\frac{y}{x}$ where y is the difference in y-values of two points and x is the difference in the x-values of the same two points. In other words, slope is the change in y over the change in x, or rise over run. The variable b is the y-intercept, where the value of x is equal to 0.

COMMON ERRORS

Since coordinates of points are named using the x-coordinate followed by the y-coordinate, students may confuse the meaning of slope as $\frac{x}{y}$. Remind them that slope is the change in y, or rise, over the change in x, or run. Draw a line on a coordinate grid and label two points. Use the points to demonstrate that a slope of $\frac{x}{y}$ is not the same as a slope of $\frac{y}{x}$.

		OBJECTIVES	CONCEPTS AND SKILLS	VOCABULARY
FOUNDATIONAL UNDERSTANDING	**PLUG IN** **Identifying the Slope and Intercept of a Line**	• Find the slope of a linear model using two coordinates. • Find the *y*-intercept of a linear model using the slope and the coordinates of a point.	Identify the slope and *y*-intercept of a linear model. **CCSS:** 8.SP.3	• **linear model** • **slope** • ***y*-intercept**
	▶ **POWER UP** **Writing Equations for Linear Models** Student Edition pp. 196–197	• Find the slope and *y*-intercept of a linear model using a graph. • Graph a linear model written in slope-intercept form.	Write the equation for a linear model. **CCSS:** 8.SP.3	
ON-LEVEL TARGET	**READY TO GO** **Solving Problems with Linear Models**	• Use the graph of a linear model to solve problems. • Use the equation of a linear model to solve problems.	Solve real-world problems using the equation of a linear model. **CCSS:** 8.SP.3	

MATERIALS

• Graph paper *(suggested)*

ENGLISH LANGUAGE LEARNERS

MP6 ELL students may need additional support understanding how to identify the coordinates of points to use to find the slope in an equation of a line. When the data is linear, the coordinates of any two data points will work. When the data is nonlinear, the points used to write the equation of a line do not have to be explicitly included in the data set. Students should understand that the coordinates of any point that lies exactly on the intersection of an *x*-value and a *y*-value may be used in the equation.

Build Background

• Talk to students about reasons to use a linear model for nonlinear data. For example, does the outside temperature affect movie attendance? A scatter plot can be used to show any relationship between the two variables. Explain that a trend line, or line of best fit, can be used to predict movie attendance based on outside temperatures.

• **MP4** Have students discuss additional examples of real situations in which nonlinear data could be represented by a linear equation.

• Tell students they will find the slope and *y*-intercept of the line of best fit for nonlinear data.

Introduce and Model

• **Introduce Concepts** Guide students through the information about writing an equation for linear models. Point out that although the data is nonlinear, there is a strong positive association represented by a line of best fit. The equation of the line of best fit can be used to predict additional similar data points.

• **Support Discussion** **MP3** Have partners discuss briefly before group discussion.

> *Prompt:* What must always be true about the coordinates of the y-intercept? Does that have any effect on the y-value of the y-intercept? Explain.
> *Sentence Starter:* The x-value of the coordinates of the y-intercept must always be…

Lesson 20

POWER UP Writing Equations For Linear Models

Cassy drew the following linear model.

I see! I can write an equation to represent a linear model.

Write an equation that represents her linear model.

1. **Identify the *y*-intercept.** The *y*-intercept is where the line intersects with the *y*-axis.

   The *y*-intercept is 10.

2. **Calculate the slope.** Find the $\frac{\text{change in } y}{\text{change in } x}$ for any pair of points on the line.

   Two points on the line are (0, 10) and (40, 30), so

   $m = \frac{30 - 10}{40 - 0} = \frac{20}{40}$ or $\frac{1}{2}$.

3. **Write the equation in slope-intercept form.** Use the form $y = mx + b$, where *m* represents the slope and *b* represents the *y*-intercept.

   $b = 10$

   $y = \frac{1}{2}x + 10$

   The equation is $y = \frac{1}{2}x + 10$.

DISCUSS Dwayne says he can't find the *y*-intercept of a linear model because the line passes through the origin. What would you tell him?
Possible response: The coordinates of the origin are (0, 0), so the *y*-intercept is 0.

A You can find the slope and *y*-intercept of a linear model using a graph.

DO Find the slope and *y*-intercept of the line. Write the equation of the line.

1. Identify the *y*-intercept.
2. Find the slope.
3. Write the equation of the line.

   The *y*-intercept is ___20___

   Use points (30, 10) and (60, 0) to find the slope.

   $\frac{0 - 10}{60 - 30} = \frac{\boxed{-10}}{\boxed{30}} = \frac{\boxed{-1}}{\boxed{3}}$

   $y = \frac{\boxed{-1}}{3}x + \boxed{20}$

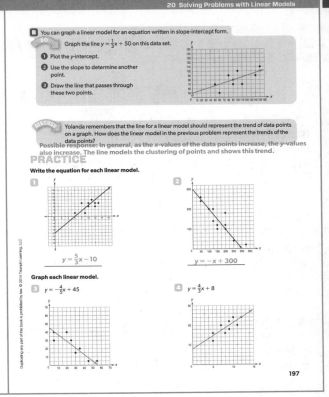

B You can graph a linear model for an equation written in slope-intercept form.

DO Graph the line $y = \frac{1}{3}x + 50$ on this data set.

1. Plot the *y*-intercept.
2. Use the slope to determine another point.
3. Draw the line that passes through these two points.

DISCUSS Yolanda remembers that the line for a linear model should represent the trend of data points on a graph. How does the linear model in the previous problem represent the trends of the data points?
Possible response: In general, as the *x*-values of the data points increase, the *y*-values also increase. The line models the clustering of points and shows this trend.

PRACTICE

Write the equation for each linear model.

1. $y = \frac{5}{3}x - 10$

2. $y = -x + 300$

Graph each linear model.

3. $y = -\frac{4}{5}x + 45$

4. $y = \frac{4}{3}x + 8$

• Model Application

DO **A** Guide students through using coordinates to find the slope and write an equation of a line. Remind students that the *x*- and *y*-coordinates must be used in corresponding order when finding the slope of the line.

DO **B** Guide students as they use the equation of a line to graph the line of best fit. Remind students that slope is $\frac{\text{rise}}{\text{run}}$; therefore, another point on the line is one unit up and three units to the right of the *y*-intercept. *What are the coordinates of the second point?*

• **Support Discussion** MP4 Have partners discuss briefly before group discussion.

> *Prompt:* What is the trend of the data? Can a linear model be used to represent the trend of any data set? Explain.
> *Sentence Starter:* The trend of the data is represented by the relationship between...

Practice and Assess

• Ask students to complete practice items 1–4 on page 197 independently or in pairs. Monitor ongoing work.

Observation	Action
Students have difficulty associating linear models and the corresponding equations of the lines.	Have students label the *y*-intercept with the variable *b* to remind students that the *y*-value of this point represents *b* in the equation of a line in slope-intercept form.

SPOTLIGHT ON MATHEMATICAL PRACTICES

MP6 Attend to Precision

Students should be aware that the exact coordinates of a point can not be identified by visually assessing its location on the coordinate grid. Points that are used in equations should be identified in the data set. Students should understand that the equation of a trend line of nonlinear data is an approximation unless they are given enough data to specifically identify the slope and *y*-intercept of the line.

	OBJECTIVES	CONCEPTS AND SKILLS	VOCABULARY
FOUNDATIONAL UNDERSTANDING — **PLUG IN** — **Identifying the Slope and Intercept of a Line**	• Find the slope of a linear model using two coordinates. • Find the *y*-intercept of a linear model using the slope and the coordinates of a point.	Identify the slope and *y*-intercept of a linear model. **CCSS:** 8.SP.3	• **linear model** • **slope** • ***y*-intercept**
POWER UP — **Writing Equations for Linear Models**	• Find the slope and *y*-intercept of a linear model using a graph. • Graph a linear model written in slope-intercept form.	Write the equation for a linear model. **CCSS:** 8.SP.3	
ON-LEVEL TARGET — **▶ READY TO GO** — **Solving Problems with Linear Models** Student Edition pp. 198–203	• Use the graph of a linear model to solve problems. • Use the equation of a linear model to solve problems.	Solve real-world problems using the equation of a linear model. **CCSS:** 8.SP.3	

MATERIALS

- Lesson 20 Quiz, Assessment Manual pp. 42–43
- Lesson 20 Quiz Answer Key, Assessment Manual
- Graph paper *(suggested)*

SPOTLIGHT ON MATHEMATICAL PRACTICES

MP1 Make Sense of Problems

Students understand that slope is defined as $n = \frac{y_1 - y_2}{x_1 - x_2}$. Discuss the impact on slope when the difference of the *x*-values equals 0. Division by 0 is undefined and the graph of the equation will be a vertical line. For this reason, the slope of a vertical line is undefined.

Build Background

- Talk to students about using linear equations and models to solve real-life problems. For example, a tree farm wants to know when they can expect different species of trees to be ready for sale. Using data collected over time, a linear model can be helpful in predicting when the saplings of difference species will be large enough to sell.

- **MP4** Have students discuss additional examples of real situations in which linear models and equations that represent data could be useful.

Introduce and Model

- **Introduce Concepts** Emphasize that sometimes the data is linear and sometimes it is nonlinear; however, a linear model or equation can be used to summarize data.

- **Support Discussion MP2** Have partners discuss briefly before group discussion. If students have difficulty explaining the meaning of the equation, suggest they write the algebraic equation of a line and evaluate the given values according to the meaning of the corresponding variables.

> *Prompt: Which variable in the algebraic equation represents the rate of change? What is another term for the rate of change?*
>
> *Sentence Starter: In the equation* y = mx + b, *the rate of change is represented by the variable…*

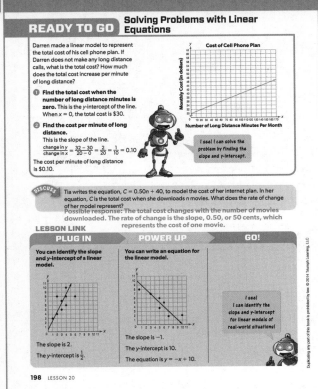

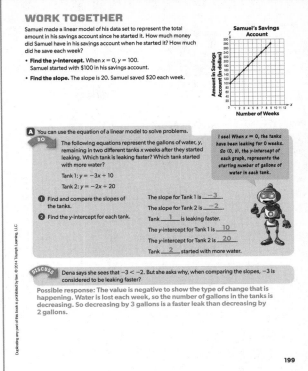

LESSON LINK

Connect to Foundational Understanding Skills learned in the **Plug In** and **Power Up** are referenced in the **Lesson Link**. Explain that the slope and *y*-intercept of a linear model are represented by the variables *m* and *b*, respectively, in the equation of a line. The value of *b* is represented by the initial value, which can be greater than, less than, or equal to 0.

- **Work Together** Explain that students will use a linear model to identify the initial value, or *y*-intercept, and the slope of the line representing a real-life situation. *Which value answers the question about how much Samuel had in his savings account when he started it? How can you find how much he saved each week?*

DO **A** Monitor students as they use linear equations to compare the rates of change. If students have difficulty working with equations, suggest they graph both lines on a single coordinate plane.

- **Support Discussion** **MP2** Have partners discuss briefly before group discussion. As needed, have students refer to a graph of the lines.

> *Prompt: How is a negative slope of a line represented on a graph? What does a negative slope mean?*
> *Sentence Starter: A line with a negative slope shows the y-values decreasing as the x-values …*

MP2 Support students in using mathematical language as they work:

- *If you were to write a linear equation for the graph of Samuel's savings account what would be the* **y-intercept**?
- *How do you know the graphs for Tank A and Tank B are* **linear models**?
- *Which value in the equation* $y = mx + b$ *represents the* **slope** *of the line?*

PRACTICE

Solve.

1 Sylvia made this linear model to represent the number of cups of dog food she will need for a given number of days. How many cups of dog food does her dog eat each day? __2 cups__

> **REMEMBER**
> When looking for a rate of change, you want to find the slope of the graph.

Cups of Dog Food Needed

(graph: Number of Cups vs Number of Days)

2 Colleen made this linear model to represent the amount of fencing needed to enclose a square garden. As the side length of the square garden increases by 1 meter, how much more fencing will she need? __4 meters__

Fencing for a Square Garden

(graph: Meters of Fencing Needed vs Side Length (in meters))

3 Jake made this linear model to represent the height of an airplane in feet x minutes after it begins its descent. What was the initial height of the airplane? __15,000 ft__

> **HINT**
> The term "initial height" means the height at the beginning of its descent. In this problem, that occurs when $x = 0$.

Height of Descending Plane

(graph: Height of Plane (in feet) vs Minutes After Descent Begins)

4 Steve made this linear model to represent the distance, y, in miles he's traveled after x hours. What was the rate of change of his distance? __55 miles__

Distance Over Time

(graph: Miles Traveled vs Time (in hours))

Solve.

5 Benny wrote the equation $y = 6x - 30$ to represent the depth of a diver under water as he swims to the surface. At what depth did the diver begin swimming to the surface? __30 ft__

6 Olivia wrote the equation $y = 25x$ to represent the total amount of money she has saved after x months. How much money will Olivia save each month? __$25__

Solve.

7 Julia wrote the equation $y = -2x + 100$ to represent the number of pencils remaining after x weeks. How many pencils did she start with? How many pencils does she use each week? __100; 2__

> I remember! In a linear model in the form $y = mx + b$, m is the slope and b is the y-intercept.

8 Justin wrote the equation $y = \frac{1}{2}x + 3$ to represent the height of a plant after x days. What was the initial height, in centimeters, of the plant? How many centimeters does the plant grow each day? __3 cm; $\frac{1}{2}$ cm__

DISCUSS

Model with Mathematics

Jill reads an order form for a company that makes shirts. She sees that the cost per shirt decreases as more shirts are ordered.

She writes the equation $y = -\frac{1}{2}x + 20$ to represent the cost per shirt when x shirts are ordered.

Based on her model, what is the rate of change in the cost for each additional shirt ordered? __$-\frac{1}{2}$, or $-\$0.50$__

Jill says her model does not work because 40 shirts would cost $0 each. Is Jill correct? __Jill is correct. If $x = 40$, $y = \$0$. Her model does not work.__

> I see!
> A linear model may represent a data set well, but it may not make sense for values outside of the data set.

ADDITIONAL PRACTICE

Provide students with additional practice to model and solve:

Use the points to graph the equation of the line. Then identify the slope and the y-intercept.

$(-4, 9)$, $(2, -6)$,
$(8, -9)$ $(2, 3)$

$(3, 8)$, $(6, -2)$,
$(1, -2)$ $(8, -2)$

COMMON ERRORS

Students often drop negative signs when doing calculations with integers. Remind them to check their solutions for reasonableness. *Does the equation of the line have a positive or negative slope? Does the slope make sense based on the context of the problem?* If the slope does not make sense, encourage students to go back and check the values in their work for the correct signs.

Support Independent Practice

1–4 Remind students to read the **HINT** and **REMEMBER**. If needed, have students write the equation of the line. Ask: *What does the initial value represent? Does the initial value make sense? Why?*

5–6 *What will be the value of b when the diver reaches the surface? Explain.*

7–8 *Is the slope of the line positive or negative? How do you know by looking at the equation?*

- **Support Discussion** MP3 Have partners discuss briefly before group discussion. As needed, suggest students use graph paper to draw a linear model of the equation.

> **Prompt:** *How can you use the equation of the line to check Jill's reasoning?*
> **Sentence Starter:** *Using the equation, substitute 40 for the variable …*

Problem Solving

- **Model the Four-Step Method** MP7 MP8 Guide students through the four-step method using think-aloud strategies. As needed, have students use a linear equation to represent the linear model.

  Think Aloud *When $x = 0$, $y = 40$, so the initial value is $40. That means the base rate to access online data storage is $40.*

- **Support Problem-Solving Practice** Have students use the Checklist as they complete each step.

PROBLEM SOLVING
READY TO GO

DATA STORAGE

READ The graph shows the relationship between the total cost of online data storage and the number of gigabytes downloaded. Use the graph to determine the cost per gigabyte and the cost if 0 gigabytes are downloaded.

PLAN • Find the __cost__ per gigabyte downloaded (slope).

• Find the cost if __0__ gigabytes are downloaded (y-intercept).

Cost of Online Data Storage

Cost per Gigabytes Downloaded (in dollars)

Number of Gigabytes Downloaded

SOLVE To find the slope, pick two points on the graph, such as (0, __40__) and (30, __46__).
Calculate the slope using these points.

$$\frac{\text{change in } y}{\text{change in } x} = \frac{46 - 40}{30 - 0} = \frac{6}{30} = 0.2$$

To find the y-intercept, find the point at which the graph intersects __the y-axis__ .
This point is (__0__ , __40__), so the y-intercept is __40__ .

CHECK Write the equation for the graph in slope-intercept form.

$y = $ __0.2__ $x + $ __40__

Substitute an x-value of a point on the line for x in the equation. Check that the y-value from the equation matches the y-value for that point on the graph.

Choose the point (50, __50__).

$y = $ __0.2__ $\times$ __50__ $+$ __40__

$y = $ __10__ $+$ __40__

$y = $ __50__

Does the value you found for y match the y-value shown on the graph? __yes__

The cost per gigabyte downloaded is __$0.20__ .
The cost if no gigabytes are downloaded is __$40__ .

PRACTICE
Use the problem-solving steps to help you.

1. Nina gets paid $200 a week plus an extra $5 per handbag she sells. Write an equation for this problem, and identify the slope and y-intercept.

$y = 5x + 200, m = 5, b = 200$

CHECKLIST
☐ READ ☐ PLAN ☐ SOLVE ☐ CHECK

2. Burt pays $20 a month for his water bill. The water company will add $0.01 per gallon used to his bill. Write an equation for this problem, and identify the slope and y-intercept.

$y = 0.01x + 20, m = 0.01, b = 20$

CHECKLIST
☐ READ ☐ PLAN ☐ SOLVE ☐ CHECK

3. When Myla visits a fruit stand, she buys a bag of oranges for $2 and several pounds of grapes at $1.50 per pound. Write an equation for this problem, and identify the slope and y-intercept.

$y = 1.5x + 2, m = 1.5, b = 2$

CHECKLIST
☐ READ ☐ PLAN ☐ SOLVE ☐ CHECK

Prompt: What is the algebraic equation of a line in slope-intercept form?

Prompt: How could this equation be used to determine the total cost of using 30 gallons of water per month?

• **Explore Student Thinking MP2** Invite students to evaluate the meaning of their equations. *Would it be possible for any of these initial values to be 0? Less than 0? Explain.*

ENGLISH LANGUAGE LEARNERS
MP6 ELL students may need additional support translating the meaning of the word problems into linear equations. Suggest that students work with a partner to read and discuss the meaning of the problem before writing an equation.

Assess
• Use the table below to address any difficulties.

	Observation	Action
1	Frequent errors when writing linear equation based on real situations. General confusion about identifying the slope and y-intercept in a linear equation.	Based on a linear graph, ask students to identify the y-intercept. Then have students put their pencil on any point on the graph. Model how to count up and over to the next point. Remind students that this is the slope, the change in y over the change in x.
2	Occasional errors when writing linear equation based on real situations. General confusion about identifying the slope and y-intercept in a linear equation.	Have students work with a partner. Using graph paper, one partner draws a line on a coordinate grid and writes the coordinates of any two points. Students trade papers and write the equation of the line. Have partners trade tasks and repeat the activity.
3	Accurately writes linear equation based on real situations and correctly identifies the slope and y-intercept.	Assign the Lesson 20 Quiz.

Appendix

Math Tools

Math Tool: Dot Paper

Name _____   Date _____

Math Tool: Coordinate Grid

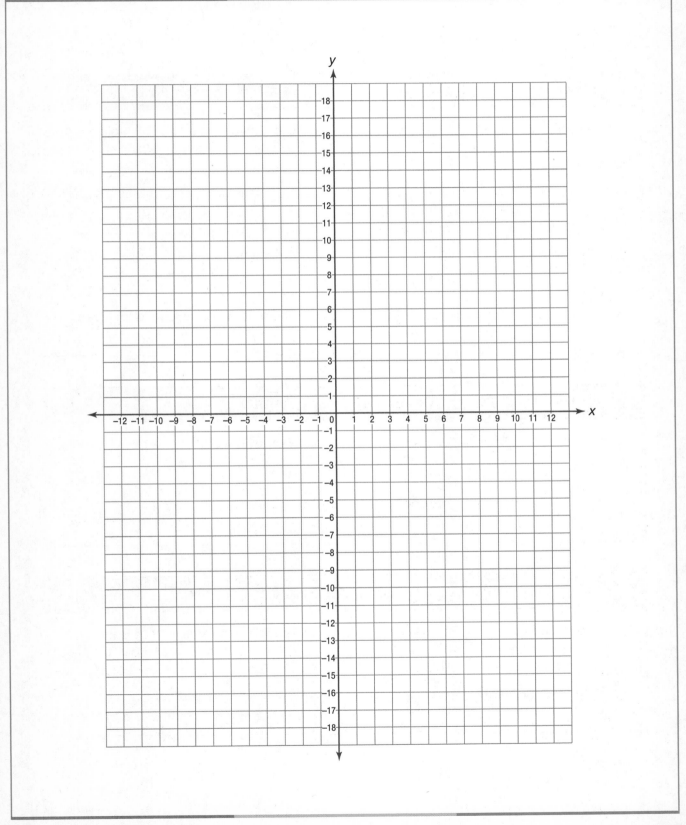

Math Tool: Properties of Multiplication

Addition Properties
Associative Property of Addition $(a + b) + c = a + (b + c)$
Commutative Property of Addition $a + b = b + a$
Additive Identity Property of 0 $a + 0 = a$
Sum of Additive Inverses $a + (-a) = 0$

Multiplication Properties
Associative Property of Multiplication $(a \times b) \times c = a \times (b \times c)$
Commutative Property of Multiplication $a \times b = b \times a$
Multiplicative Identity Property of 1 $a \times 1 = a$
Product of Multiplicative Inverses $a \times \frac{1}{a} = 1$

Addition and Multiplication
Distributive Property of Multiplication over Addition $a \times (b + c) = (a \times b) + (a \times c)$
Distributive Property of Multiplication over Subtraction $a \times (b - c) = (a \times b) - (a \times c)$

Properties of Equality	
Addition Property of Equality If $a = b$, then $a + c = b + c$.	Multiplication Property of Equality If $a = b$, then $a \times c = b \times c$.
Subtraction Property of Equality If $a = b$, then $a - c = b - c$.	Division Property of Equality If $a = b$ and $c \neq 0$, then $a \div c = b \div c$.

Math Tool: Grid Paper

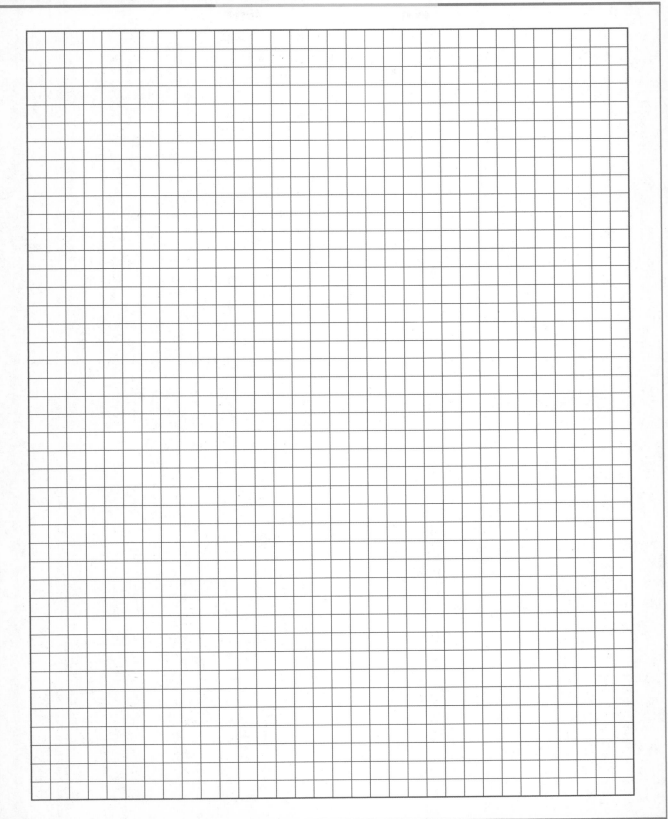

Name _____   Date _____

Math Tool: Grid Paper

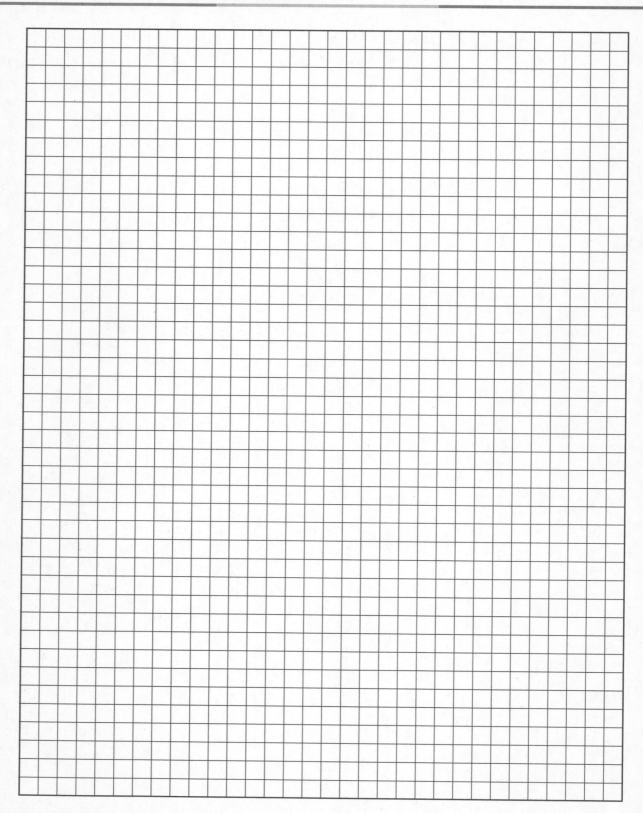

Name _____ Date _____

Math Tool: Pythagorean Theorem Proof

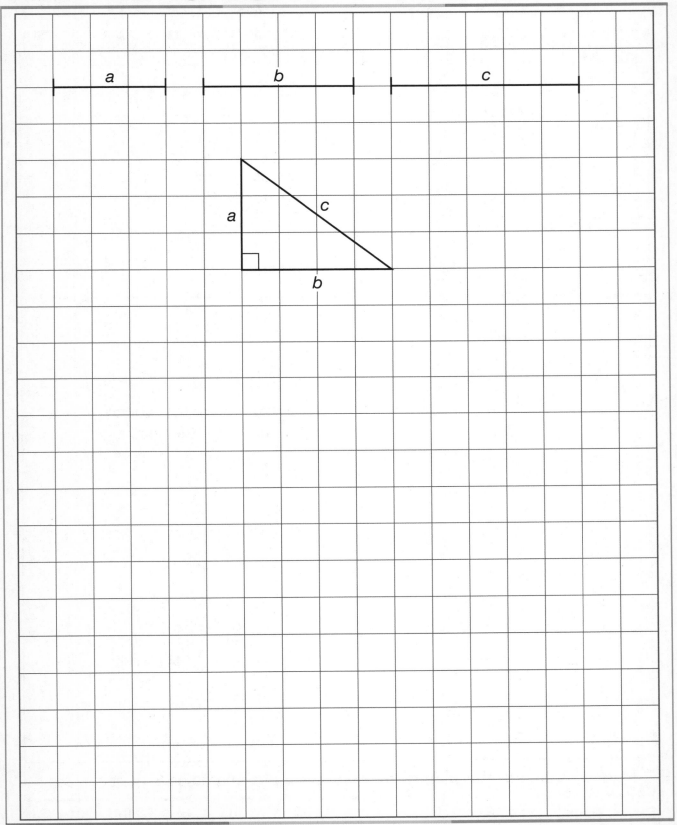

Name _____   Date _____

Math Tool: Volume Formulas

Formulas for Volume, *V*

Cylinder

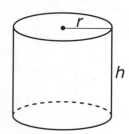

$$V = \pi r^2 h,$$

where *r* stands for the radius
and *h* stands for the height

Cone

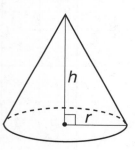

$$V = \frac{1}{3}\pi r^2 h,$$

where *r* stands for the radius
and *h* stands for the height

Sphere

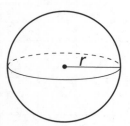

$$V = \frac{4}{3}\pi r^3,$$

where *r* stands for the radius

Pi, or π, is an irrational number than can be approximated as 3.14 or $\frac{22}{7}$.

Name _____ Date _____

Math Tool: Grid Paper

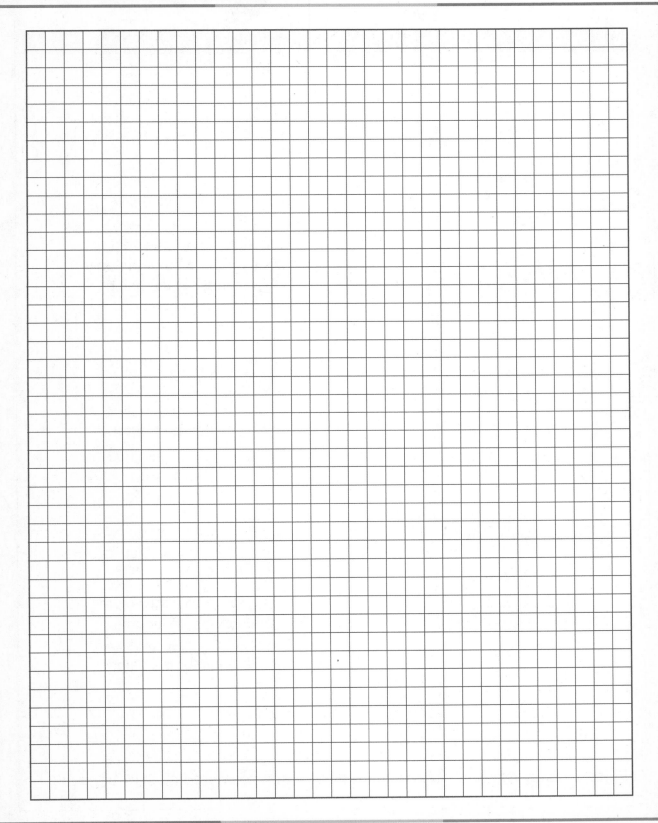

Math Tool: Volume Formulas

Formulas for Volume, *V*

Rectangular Prism

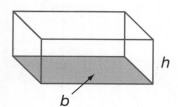

$$V = b \times h,$$

where *V* stands for the volume,
b stands for the area of the base,
and *h* stands for the height.

Rectangular Prism

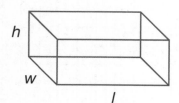

$$V = l \times w \times h,$$

where *V* stands for the volume,
l stands for the length,
w stands for the width,
and *h* stands for the height.

Name _____ Date _____

Math Tool: Grid Paper

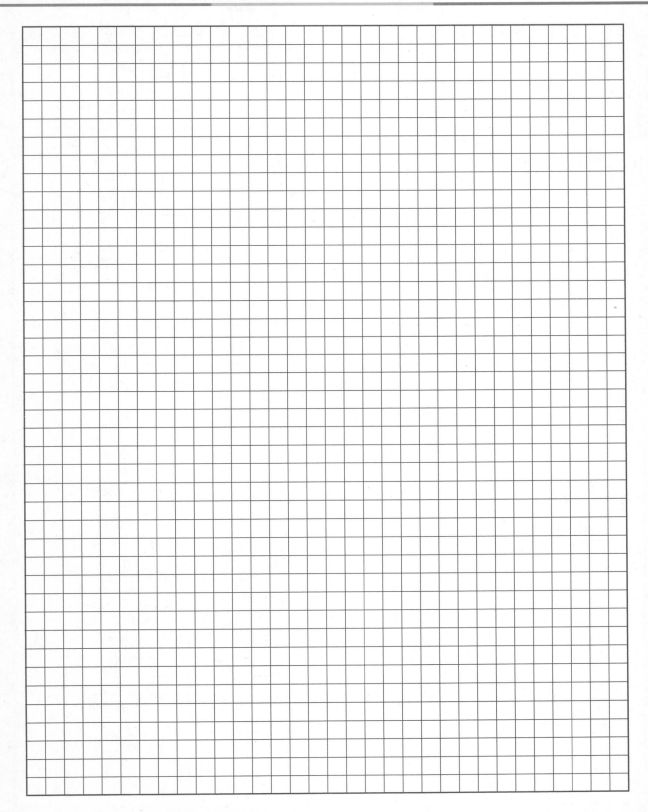

Name _____   Date _____

Math Tool: Coordinate Grids

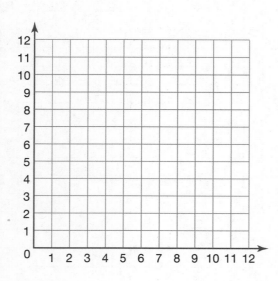
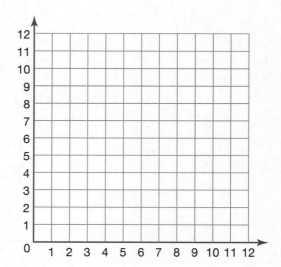
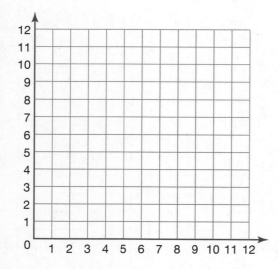
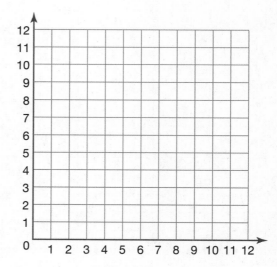

Math Tool: Coordinate Grids

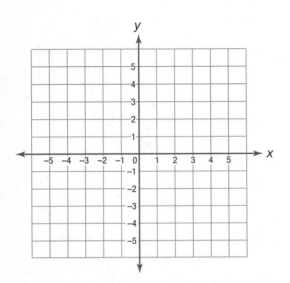

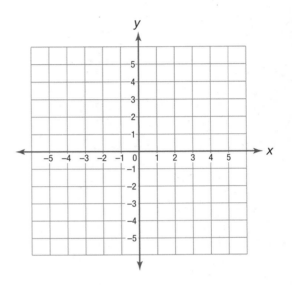

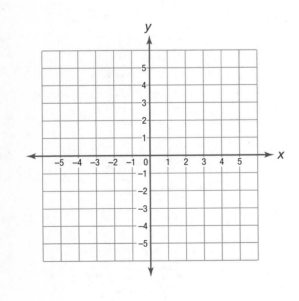

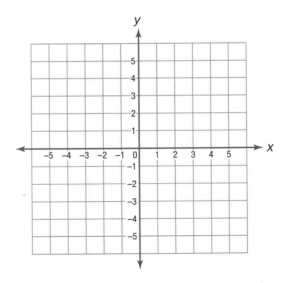

Math Tool: Fraction Strips

1

$\frac{1}{2}$	$\frac{1}{2}$

$\frac{1}{3}$	$\frac{1}{3}$	$\frac{1}{3}$

$\frac{1}{4}$	$\frac{1}{4}$	$\frac{1}{4}$	$\frac{1}{4}$

$\frac{1}{5}$	$\frac{1}{5}$	$\frac{1}{5}$	$\frac{1}{5}$	$\frac{1}{5}$

$\frac{1}{6}$	$\frac{1}{6}$	$\frac{1}{6}$	$\frac{1}{6}$	$\frac{1}{6}$	$\frac{1}{6}$

$\frac{1}{8}$	$\frac{1}{8}$	$\frac{1}{8}$	$\frac{1}{8}$	$\frac{1}{8}$	$\frac{1}{8}$	$\frac{1}{8}$	$\frac{1}{8}$

$\frac{1}{10}$	$\frac{1}{10}$	$\frac{1}{10}$	$\frac{1}{10}$	$\frac{1}{10}$	$\frac{1}{10}$	$\frac{1}{10}$	$\frac{1}{10}$	$\frac{1}{10}$	$\frac{1}{10}$

$\frac{1}{12}$	$\frac{1}{12}$	$\frac{1}{12}$	$\frac{1}{12}$	$\frac{1}{12}$	$\frac{1}{12}$	$\frac{1}{12}$	$\frac{1}{12}$	$\frac{1}{12}$	$\frac{1}{12}$	$\frac{1}{12}$	$\frac{1}{12}$

Name _____ Date _____

Math Tool: Coordinate Grid

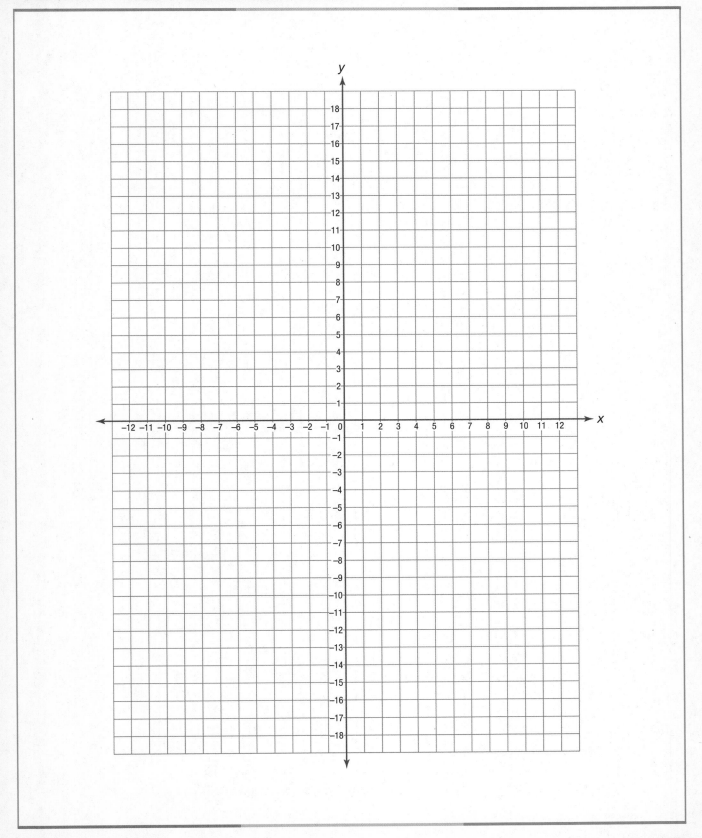

Math Tool: Coordinate Grid

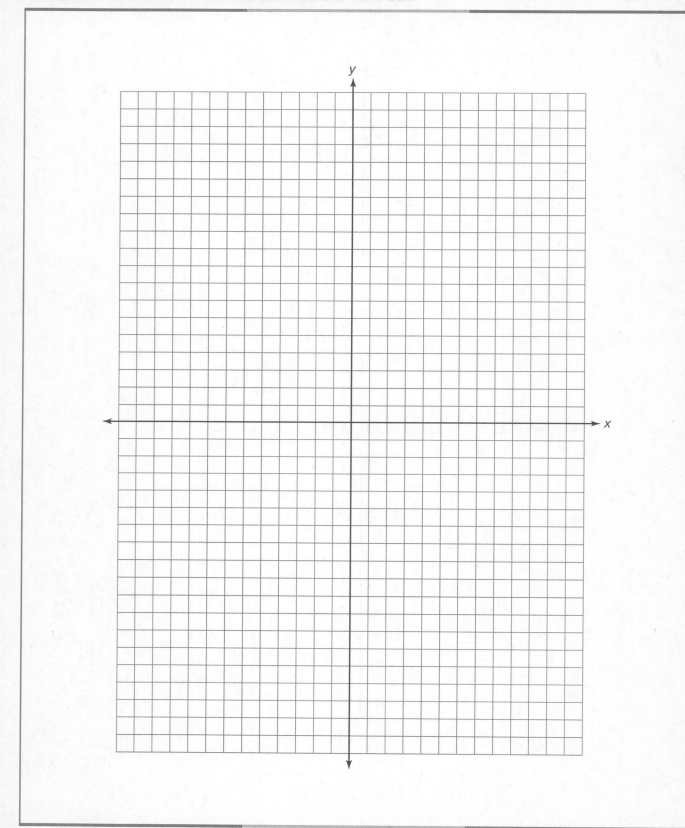

Math Tool: Grids

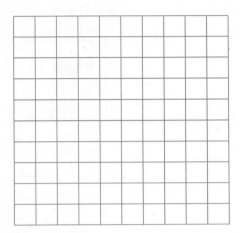
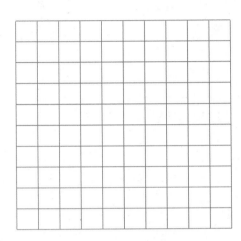
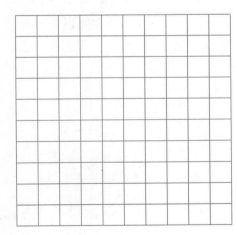
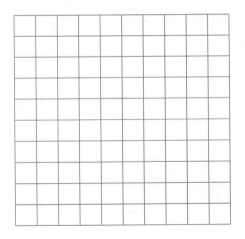

Math Tool: Two-Dimensional Shapes

circle
0 sides
0 angles

oval
0 sides
0 angles

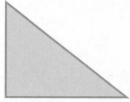

triangle
3 sides
3 angles

square
4 equal sides
4 right angles

rectangle
4 sides
4 right angles

rhombus
4 equal sides
4 angles

pentagon
5 sides
5 angles

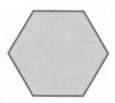

hexagon
6 sides
6 angles

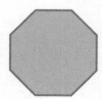

octagon
8 sides
8 angles

Notes

Notes

Notes

Notes